MARK CATESBY *The Colonial Audubon*

University of Illinois Press, Urbana, 1961

GEORGE FREDERICK FRICK AND
RAYMOND PHINEAS STEARNS

MARK CATESBY

THE COLONIAL AUDUBON

Preface

This book is an attempt to set forth from the original sources a biography of Mark Catesby, an evaluation of his work as a naturalist, and an estimate of his enduring influences in the history of science. In the eighteenth century Catesby was well known, widely admired, and frequently quoted in the circles of the virtuosi and early natural science both in Europe and America. Though his works were pre-Linnaean, they weathered the Linnaean revolution remarkably well and survived into the nineteenth century. Indeed, so much of Catesby has been preserved in natural history to this day that it is difficult to understand why he has gone so long without an adequate biographical sketch and scientific evaluation.

Catesby was close to the circle of naturalists in his day, and his life and works constitute overlooked chapters which illuminate many facets in the development of the natural sciences in the eighteenth century. His *Natural History of Carolina,* Catesby's greatest work, was a pioneer in the field of scientific illustration. In botany, zoology, ichthyology, and especially in ornithology, Catesby explored new and untried fields with high acclaim. For well over a century his work was the best single treatment of the flora and fauna of the mainland of North America, and his method of illustrating his subjects won him the posthumous compliment of imitation by no less a person than John James Audubon.

It is hoped that this volume will both rescue Mark Catesby from undeserved oblivion and prove a helpful addition to the literature of the history of science in the eighteenth century.

The authors wish to express deep appreciation to the various libraries and library staffs who freely gave them access to materials and aided them during their searches in the widely scattered sources upon which this book is based. They especially thank the President and Fellows of the Royal Society of London for permission to search among and quote from the various records and manuscripts in the Library of the Society. They also acknowledge with gratitude the assistance of the Library of the British Museum, especially the Manuscripts Division, the Bodleian Library, Oxford, the Library of Congress, Washington, D.C., and the Library of the University of Illinois. With the aid of funds supplied by the Research Board of the Graduate College, the University of Illinois Library purchased a splendid copy of the first edition of Mark Catesby's *Natural History of Carolina,* without which this work could hardly have been completed.   G.F.F.
                                                              R.P.S.

Abbreviations Used in Footnotes

Allen, *Am. Ornith.* — Elsa G. Allen, *History of American Ornithology Before Audubon* (*Transactions of the American Philosophical Society,* XLI, Philadelphia, 1951).

Carolina — Mark Catesby, *The Natural History of Carolina, Florida, and the Bahama Islands* (ed. 1, 2 vols., London, 1731-43 [1729-47]).

C.S.P., Col. and *Dom.* — *Calendar of State Papers, Colonial* and *Domestic* (London, 1856———).

Darlington, *Memorials* — William Darlington, ed., *Memorials of John Bartram and Humphrey Marshall with Notices of Their Contemporaries* (Philadelphia, 1849).

Jones, *Capt. Roger Jones* — Lewis Hampton Jones, *Captain Roger Jones of London and Virginia. Some of His Antecedents and Descendants* (Albany, N.Y., 1891 [1911]).

MS Radcliffe Trust — *Richardson Correspondence. MS Radcliffe Trust* (MSS in the Bodleian Library, Oxford).

Nichols, *Illust. Lit. Hist.* — John Nichols, *Illustrations of the Literary History of the Eighteenth Century* (8 vols., London, 1817-58).

Phil. Trans. — *Philosophical Transactions of the Royal Society of London* (London, 1665/66———).

Pulteney — Richard Pulteney, *The Historical and Biographical Sketches of the Progress of Botany in England from Its Origin to the Introduction of the Linnaean System* (2 vols., London, 1790).

Richardson Extracts — Dawson Turner, ed., *Extracts from the Literary and Scientific Correspondence of Richard Richardson . . .* (Yarmouth, 1835).

R.S. Council Minutes — *Council Minutes* (MSS in the Library of the Royal Society of London, Burlington House, London).

R.S. Journal Book — *Journal Books* (MSS in the Library of the Royal Society of London).

R.S. Letter Book — *Letter Books* (MSS in the Library of the Royal Society of London).

Sherard Letters — *Dr. [William] Sherard's Philosophical Letters* (5 vols., MSS in the Library of the Royal Society of London).

Sloane — *Sloane MSS* (MSS in the Manuscripts Division, British Museum, London).

Smith, *Corresp. Linnaeus* — Sir James Edward Smith, ed., *Selections of the Correspondence of Linnaeus* (2 vols., London, 1821).

Note on quotations: We have expanded most abbreviations quoted from manuscript sources, and, in the interest of clarity for the present-day reader, we have added punctuation marks. Dates are left as they appeared in the originals and, in nearly every case, they are Old Style.

Contents

Introduction

If by discovery is meant a familiarity with a land and its products as opposed to a mere landfall or a first view, then the discovery of America was by neither Leif the Lucky nor Christopher Columbus. Rather, it is a continuous and cumulative process which began in the Middle Ages and still goes on. Great advances were made between the mid-sixteenth century and the mid-eighteenth. Two great natural histories will serve to illustrate this fact. Konrad Gesner's *Historia animalium*,[1] which marked the beginnings of modern zoology, contained virtually no distinctively American fauna, whereas Carl Linnaeus' *Systema naturae*,[2] the starting point of modern zoological nomenclature, abounded with references to animals from many parts of the New World. By what means was this difference in scope made possible?

It was made possible by explorers and field naturalists, collectors and scholars, both amateur and professional, nearly all of whom exchanged data widely and cooperated freely with little concern for social or national boundaries. Some were supported by their sovereigns; some were patronized by the Church,

wealthy noblemen, or merchants; some drew upon their own purses. Their motives were mixed, ranging from mere curiosity and a search for wealth and fame to a genuinely scholarly pursuit of Truth. Their activity increased markedly both in frequency and in quality after the middle of the seventeenth century, owing in large part to the efforts of the Royal Society of London and of English naturalists closely associated with it. Almost from its founding in 1662 the Society was instrumental in encouraging collectors in America and throughout the world to send their specimens and reports back to England.

Mark Catesby was one of those collectors encouraged by the Society to travel to the British lands in North America in order to send back specimens which would swell British collections and enlarge Englishmen's knowledge of their distant dominions. Indeed, Mark Catesby was the most significant of these gatherers of plants and animals dispatched from England to America in the seventeenth and eighteenth centuries. He was not only an exceptionally efficient collector but also, what was more important, he produced the most outstanding work

[1] (4 pts., Zurich, 1551-58). A fifth part was published posthumously at Zurich in 1587.

[2] (ed. 10, 2 vols., Stockholm, 1758-59).

on the natural history of the British possessions in North America published before the American Revolution, *The Natural History of Carolina, Florida, and the Bahama Islands.*

Unfortunately, Catesby's reputation has languished. He belonged to that group of naturalists who flourished after the time of the great systematists of the late seventeenth century, such as John Ray, Joseph Pitton de Tournefort, and Robert Morison, and before the general adoption of the taxonomic system of Carl Linnaeus after the middle of the eighteenth. Many of the historians of the natural sciences have been so dazzled by these giants that they have failed to realize the importance of those who came between. Julius von Sachs, the great nineteenth-century German botanical historian, scornfully dismissed the botanists of the first three decades of the eighteenth century as "mere plant collectors,"[3] and Joseph Reynolds Green, the historian of British botany, pictured the years after the deaths of John Ray (1705) and Nehemiah Grew (1712) as a period of inactivity during which British botanists worked sluggishly along lines already laid down.[4] Both of these authors were plant physiologists, but they were still heavily under the influence of system, and they exaggerated the importance of naming and classifying the products of nature.

The American Revolution may also have been a factor in causing Catesby's relative obscurity. His work was almost entirely concerned with America, but he spent only a small part of his life there. He was born in England and returned there to write and illustrate his book. Accordingly, he did not seem to rate consideration as a British naturalist for writers like Green, who wrote along national lines; and for Americans he was, at best, a transient visitor, who could not qualify as an American and whose letters were located inaccessibly in England. As a consequence, he has, until recent years, been neglected by historians and scientific antiquaries on both sides of the Atlantic.

Mark Catesby, together with his contemporaries in the field of natural history, deserves better treatment. Although it is true that Catesby was principally a collector and that he constructed no great system of classification, he contributed tremendously to the Old World's knowledge of the New, both in the specimens which he sent home and, even more, in those animals and plants which he figured in the grand folio pages of his *Natural History.* Without his help, the systems of Linnaeus and the other great taxonomists of the eighteenth century would have been far less complete. And more than this, he was a talented and original (if largely self-trained) scientific artist, upon whose work the later illustrators of the North American flora and fauna could (and did) build and expand.

The chapters which follow seek to clear away much of the obscurity which has surrounded Mark Catesby's life, to evaluate his accomplishments by the standards of his own time, and to assess his lasting importance in the centuries which followed his death. To that end, Catesby's own letters and published writings, along with those of his contemporaries, have been consulted; and the works of naturalists who came after him have been examined carefully in order to find the extent to which they leaned upon or borrowed from his works. In this fashion, it is hoped that a sound perspective has been established for an estimate of Catesby's contributions to scientific knowledge.

[3] Julius von Sachs, *History of Botany, 1530-1860* (tr. by Henry E. F. Garnsey, rev. by Isaac Bayley Balfour, second impression, Oxford, 1906), 79.

[4] Joseph Reynolds Green, *A History of Botany in the United Kingdom from the Earliest Times to the End of the 19th Century* (London, 1914), 149.

PART I | CATESBY THE MAN

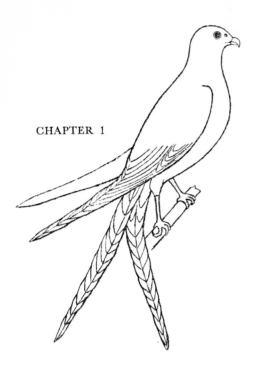

CHAPTER 1

The Background of a Naturalist

The early years of Mark Catesby, like those of many another early laborer in the fields of natural science, have left only a scanty record for the biographer. Until recently no one knew even the year of his birth. Most of those who have written about him have assumed that he was born in Sudbury, Suffolk, about 1679 or 1680. These assumptions derived from the notices of his death in the *Gentleman's Magazine,* which reported his age at the time of his death in 1749 to have been seventy.[1] Fortunately, Mrs. Elsa G. Allen, in the course of her researches into the lives of early American ornithologists, found the record of Catesby's baptism in the parish register of St. Nicholas Church, Castle Hedingham, Essex. The register records, "Mark Catesby, son of John Catesby, gent and Elizabeth, his wife, Baptize March 30, 1683, Nates March 24th, 1682."[2] Thus the future naturalist first saw light on the last day of the year 1682

according to the reckoning of the Julian Calendar, or April 3, 1683, by the Gregorian Calendar, and was christened six days later.[3] It seems likely, then, that he was born in Castle Hedingham, in the home of his maternal grandparents, as his parents hardly would have taken so tender a babe even the few miles from Sudbury to the hamlet across the Stour.

Mark was the youngest son of John Catesby and Elizabeth Jekyll, the fourth of five children who were alive when John Catesby drew up his will in November, 1700.[4] His parents were married in London in 1670, where on May 16 they had made the following allegation for a marriage license: "John Catesby, of Sudbury, Suffolk, Gent., Bachelor, about 28, and Elizabeth Jekyll, of Hedingham Castle, Essex, Spinster, about 18; her father's consent; at St. Andrew's Holborne, or Gray's Inn, or Charterhouse Chapel, London."[5] Within the year, the eldest son, also

---

[1] *Gentleman's Magazine,* XIX (1749), 573; XX (1750), 31-32.

[2] Quoted in Allen, *Am. Ornith.,* 469. Confirmed by a letter from the Rev. C. S. G. Godfrey-Thomas, Rector of St. Nicholas Church, Castle Hedingham, Essex, Feb. 7, 1956.

[3] Mrs. Allen, *Am. Ornith.,* 469, assumes that the entry means March 24, 1681/82, but this seems unlikely in view of the baptismal date, which would place the natal day in 1682/83.

[4] "The Will of John Catesby of Sudbury, Suffolk, Gentleman," made Nov. 18, 1700, proved Jan. 22, 1704/5, *P.C.C. Gee,* 4 (Principal Probate Registry, London).

[5] George J. Armytage, ed., *Allegations for Marriage Licences Issued by the Dean and Chapter of Westminster, 1558 to 1699; Also for the Vicar-General of the Archbishop of Canterbury, 1660 to 1679* (extracted by Joseph L. Chester, *Publications of the Harleian Society,* XXIII, London, 1886), 178.

named John, was baptized at Castle Hedingham, where his brother Jekyll was also carried to the font in 1672.[6] Twin sons, born in 1675, were recorded in 1675 in the registers of St. Gregory's Church, Sudbury, but they do not appear to have survived infancy.[7] Several other children died either at birth or shortly afterward, as they were buried in Castle Hedingham apparently before baptism. The next child, Elizabeth, must have been made of tougher stuff, because she lived four years beyond three-score and ten, dying in March of 1753.[8] She was born, therefore, in either 1680 or 1681. Elizabeth, described by her father as "my disobedient daughter" because she married William Cocke without parental consent, was to have great importance for her brother Mark.[9] It was her residence in Virginia which made it possible for him to make his first trip to America.[10] The family was then completed with Mark and with Ann, the youngest, born in Sudbury in 1688.[11]

The records reveal little that is certain about Mark Catesby's paternal ancestry beyond his father. Apparently the family stemmed from the Catesbys of Northamptonshire and Warwickshire, but the connections are not clear. The family name derived from the Parish of Catesby in Northamptonshire near Daventry.[12] The surname began with one Philip de Catesby, a younger son of the family of Esseby or Ashby in the twelfth century — or so states an "antient pedigree" cited by the great seventeenth-century

Warwickshire antiquary, William Dugdale.[13] The Catesbys embraced several men of local prominence and even of national notoriety.

These included George Catesby of Ecton and Whiston in Northamptonshire, who fell afoul of the law in 1627 for refusing to subscribe to forced loans levied by Charles I and, a decade later, was before the Court of High Commission for alleged Puritan sympathies;[14] Robert Catesby (1573-1605), a principal in the Gunpowder Plot (1604), who won a bullet and a bill of attainder for his pains;[15] and William Catesby (d. 1485), the servant of Richard III and, according to Hall's Chronicle, the "Cat" in the couplet,

> The Rat, the Cat and Lovell our dog
> Rule all England under the Hog.[16]

It seems likely that William Catesby, like his royal master, was traduced by Tudor chroniclers whose slanders were given currency by Shakespeare. But his evil reputation can hardly have been wholly undeserved.

According to Emanuel Mendez da Costa (1717-91), a contemporary and acquaintance of Mark Catesby, William Catesby was one of the latter's direct ancestors.[17] But da Costa, who was dismissed as a clerk of the Royal Society of London in 1767 for having made off with nearly fifteen hundred pounds of the Society's funds, is not the most trustworthy witness.[18] Still, there is no reason to suspect

[6] Letter from the Rev. C. S. G. Godfrey-Thomas.
[7] Allen, Am. Ornith., 469.
[8] Jones, Capt. Roger Jones, 215.
[9] P.C.C. Gee, 4.
[10] Carolina, I, v.
[11] Allen, Am. Ornith., 469.
[12] S[ydenham] H. A. H[ervey], Ladbroke and Its Owners (Bury St. Edmunds, 1914), 66.
[13] William Dugdale, The Antiquities of Warwickshire . . . (London, 1656), 585-87.
[14] Letter to the Rev. Joseph Mead, London, Feb. 23, 1726/27, quoted in Robert F. Williams, ed., The Court and Times of Charles I . . . Transcribed by Thomas Birch (2 vols., London, 1849), I, 196-99; C.S.P., Dom., Charles I, 1637-1638, XII, 64; Acts of the Privy Council, 1627-1628 (London, 1940), 10, 58; Henry Isham Longden, ed., The Visitations of the County of Northampton in the Year 1681 (Pub. of the Harleian Society, LXXXVII, London, 1936), 43-44.
[15] D.N.B.; S. R. Gardiner, History of England from the Accession of James I to the Outbreak of the Civil War (new ed., 10 vols., London, 1895), I, 234-64, 286.
[16] Edward Hall, Hall's Chronicle (London, 1809), 393.
[17] Emanuel Mendez da Costa, "Notices and Anecdotes of Literati, Collectors, Etc., from a MS by the Late Mendez da Costa, and Collected Between 1747 and 1788," Gentleman's Magazine, LXXXII, pt. 1 (1812), 206.
[18] Sir Henry Lyons, The Royal Society 1660-1940: A History of Its Administration Under Its Charters (Cambridge, 1940), 169.

that he bore ill will toward Mark Catesby — nor that the latter would have selected William Catesby had he been fabricating ancestors.

Again, according to W. W. Hodson, the Sudbury antiquary, George Catesby, Esq., the early seventeenth-century Puritan, was Mark Catesby's grandfather.[19] If so, the relationship is difficult, if not impossible, to establish. He did not appear to have a son named John, and his grandson of that name, born in 1631, is obviously not the John Catesby who married Elizabeth Jekyll in 1670, as the latter's age at that time was "about 28." All of which seems a pity, for George Catesby would have made an ideal grandfather for the naturalist. He betrayed strong qualities of stubbornness and tenacity similar to those of Mark Catesby, and his Puritan strain could have helped to explain the easy attitude taken by Mark's father in his dealings with the Nonconformists of Sudbury.

But the plain fact is that we cannot name Mark Catesby's remote forebears with any certainty. So we turn to his father, John Catesby of Sudbury, whose activities are of greater significance in a study of his youngest son than are those of more distant relatives. He was, like so many of the Catesbys, a lawyer, although a solicitor rather than a barrister.[20] Certainly he became a gentleman of some substance, for near the time of his death he possessed an estate which should have permitted the family to live in considerable comfort. According to his will, he had a farm, Holgate, and houses in Sudbury. One of these may have been the one listed in 1674 for a "Mr. Cattesby" in St. Peter's parish. It had five hearths, a number which did not indicate a mansion but was a better-than-average dwelling.[21] The will also listed lands in the nearby parishes of Chilton, Great Cornard, and

Cavendish in Suffolk and in Pentlow in Essex, just across the River Stour from Cavendish. In Pentlow also John Catesby held the advowson to the rectory. Further, he owned a number of houses in the vicinity of Fleet Street, London, which must have been a valuable bit of property even in that day.[22]

John Catesby's name appears often in the records of the political life of the borough of Sudbury in the late seventeenth century. He was a member of a tight little group which governed this cloth-manufacturing town up to the time of the loss of its charter in 1684, and possibly afterward.[23] In 1669, the year before his marriage, he was chosen Town Clerk and Clerk of the Peace, a choice which, after petitions covering a period of five months, was finally confirmed by the King at Whitehall.[24] From 1674 through 1684, Catesby served four one-year terms as Mayor of the municipality and may have held the office again, since the list of mayors compiled by C. F. D. Sperling is blank, except for one year, for the rest of the century.[25]

The events of 1684 throw a good deal of light on the activities of John Catesby. In that year an action for a writ of quo warranto was brought against the corporation of Sudbury to nullify its charter. Catesby, as Mayor, and the rest of the clique which governed the town, apparently attempted to retain control by surrendering their charter. After the fall of the London charter in the previous year, there was little else for the smaller boroughs to do but to acquiesce in this attack on these privileged centers of opposition.[26]

From the point of view of the Court, and especially of the High-Churchmen of Sudbury, the attack was warranted in the case of John Catesby and his cohorts. They were tolerant of Nonconformists, of In-

[19] William Walter Hodson, *The Meeting House and the Manse, or the Story of the Independents of Sudbury* (London, 1893), 58.
[20] Hodson, *Independents of Sudbury*, 52.
[21] *Suffolk in 1674, Being the Hearth Tax Returns* (Suffolk Green Books, No. 11, Woodbridge, 1905), 274.
[22] *P.C.C. Gee*, 4.
[23] Charles Frederick Denne Sperling, *A Short History of the Borough of Sudbury in the County of Suffolk Compiled from Materials Collected by W. W. Hodson* (Sudbury, 1896), 34.
[24] *C.S.P., Dom., Charles II, 1684-1685*, XXVII, 48.
[25] Sperling, *Sudbury*, 78.
[26] *C.S.P., Dom., Charles II, 1684-1685*, XXVII, 48; G. N. Clarke, *The Later Stuarts 1660-1714* (*The Oxford History of England*, VIII, Oxford, 1934), 103-4.

dependents, and even of Anabaptists, a course of action which was not unusual in Puritan East Anglia.[27] This tolerance was no doubt politic, but it was not accomplished with discretion. According to one of the allegations against John Catesby, "Mr. Petto, a Non-conformist and settled preacher to one of the conventicles, constantly lived within the Corporation for ten years last, past, in no more private place than the vicarage house belonging to All Saints Church."[28]

Probably there was some truth in this contention, but there seems to have been a good deal of factional politics in it as well. The principal accuser of John Catesby was Sir John Cordell, who, among other things, obtained the right to search the house of the Mayor and his principal supporters for seditious letters and papers.[29] Among the charges laid against the group in power was one which said that the corporation had been dissuaded from casting its vote for Sir Robert Cordell (Sir John's father) by the "wheadles of Mr. Catesby," who, because Sir Robert's opponent, Sir Gervase Elwes, had made a gift to the corporation of a silver tankard, had built up such support for the latter "as all the Gentlemen in the County could never destroy it."[30] This support does not seem to have survived the upheaval of 1684, as Sir Gervase lost his seat in that year; but thirteen years later John Catesby was still trying to resurrect it and did so successfully.[31]

Such was the immediate paternal background of Mark Catesby. The maternal side was not far different. The Jekylls, like the Catesbys, were a family of lawyers. There is a difference, perhaps, in that the pedigree is clear at least as far back as Bartholemew Jekyll, who lived in Lincolnshire in the time of Henry VI. Perhaps the first notable member of the family was Thomas Jekyll of Bocking, Essex, a member of Clifford's Inn and the Chief Clerk in the Paper Office of the Court of King's Bench. A contemporary of the great William Camden, Thomas Jekyll made the antiquarian collections which later found their way into William Holman's *History of Essex*. John, the fourth son, sired two sons of some eminence: Thomas, who attained some fame for his sermons and other religious works published in the late seventeenth century; and Sir Joseph, who was Master of the Rolls from 1717 to 1742. The fifth and youngest son of the antiquary was Nicholas Jekyll, the maternal grandfather of Mark Catesby. He was a lawyer at Castle Hedingham, and, like his father, was a member of Clifford's Inn.[32] He and his son, also named Nicholas, shared the antiquarian interests of Thomas Jekyll, and they, in turn, inherited his manuscripts and made considerable use of them.[33]

With this picture of lawyers and antiquaries in the background, it is perhaps surprising that Mark Catesby chose to follow natural history rather than the law. Certainly it is difficult to trace influences which might have turned him in the direction in which he went, especially because little documentary evidence of his early years is available. For his own testimony about these years, we have only a few words in the Preface to his great life's work.

The early Inclination I had to search after Plants and other Productions in Nature, being much suppressed by my residing too remote from London, the Center of all Science, I was deprived of all Opportunities and Examples to excite me to a stronger Pursuit after those Things to which I was naturally bent: yet my Curiosity was such, that not being content with contemplating the Products of our own Country, I soon imbibed a passionate desire of viewing as well the Animal as Vegetable Productions in their Native Countries; which were Strangers to England.[34]

[27] C. G. Grimwood and S. A. Kay, *History of Sudbury, Suffolk* (Sudbury, 1952), 68.

[28] Quoted in Sperling, *Sudbury*, 153.

[29] *C.S.P., Dom., Charles II, 1684-1685*, XXVII, 48.

[30] Quoted in W. W. Hodson, "Sudbury Corporation Regalia," *Proceedings of the Suffolk Institute of Archeology and Natural History*, VIII (1894), 1-8.

[31] Hodson, "Sudbury Corporation Regalia"; John Gurdon to [?], Feb. 28, 1689, quoted in Sperling, *Sudbury*, 85.

[32] C. F. D. Sperling, "Thomas Jekyll," *Essex Review*, III (1894), 255, 258-59.

[33] C. F. D. Sperling, "Philip Morant," *Essex Review*, III (1894) 33-34.

[34] *Carolina*, I, v.

There is little positive evidence as to where Mark Catesby was educated. He does not appear to have attended either of the universities, and probably he was not at one of the Inns of Court or Chancery, although John, his eldest brother, was admitted to Clifford's Inn and subsequently matriculated at Cambridge in 1690 before migrating to the Inner Temple.[35] Mark surely had some schooling, as both his correspondence and his *Natural History of Carolina* indicate that he knew a certain amount of Latin. The suggestion by Mrs. Allen that he attended Sudbury Grammar School is a likely conjecture.[36] Unfortunately, that venerable institution, founded in 1491 by William Wood, the Dean of Sudbury College, fell into evil ways, and its records for the period do not survive. A later and more famous Sudbury painter, Thomas Gainsborough, attended the school, but there is no positive evidence that the less celebrated delineator of plants and animals ever entered its doors.[37]

Still another possible source of Mark Catesby's education was Samuel Petto, the minister to the Independents of Sudbury already mentioned. Petto had graduated from St. Catharine's College, Cambridge, in 1644, and he had left his living at Sandcroft, Suffolk, early in 1662, even before the enforcement of the Act of Uniformity. After preaching to conventicles in Norfolk, he transferred his activities to Sudbury before 1675 and remained there until his death in 1711.[38]

Young Mark may have been tutored by this minister whom his father protected. And whether or not the relationship was that of tutor and pupil, Mark Catesby may well have developed a bent toward "natural philosophy" at the hands of this Noncon-

formist preacher. Certainly he must have known the "Grave Divine," as Petto was called in the *Philosophical Transactions*, which published (1699) an account of parhelia seen by him the year before.[39] This could explain the boy's inclination toward science, an inclination strong enough to impel him later to brave the hardships of the Carolina wilderness. However, to say that Mark Catesby studied under the direction of the Reverend Samuel Petto is mere conjecture, and the latter's devotion to natural phenomena may easily be overemphasized. The minister was apparently quite adept at seeing mock suns. He wrote to Increase Mather of an earlier appearance and lamented that after it had occurred there was "no appearance of a deep humiliation in any sort of men, for the Crying sins which provoke the Lord to wrath against us. . . ."[40] This, however, could hardly discredit a late seventeenth-century parson's genuine interest in natural science.

The Jekyll connection at Castle Hedingham was far more important, though, in turning Mark Catesby's mind and hand to the study of nature. Judging from the frequency of the appearance of their names in the registers of St. Nicholas Church, the Catesbys spent a good deal of time in the home of their grandfather, Nicholas Jekyll, until his death in November, 1683, and then in that of their uncle, his namesake.[41] This last Nicholas Jekyll, as has already been said, carried on the antiquarian pursuits of his grandfather. His was more than a passive interest arising from his possession of Thomas Jekyll's manuscripts, as was attested by his fellow laborers in the field. In the edition of Camden's *Britannia* published by Edmund Gibson in 1695, Nicholas Jekyll is mentioned among the authorities on Essex history as "that hope-

[35] J. and J. A. Venn, *Alumni Cantabrigienses . . .* (4 vols., Cambridge, 1922-27), pt. I, I, 307.

[36] Allen, *Am. Ornith.*, 469.

[37] See W. W. Hodson, "The Sudbury Grammar School," *Proceedings of the Suffolk Inst.*, VII (1891), 311-19; William Page, ed., *The Victoria History of the County of Suffolk* (2 vols., London, 1907-11), I, 341.

[38] *D.N.B.* For a bibliography of Petto see Arnold Gwynn

Matthews, *Calamy Revised* (Oxford, 1934), 388.

[39] *Phil. Trans.*, XXI (1699), 107-8.

[40] *Collections of the Massachusetts Historical Society*, ser. 4, VII (1868), 349-50. Nathaniel Mather, brother of the Massachusetts divine, was apparently a predecessor of Petto in Sudbury. See "Will of Samuel Mather," *New-England Historical and Genealogical Register*, LII (1898), 366-68.

[41] Letter from the Rev. C. S. G. Godfrey-Thomas.

ful young Gentleman" who aided the Reverend John Ouseley, then Rector of Pantfield, in his researches.[42] Jekyll's aid apparently included giving Ouseley some of the manuscripts inherited from his grandfather, and from Mr. Ouseley's hands they found their way into the collections of William Holman, whose unpublished history formed the basis for Philip Morant's *History of Essex*. Nicholas Jekyll also worked directly with Holman and eventually gave or sold him the rest of the papers in his possession.[43]

These activities of Nicholas Jekyll placed him in the direct line of descent of Essex historians, but more than that, they brought him into contact with the man who was the premier naturalist of England and, after Isaac Newton, perhaps her foremost scientist. This, of course, was John Ray, who in the second edition of his *Collection of English Words* wrote: "The greater part of the additional Words in the Southern Collection were contributed by my ingenious Friends Mr. Nicholas Jekyll of Sibble Heveningham,[44] and Mr. Mansell Courtman, Minister of Castle Heveningham in Essex."[45] This connection, then, between John Ray and the uncle of Mark Catesby was primarily in matters of philology, as Ray, who conscientiously credited his helpers, does not appear to have mentioned Jekyll's name in any of his other works. The two men, however, shared still another interest, that of botany, though on quite different levels. Nicholas Jekyll, like many another English gentleman of the time, was the owner of a botanical garden.[46]

Yet another possible connection existed between young Mark Catesby and John Ray. This was by means of Mansell Courtman, the associate of Nicholas Jekyll in his contribution to Ray's *Collection of English Words*. Courtman must have served as Rector of St. Nicholas in Mark Catesby's native village during the period between 1685, when he was ordained, and 1691, when he became vicar at Draughton, Northamptonshire.[47] Courtman was the conforming son of a Nonconformist father, John Courtman, who had been ejected from his living in 1662, just as Ray had been forced to leave his fellowship at Trinity College, Cambridge.[48] The younger Courtman, who received both his B.A. and M.A. from Trinity, shared with the sometime Fellow other things than the fact that both were men of the cloth and that both had an interest in English dialects. He was something of a naturalist, or at least a collector, and contributed some seven specimens to Ray's *History of Insects*.[49] His work in natural history probably was stimulated by the fact that he was a physician as well as a priest, though he lacked a degree in "physic." According to his monumental inscription at Draughton, Mr. Courtman was, even without a diploma, as adept at the cure of bodies as of souls.[50]

There is no real evidence to associate Mansell Courtman with the young Mark Catesby, who was, at the most, eight years old when the clergyman moved to his new benefice in Northamptonshire. Still, parson and child could hardly have missed each other in the hamlet, and there is a good possibility that the well-lettered clerk may have taught the boy about the ways of east-country moths. Whatever his connection with Catesby, Courtman established a further tie between Castle Hedingham and the Jekylls and the

[42] Edmund Gibson, ed., *Camden's Britannia Newly Translated into English* . . . (London, 1695), unpaged Preface, "f 2."

[43] C. F. D. Sperling, "William Holman," *Essex Review*, III (1894), 34-35.

[44] Syble Hedingham lies next to Castle Hedingham, and the two might easily have been confused.

[45] John Ray, *A Collection of English Words Not Generally Used* . . . (ed. 2, London, 1691), unpaged Preface, 2nd p.

[46] George Symonds Boulger, "Samuel Dale," *Journal of Botany, British and Foreign* . . . , XXI (1883), 193.

[47] *Alumni Cantab.*, I, 275. The first name is also given as Maunsell. See Henry Isham Longden, *Northamptonshire and Rutland Clergy* (16 vols., Northampton, 1938-52), III, 275.

[48] Matthews, *Calamy Revised*, 138-39; Charles E. Raven, *John Ray, Naturalist: His Life and Works* (Cambridge, 1942), 61. We are principally indebted to this fine biography for material on Ray.

[49] John Ray, *Historia insectorum* (London, 1710), 127, 337.

[50] Longden, *Northants. Clergy*, III, 275.

world of natural history, and especially with that world as it was personified in John Ray.[51]

From these associations, Mark Catesby, in the words of his friend and fellow ornithological illustrator, George Edwards, "Hapned to fall into the acquaintance of the great naturalist Mr. Ray, who then lived in Essex not far from him. This acquaintance inspir'd Catesby with a gen[i]us for natural history."[52] The distances between them were indeed not great — less than ten miles from Black Notley, the parish in which Ray lived, to Castle Hedingham, and not more than sixteen to Sudbury. Moreover, the way to London from either of these places lay through Braintree, which was but a short walk from Dewlands, the home of Ray.[53] Young Mark, still in his early twenties, would have had ample chance to sit at the feet of the ill and aging naturalist before the death of the latter in 1705.

Through Ray and again through Nicholas Jekyll, Catesby met still another man who was to have great importance for him. This was Samuel Dale, the widely recognized apothecary and physician of Braintree. Dale played somewhat the same role in Ray's later years that Francis Willughby had performed earlier. However, he was more assistant than co-worker and patron, as Willughby, the wealthy scientific amateur, had been.[54] In addition to being counselor to and principal collector for his famous friend

during the years when Ray was a partial invalid, Dale won recognition in his own right for his *Pharmacologia.*[55] First published in 1693 with a supplement in 1705, this work, which Pulteney called "one of the first rational books on the subject," saw a third edition before the death of the author in 1739.[56] Dale also contributed frequently to the *Philosophical Transactions,* but his only other major work was his edition of Silas Taylor's *History and Antiquities of Harwich and Dovercourt,* which appeared in 1730 and was so popular that it was reprinted two years later.[57] His principal contribution to the volume was an Appendix devoted to the natural history of the area which has been called almost complete.[58] Although Dale was primarily a collector, in which capacity Mark Catesby served him well, his works demonstrate that he was also a capable and reasonably critical botanist.[59]

Mark Catesby had ample opportunity to gain the friendship and confidence of Samuel Dale, both in their common contact with Ray and also during collecting trips which carried Dale through Castle Hedingham.[60] There the Braintree apothecary must have visited often with Nicholas Jekyll, with whom he shared, in addition to a love for botany, an interest in Essex antiquities.[61] On one of these visits, in 1711, Dale obtained specimens from the garden of Nicholas Jekyll.[62] More than that, this may well have been

---

[51] There is some confusion surrounding Courtman, as his brother Richard, also a physician, held the living at Castle Hedingham, apparently as a sinecure, in 1705. Possibly the "D. Courtman" mentioned in the *Historia insectorum* was Richard rather than Mansell. If so, he may have been in the village when he could have known a more mature Mark Catesby. See *Alumni Cantab.,* I, 275; and Philip Morant, *The History and Antiquities of the County of Essex* (ed. 2, 2 vols., Chelmsford, 1816), II, 299.

[52] George Edwards to Thomas Pennant, London, Dec. 5, 1761, in G. F. Frick, "Mark Catesby . . . ," *Papers of the Bibliographical Society of America,* LVI (1960), 172-75.

[53] Raven, *Ray,* 1-2, 179-80.

[54] Boulger, "Samuel Dale," 194.

[55] Samuel Dale, *Pharmacologia, seu manuductio ad materiam medicam . . .* (London, 1693).

[56] *Pulteney,* II, 123.

[57] See Paul Henry Maty, *A General Index to the Philosophical Transactions . . .* (London, 1787), 602, for a list of Dale's contributions. Silas Taylor, *The History and Antiquities of Dovercourt . . . Now Much Enlarged with Notes and Observations Relating to Natural History by . . . Samuel Dale* (London, 1730).

[58] *D.N.B.*

[59] Boulger, "Samuel Dale," 193.

[60] Miller Christie, "Samuel Dale (1659?-1739) of Braintree, Botanist, and the Dale Family . . . ," *Essex Naturalist,* XIX (1919), 52-53, has suggested incorrectly that Catesby and Samuel Dale became acquainted through Dale's nephew, Francis Dale, who was also a Bahaman traveler. For some of Dale's visits to Castle Hedingham see John Ray's list of Essex plants in Gibson, ed., *Camden's Britannia,* col. 363.

[61] Morant, *Hist. of Essex,* I, vii; II, 397n.

[62] Boulger, "Samuel Dale," 193.

the occasion which set in motion the events which culminated in Catesby's famous *Natural History of Carolina*. The visit was made during the year before Mark Catesby set out for Virginia, where he first tried his hand as a naturalist. In all probability, arrangements were made at this time for the younger man to send specimens of the Virginian flora to the Essex botanist.

In 1711 Mark Catesby was twenty-seven years old, and perhaps that is as much as can be safely said about him. He must, however, have done more in these years than learn a bit of Latin. According to Richard Pulteney, this young man who so passionately wanted to follow the ways of a naturalist went early in his life to London.[63] This may be so, although there would seem to be nothing to corroborate it. *The Historical and Biographical Sketches of the Progress of Botany in England* is still, in many ways, the best book ever written on the subject and has often been treated almost as a primary source. In the case of Catesby this has been especially true. Pulteney, though he wrote forty years after the death of Catesby, knew at least some men who had known the modest author of *The Natural History of Carolina*, such as Philip Miller, John Martyn, and Emanuel Mendez da Costa.[64] He may have had oral

evidence, then, in support of this statement. On the other hand, he may have based it on the passage of Catesby's Preface which said only that its author lived "remote from London. . . ."[65]

Certainly Mark Catesby would have been at some liberty to have gone to the metropolis in 1705 after the death of his father. John Catesby divided his properties rather equitably among his children, and he bequeathed to his youngest son his houses in Sudbury and in the Parish of St. Brides in London and lands in Chilton and Great Cornard in Suffolk.[66] Thus provided with a modest competence, the young man of twenty-one or twenty-two may have headed for the capital, possibly to one of the great nurserymen such as Thomas Fairchild, to whom he later supplied plants and seeds from Virginia.[67]

It seems more likely, however, that during the years of his youth and early manhood Mark Catesby remained in his little part of East Anglia, possibly making a few journeys to London. Here, "Contemplating the Products" of the valley of the Stour amidst the eminent circle of his Uncle Jekyll's friends, he could domesticate a few plants in his uncle's garden and prepare himself for greater things. Then, when the opportunity arose, he made his way across the sea to Virginia, where his life's adventures began.

---

[63] *Pulteney*, II, 220.
[64] *D.N.B.; Pulteney*, II, 241.
[65] *Carolina*, I, v.

[66] *P.C.C. Gee*, 4.
[67] *Phil. Trans.*, XXIX (1715), 357.

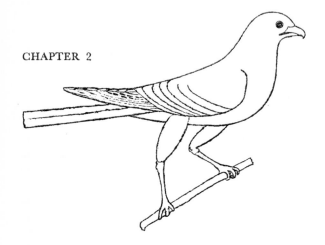

CHAPTER 2

The Apprenticeship of a Naturalist, 1712-22

"Virginia was the Place," wrote Mark Catesby, as he looked back on his first voyage to America. It was a place which might stir the imagination of a young man who sought a new and more exciting life. But more than a search for adventure drew him to the land on Chesapeake Bay. He was a practical man whose resources were modest and, although he had an intense interest in natural history, he had no patrons to ease his way. "Virginia was the Place (I having Relations there) suited most with my Convenience to go. . . ."[1] This was Catesby's prosaic and somewhat anticlimactic account of his first voyage to Virginia. The young naturalist, like many another traveler with large ideas and small purse, stayed with relatives, with his sister Elizabeth and her husband Dr. William Cocke.

Elizabeth Catesby had married William Cocke "the younger" some time before her father's will was

drawn in November, 1700. John Catesby, who did not approve of the marriage, tartly made a small bequest to his eldest daughter in the event her "supposed Husband" should "be imprisoned for debt or other cause or . . . goe beyond sea or otherwise absent and abscond himself from her. . . ."[2] The inclusion of the second of these dire possibilities suggests that Dr. Cocke may have been planning to emigrate for some time. When he did — it was apparently shortly after 1700 — he took his wife with him. More than that, he prospered, and his descendants helped populate the American South with a goodly number of people bearing Catesby as a Christian name.[3] Surely this confounded the gloomy predictions of the testy magistrate.

William Cocke, unlike a great many "doctors of physic" in his day, had at least some university training in medicine, having received his M.B. at Queens'

[1] *Carolina*, I, v.

[2] "The Will of John Catesby of Sudbury, Suffolk, Gentleman," made Nov. 18, 1700, proved Jan. 22, 1704/5, *P.C.C. Gee,* 4 (Principal Probate Registry, London).

[3] See Jones, *Capt. Roger Jones, passim.* One of the more famous of these was Commander Catesby ap Roger Jones, U.S.N. and then of the Confederate Navy, who commanded

the *Virginia* (the *Merrimac*) in its struggle with the *Monitor.* "We cannot choose but pause a moment," according to a loyal Southerner, "to uncover and salute the heroic shade of this glorious sailor, whose place is assured in the naval annals of the world alongside that of Sir Richard Grenville . . . and of the mighty seamen of 'the spacious times of the Great Elizabeth.'" "Proceedings of the Virginia Historical Society, 1919," *Va. Mag.,* XXVII (1919), xxvii.

College, Cambridge, in 1693.[4] According to a tablet in his memory in Bruton Parish Church at Williamsburg, this pioneer of Virginia medicine was "learned and polite, of undisputed Skill in his profession, Of unbounded generosity in his practice. . . ."[5] Moreover, Cocke was an unqualified success politically and socially in Virginia. He obtained the patronage of Lieutenant Governor Alexander Spotswood and, shortly after his brother-in-law arrived in America, was sworn in as Secretary to the colony.[6] In a little more than a year, on August 8, 1713, he was, by an order in Council, elevated further in the political life in Virginia and became one of Her Majesty's councilors.[7]

It was to Williamsburg and to the Cockes that Mark Catesby went on April 23, 1712.[8] The little capital should not have disappointed him. With its capitol, college, and the still-unfinished governor's palace, Williamsburg was reputed by a near contemporary of Catesby to have the finest buildings in British America, structures which were "exceeded by a few of their kind in England." Here, too, many people of quality lived the year round and were joined by many others during "publick times." "They live," said this observer, "in the same neat manner, dress after the same modes, and behave themselves exactly as the gentry in London; most families of any note having a coach, chariot, berlin, or chaise."[9]

Only a week after his arrival, Catesby met the head of one of the principal families of the colony, William Byrd of Westover, the second of that name,

F.R.S. and a member of the Council of Virginia.[10] Certainly the naturalist wasted no time in meeting the people who would enable him to learn the natural history of this new land. Through William Cocke he had access to men like Byrd, who was at this time still on good terms with the Doctor. We are fortunate that the acquaintance was made, because the few pages of the diary of William Byrd which were crossed by Catesby provide us with the most intimate and detailed account available for any period in his life.

A short time after this first visit, on May 24 to be exact, Mark Catesby, his sister and brother-in-law and their daughter again went from Williamsburg to Westover, Byrd's seat on the James River. Dr. Cocke left for home again in a few days; but Catesby stayed on, in good Virginian fashion, for more than three weeks.[11] Evidently the visit was a pleasant one. The master of Westover met his guests with cakes and a bottle of canary, and, in the late afternoon, Catesby and his niece were led by their host into the swamp, where they looked for the nest of a hummingbird. Byrd and his guest took a number of walks around the plantation, which must have provided Catesby with a good introduction to the American flora and fauna. Even though Byrd was at best an enthusiastic, and often gullible, amateur naturalist, he did know a great deal about the natural products of Virginia. Catesby, with his experience in gardening, was able to assist his new-found friend. Byrd confided to his diary that "Mr. Catesby directed how I should mend my garden and put it into better fashion than it is at present."

[4] J. and J. A. Venn, *Alumni Cantabrigienses* . . . (4 vols., Cambridge, 1922-27), pt. I, I, 362.

[5] "The Cocke Family of Virginia," *Va. Mag.*, V (1897), 190.

[6] Henry Read McIlwaine and Wilmer L. Hall, eds., *The Executive Journals of the Council of Colonial Virginia* (5 vols., Richmond, 1925-45), III, 317.

[7] *C.S.P., Col., 1711-1712*, XXVII, 276.

[8] *Carolina*, I, v.

[9] Hugh Jones, *The Present State of Virginia* . . . (Richard L. Morton, ed., Chapel Hill, N.C., [1956]), 70-71.

[10] Louis B. Wright and Marion Tinling, eds., *The Secret Diary of William Byrd of Westover, 1709-1712* (Richmond, 1941), 523. There is much material on Byrd. For bio-

graphical information see Richard C. Beatty, *William Byrd of Westover* (Boston and New York, 1932); John Spencer Bassett, ed., *The Writings of Colonel William Byrd* . . . (New York, 1901), Introduction, ix-lxxxviii; Raymond P. Stearns, "Colonial Fellows of the Royal Society of London, 1661-1788," *Notes and Records of the Royal Society of London*, VIII (1951), 197; Maude H. Woodfin, "William Byrd and the Royal Society," *Va. Mag.*, XL (1932), 23-24, 111-23; Louis B. Wright, *The First Gentlemen of Virginia* (San Marino, Calif., 1940), 320-47.

[11] Wright and Tinling, eds., *Byrd Diary*, supply the sources for Catesby's visits. See 534-44, 585-92. This second visit apparently ended on June 15.

However, the two men did not spend all their time in the pursuit of natural history. In the evenings they frequently drank a bottle, and on at least one occasion had so much that the pious master of Westover neglected to say his prayers at bedtime. One day they spent a rather festive time aboard ship and, on the way home, "were so merry that Mr. Catesby sang." The implication was that this was an unwonted amount of levity for the reserved East Anglian newcomer to Virginia.

Mark Catesby made another visit to Westover in the early autumn of 1712. He arrived on September 17, bearing a letter from Dr. Cocke with news from Williamsburg. The two men appear to have repeated much the same sort of schedule followed during the earlier sojourn — at least for the first few days. Shortly afterward, however, the routine was broken by another letter from Cocke summoning Colonel Byrd to meet Governor Spotswood and his company at the Pamunkey Indian town on the Pamunkey River. Apparently, difficulties between the Councilor and Governor were already beginning and Byrd had to prove loyalty in attendance.[12] Mark Catesby accompanied his host.

This visit to Pamunkey probably afforded Catesby his first opportunity to view the Indians, other than those he may have seen previously in the capital. Accordingly, it was the beginning of his observations which would eventually develop into his fine discourse on the aborigines of North America.[13] The Colonel and his guest rode north from Westover on September 22, and, after spending the night at the plantation of Sherwood Lightfoot on the Pamunkey River, met the Governor the next day at the Indian town. Their view of its inhabitants was, perhaps, diminished by rain. Byrd, however, commented on one Indian who had twenty wives and of another "who was ill of a bite of a rattlesnake but was on the recovery having taken some snakeroot." Thus was Catesby introduced early to one of the persistent myths of the American pharmacopoeia — a myth stubbornly upheld by William Byrd.

On the following day, the two men rode south and east to the plantation of Colonel William Bassett, located on the Pamunkey River just a short distance from where it flows into the York.[14] Along the way, Catesby was able to witness other customs of Virginia, this time of the white inhabitants. He stayed briefly at New Kent Court House for the election of burgesses, proceedings which could scarcely have surprised the son of a Sudbury politician. Much more exciting was the walk he and Byrd took the next day around the Bassett holdings, during the course of which Catesby killed two snakes.

Travel, or even living in these lowland areas, was not without its hazards. Colonel Bassett, whose lands were surrounded by swamps, was suffering from a malarial fever while his guests were tramping his fields in search of natural history specimens. On September 27, after they had returned home, the travelers too were seized with the ague, a common complaint among the inhabitants of the Virginia Tidewater.[15] Byrd, who was something of a hypochondriac, prescribed a rather uncomfortable treatment, a chilly dip in the James. But it — or perhaps something else — precipitated a cure, for Byrd recorded that Catesby "was seized with a violent loose-

[12] The difficulties between Byrd and Spotswood at this time were apparently the work of a Mrs. Russell, who told the Governor that Byrd was only giving himself "an air" in waiting on Spotswood. Their later and more serious disputes concerned the collection of quitrents in the colony. Byrd went to London in 1715, as an agent of the Assembly, to press his case. Wright and Tinling, eds., *Byrd Diary,* 586; Beatty, *William Byrd,* 81-86.

[13] *Carolina,* II, vii-xvi.

[14] See Peter Jefferson and Joshua Fry, *A Map of the Most Inhabited Part of Virginia Containing the Whole Provence*

of Maryland with Part of Pensilvania, New Jersey and North Carolina (London, [1754?]). Available in a facsimile edition, with Introduction by Dumas Malone (Princeton, N.J., 1940).

[15] Richard L. Morton, ed., Hugh Jones, *Present State,* 207n, seems to try to minimize the prevalence of malaria, using Wyndham B. Blanton's *Medicine in Virginia in the Seventeenth Century* (Richmond, 1930) as an authority. However, malaria seems to have been endemic among Byrd's friends, and Hugh Jones called it the "country distemper." Wright and Tinling, eds., *Byrd Diary,* 587-90; Hugh Jones, *Present State,* 85.

ness which carried away his fever." That is, without doubt, the most intimate record we have of any incident in Catesby's life.

Unfortunately, he figures in the events of only one more day in Byrd's diaries. On September 12 the Colonel recorded that his guest shot a bear — a cub — which sat in a tree eating grapes. The incident does not testify to Catesby's prowess as a hunter, but it underscores his constant interest in the wildlife of Virginia.

These days at Westover marked the beginning of a long friendship between Mark Catesby and William Byrd, a friendship which was continued by correspondence in later years.[16] Despite the fact that Dr. Cocke favored Governor Spotswood, when the Governor and Byrd quarreled, apparently Catesby did not become involved. Though Byrd later referred disdainfully to the Doctor as a "devoted Creature to the Lieut. Governor," his disdain did not extend to the brother-in-law of Secretary Cocke.[17]

Catesby did not, as these days spent with Byrd would seem to indicate, indulge merely in aimless sightseeing during this first summer and autumn in America. He was also busy collecting botanical specimens. One product of his efforts was a small packet of seeds which Governor Spotswood sent, in the spring of 1713, to Henry Compton, Bishop of London, the enthusiastic amateur botanist whose garden at Fulham Palace was famed for its exotics. "These are collected," wrote the Governor, "by a Gentleman now in this Country, a nephew of Mr. Jekyll's of Castle Haningham [Hedingham] and one very curious in such things."[18] Unfortunately for Spotswood, who was no doubt attempting to curry favor with this clerical member of the Council of Trade and Plantations, Bishop Compton died without having acknowledged the gift and possibly even before its arrival.[19]

Catesby also collected "botanicals" for Samuel Dale, a project which became his repeated concern throughout his stay in America, thereby maintaining a relationship which was to become so very important to him.[20] It is likely, too, that some of his collections were sent home to his uncle, Nicholas Jekyll. At least, in later years, Catesby wrote of several "Sweet flowering Acacia" trees growing at Castle Hedingham which probably had been planted at about this time.[21] Still other seeds went to Thomas Fairchild, the nurseryman of Hoxton and the author of the *City Gardener,* a manual for those who wanted to cultivate plants in a London which was already affected by the smoke of "sea coal." The shipments to Fairchild helped to bring the name of "that curious Botanist Mr. Mark Catesby of Virginia" before scientific circles in London, as they were publicized by James Petiver, that indefatigable promoter of botany and natural history.[22]

Besides the items sent to England, Mark Catesby aided his new-found American friends, and in doing so enlarged his knowledge of gardening. Among those whom he aided were Thomas Jones, a prosperous merchant and planter who later married his niece,

[16] See below, pp. 92-93.

[17] Quoted by Bassett, ed., *Writings of Wm. Byrd,* lxix.

[18] Gov. Spotswood to the Bishop of London, Nov. 16, 1713, in Robert Alonzo Brock, ed., *The Official Letters of Governor Alexander Spotswood (Collections of the Virginia Historical Society,* Vols. I, II, Richmond, 1882-85), II, 44-45.

[19] For Compton see *D.N.B.* Brock states that the letter was sent to Compton's successor, John Robinson. This appears unlikely, considering the subject. The letter is badly annotated. Edward Carpenter's *The Protestant Bishop, Being the Life of Henry Compton, 1632-1713* (New York, 1956) ignores Compton's scientific interests and associations.

[20] George Symonds Boulger, "Samuel Dale," *Journal of Botany, British and Foreign . . . ,* XXI (1883), 225; "Seeds from Virginia Sent by Mr. Catesby to Mr. Dale," *Sloane*

3339, fols. 73b-75, may date from this early period.

[21] Catesby to [William Sherard?], Charles Town, Jan. 17, 1723/24, *Sherard Letters,* II, No. 175. For the opportunity to consult and permission to quote from these and other manuscript sources in the archives of the Royal Society of London the authors wish to express their deep appreciation to the President and Fellows of the Society and their sincere thanks to the Society's librarians, Messrs. I. Kaye and N. H. Robinson.

[22] James Petiver, "Botanicum hortense, IV," *Phil. Trans.,* XXIX (1715), 357, 358, 359, 362. For Petiver's activities see Raymond P. Stearns, "James Petiver, Promoter of Natural Science," *Proceedings of the American Antiquarian Society,* n.s., LXII (1952), 243-365.

Elizabeth Cocke, and John Custis, who was a talented amateur botanist in his own right. Years later Peter Collinson, the prominent and much-beloved Quaker collector and scientific entrepreneur, wrote to Custis expressing Catesby's concern that "the Race of that Curious peach colour'd Dogwood is lost." The young visitor from England had planted shoots of this plant in the gardens of both men. Those in the Jones garden were destroyed by fire, and Catesby feared for those of Custis. His fears were not unfounded, for apparently the Custis plants never flowered.[23]

Catesby's must have been a pleasant life during his first years in Virginia. He explored the fields in the Tidewater plantations, enjoyed the bounties of hospitality of the gentlemen of the area, and rewarded them with occasional blooms for their gardens. However, he did not confine himself to the Tidewater. In 1714, according to one of the finest descriptive passages in his *Natural History*, Catesby, in company with others not identified, "travelled from the lower part of St. James River in Virginia to that part of the Apalatchian mountains where the sources of that river rise. . . ." Despite the statement, it does not appear that Catesby and his party traced the James to its sources. Some twelve miles from the mountains, according to Catesby, his party left the river and began their climb toward the first of the mountains. There is no indication that they went much beyond.[24]

During this same year (1714), Catesby also made a voyage to the West Indies, primarily to visit Jamaica. Undoubtedly a powerful influence which drew him to the sugar island was *The Natural History of Jamaica* by Dr. Hans Sloane, the first volume of which had elicited high praise and had quickened

interests farther, even, than Sudbury when it was published in 1707.[25] Sloane, as patron, and his work, as example, were later to figure strongly in the efforts of the younger naturalist to provide a similar treatment for Carolina and the Bahamas. Catesby shipped on a vessel carrying provisions for the island, sharing his accommodations with a load of sheep, "which as they approached the South, gradually dropt their Fleeces, which by the Time they arrived at the Island, was all fallen off, and was succeeded by Hair like that of Goats."[26] It was on this voyage, also, that Catesby got a glimpse of the Bermudas. Catesby left little account of what he did on his excursion into the Caribbean. He recorded having seen the remains of "Cacao-Walks," which had been planted by the Spaniards in Jamaica, and the "Plat Palmetto" in Bermuda.[27] But again, as in Virginia, he did not confine himself to mere observation. In Jamaica, and perhaps in Bermuda as well, the eager botanist made collections to confirm and to supplement those of Sloane. Samuel Dale mentioned Jamaican plants in his possession in January, 1718/19, which most likely had been received from Catesby's hand,[28] and the apothecary also recorded "two Quiers [quires] of Jamaica plants sent me by Mr. Catesby," which he had received before April 1 of the same year.[29]

Of the remaining years of Catesby's residence in Virginia very little evidence remains. Quite possibly a good part of his time was spent at Windsor, the plantation of Major William Woodward in Caroline County. At least we have the word of the genealogist of the descendants of Elizabeth Catesby Cocke to this effect.[30] The family papers hardly substantiate this,

[23] Collinson to Custis, Feb. 20, 1737/38, quoted in Earl G. Swem, ed., "Brothers of the Spade: Correspondence of Peter Collinson, of London, and of John Custis, of Williamsburg, Virginia, 1734-1746," *Proceedings of the American Antiquarian Society*, LVIII (1948), 67; same to same, 1738, *ibid.*, 70; *Carolina*, I, 27.

[24] *Carolina*, II, v, vi.

[25] Hans Sloane, *A Voyage to the Ilands Madera, Barbados, Nieves, S. Christophers and Jamaica with the Natural History of the Herbs and Trees, Four-footed Beasts, Fishes,*

Birds, Insects, Reptiles Etc. . . . (2 vols., London, 1707-25), commonly called *The Natural History of Jamaica.*

[26] *Carolina*, II, xxxi.

[27] *Carolina*, I, xli; II, *Appendix*, 6; "Plat Palmetto" — *Sabal palmetto* (Walter) Loddiges.

[28] Dale to William Sherard, Braintree, Jan. 19, 1718/19, *Sherard Letters*, II, No. 203; same to same, Feb. 2, 1718/19, *ibid.*, No. 204.

[29] Same to same, Braintree, April 1, 1719, *Sherard Letters*, II, No. 206a.

[30] Jones, *Capt. Roger Jones*, 120.

but neither do they refute it.[31] Catesby wrote of fossilized shells found at a depth of seventy feet in the shaft of a well which was dug at Windsor. He did not say, however, that he saw them; and since his niece, Ann Cocke, later married Major Woodward, he may have heard about the incident by a letter received after his return to England.[32]

At least a part of Catesby's last years in Virginia may have been devoted to the management of the affairs of William Cocke while the latter was in England. The good Doctor left Virginia in the late spring of 1716 and did not return until almost two years later.[33] Ostensibly, the principal object of his leave, which was officially for one year, was to oversee the publication of the laws of the colony. Actually, however, he appears to have gone to strengthen the case of Governor Spotswood against William Byrd, who was already in London.[34] While Cocke was waiting upon the English Board of Trade, his interests in Virginia must have required considerable superintendence, for he was a member of the official company trading with the Indians and he had acquired a considerable amount of land.[35] Moreover, his children were all relatively young;[36] and, in these circumstances, it seems likely that his brother-in-law lent a helping hand in the oversight of his private affairs and gave protective comfort to his family.

What did Catesby accomplish during his years in Virginia? His own estimate of his accomplishments was rather low. In the first volume of his *Natural History of Carolina* he wrote:

I thought then so little of prosecuting a Design of the Nature of this Work, that in the Seven Years I resided in that Country, (I am ashamed to own it) I chiefly gratified my Inclination in observing and admiring the various Pro-

ductions of those Countries . . . only sending from thence some dried Specimens of Plants and some of the most Specious of them in Tubs of Earth, at the Request of some curious Friends, amongst whom was Mr. Dale of Braintree. . . .

These, along with a "few observations on the country" which he also sent to Dale, were the only results he would claim for those years.[37]

Still, Catesby's residence in Virginia from the spring of 1712 until the autumn of 1719 had not been as barren as his words indicated. During these seven years, the naturalist had learned a great deal about America which was of invaluable assistance to him when, in 1722, he returned with greater purpose. *The Natural History of Carolina* was much richer for the undisciplined "observing and admiring" of these earlier years. Indeed, it abounded with references to Virginia and comparisons with the products of the more northerly colony. Some of its plates were copies of drawings made during Catesby's residence in Virginia.[38] These years spent by the James, the York, and the Rappahannock gave Catesby wider experience and greater perception when he later worked along the Ashley, the Cooper, and the Savannah than he could possibly have had had he come fresh from Britain with no previous knowledge of or personal acquaintances in America.

Actually, Catesby himself did not fully appreciate the most important results of his American sojourn. These were the good impressions which he and his collections had made on such men as Samuel Dale and, through Dale and possibly others, on William Sherard. Sherard was, in Catesby's words, "one of the most celebrated Botanists of this Age."[39] Indeed, after the death of the great John Ray, Sherard was the foremost English botanist.[40] He has fallen into

[31] *The Papers of the Jones Family* . . . (MSS in the Library of Congress).

[32] *Carolina*, II, vii; Jones, *Capt. Roger Jones*, 120.

[33] Cocke was absent from the Council after May 2, 1716, and was not present again until April 30, 1718. McIlwaine and Hall, eds., *Va. Counc. Journ.*, III, 424-66.

[34] *C.S.P., Col., 1715-1716*, XXIX, 92, 163; *Journal of the Commissioners for Trade and Plantations* (14 vols., London, 1920-38), III, 179, 289, 291.

[35] *C.S.P., Col., 1715-1716*, XXIX, 74; *Va. Mag.*, V (1897), 192.

[36] See Jones, *Capt. Roger Jones*, 215-16.

[37] *Carolina*, I, v.

[38] *Carolina*, I, 48, 67, 70.

[39] *Carolina*, I, v.

[40] See George Pasti, Jr., *Consul Sherard; Amateur Botanist and Patron of Learning* (unpublished Ph.D. dissertation, University of Illinois, 1950).

the obscurity so widely accorded the followers of botany in the pre-Linnaean decades of the eighteenth century, an obscurity partially explained by the fact that he published so little. He made a few contributions to the *Philosophical Transactions,* edited the *Paradisus Batavus* of Paul Hermann,[41] and compiled the *Schola botanica,* a catalog of plants in French and Dutch gardens;[42] but even these two books were published anonymously. His great work, an attempt to bring up to date the *Pinax* of Caspar Bauhin, was unfinished at his death and lies buried, still in manuscript, in the Library of the Oxford Botanical Garden. This work was an attempt to gather together the entire synonymy for all plants. As such it proved beyond the reach of the lifetime of such an exacting man as Sherard. J. J. Dillenius, who was brought by Sherard from the Continent to help in this task, failed him in the end. The first to hold the chair of botany at Oxford which was founded by Sherard, Dillenius became too involved in his own work on the mosses, and in compiling the *Hortus Elthamensis,* ever to complete Sherard's great project.[43]

The *Pinax* was to have great importance for Mark Catesby. Late in 1717 Sherard arrived in England, after making a tour of the Continent on his way home from the Levant. He had sought, and quite successfully, to gain a fortune as Consul to the British factory at Smyrna.[44] Unfortunately he had not found time to pursue his great work in Turkey and, worse still, his collections had been depleted by time and excessive generosity.[45] His plans and the arrival of Catesby from America within two years after Sherard's return from the Near East turned out to be mutually advantageous to the two men.

As early as August 17, 1718, Samuel Dale had written to Sherard about plants he had received from Catesby in Virginia and offered to permit the Consul

to see them.[46] On February 24, 1718/19, the Braintree apothecary had sent some of the plants to Sherard, and, in the next few months, he followed them with others.[47] Already Dale had thought about the possibility of securing Sherard's patronage for his friend in America, as his correspondence with the Consul amply demonstrates.

Apparently, however, he had not accomplished his object before Catesby's return to England. On October 15 of the same year (1719), Dale announced to Sherard: "Mr. Catesby is come from Virginia. . . ." This is the nearest we can come to dating Catesby's arrival in England. It was also the beginning of a more determined effort on the part of Dale to persuade the Consul to take an active interest in Catesby. "He intends againe to returne," the apothecary continued, "and will take an opportunity to waite upon you with some paintings of Birds etc., which he hath done. It's [a] pitty some incouragement can't be found for him; he may be very useful for the perfecting of Natural History."[48] A little more than two months later Dale repeated these sentiments in a letter to Sherard, saying that Catesby intended soon to go to London and would wait upon him then.[49] The meeting, however, did not take place so soon. The letter of introduction which Catesby carried from his friend in Essex to Sherard in London was dated May 11, 1720.[50]

Such a project as Catesby would undertake in Carolina had been under consideration in English scientific circles for more than a decade, perhaps since the death of the Reverend John Bannister of Virginia in 1692. In England, an enthusiastic group of collectors, many of them associated with the Royal Society, who met together often during the 1690's and the early years of the eighteenth century as the

[41] *Paradisus Batavus, continens plus centum plantas . . .* (Leyden, 1698). See Pasti, *Sherard,* 72.

[42] *Schola botanica, sive catalogus plantarum . . .* (Amsterdam, 1698). See Pasti, *Sherard,* 43-45.

[43] Pasti, *Sherard,* 227.

[44] Pasti, *Sherard,* 118, 171.

[45] James Sherard to Richard Richardson, London, Aug. 4, 1716, *MS Radcliffe Trust,* C. III, fol. 37.

[46] *Sherard Letters,* II, No. 198.

[47] *Sherard Letters,* II, Nos. 196, 203, 244, 206a.

[48] *Sherard Letters,* II, No. 211.

[49] *Sherard Letters,* II, No. 212, Dec. 23, 1719.

[50] *Sherard Letters,* II, No. 215.

Temple Coffee House Club, had supplied both ideas and funds for ventures of this sort. William Sherard and Hans Sloane had been members of this informal coterie of botanists and others interested in natural science; and Samuel Dale had attended meetings when in London.[51] Probably no single member, though, had done as much to promote collections overseas as James Petiver, the apothecary, who maintained a tremendous correspondence with like-minded people in the British colonies and throughout the world. The most ambitious plan, prior to Catesby's, and which may have provided the idea for the later expedition, was that which had been advanced by one of Petiver's correspondents, John Lawson, the Surveyor General of North Carolina. Lawson was the author of *A New Voyage to Carolina,* published in 1709, which reappeared in 1714 and later as *The History of Carolina: Containing the Exact Descriptions and Natural History of that Country: Together with the Present State Thereof,* a work which, in itself, provided the best (though somewhat credulous) account of the flora and fauna of Carolina which had been published before Catesby produced his *Natural History of Carolina.* At Petiver's urging, Lawson, late in 1710, had promised that he would compile what would have amounted to a complete natural history of the area. Unfortunately for science (but fortunately perhaps for Catesby), Lawson was never able to carry his grand project to a successful conclusion, as he met death at the hands of some Tuscarora Indians in the following year. While Lawson's death had been a severe blow to the hopes of English promoters, it had not extinguished their hopes altogether. James Petiver, too, had died in 1718, so now it fell partly to William Sherard to fill the gap and to assume leadership in undertakings of this kind.[52]

Just when the project to send Catesby to Carolina was formulated is not clear from the correspondence of Consul Sherard. There was no mention of it during the summer of 1720. By September, though, plans to send a painter to America were developing. Sherard wrote to his friend, Dr. Richard Richardson of North Bierly, Yorkshire, on September 20: "Albin thinks of doing the English Scarabaei, Libellae, and Araneae; but has proposals of going to Carolina, to paint there in the summer months, and in the winter to paint in the Carribbe ilands."[53] The reference was to Eleazer Albin, whose *Natural History of English Insects* had first been published in this year. Dawson Turner, the editor of the Richardson correspondence, suggests that when Albin declined the offer, the negotiations were transferred to Catesby.[54] This is quite plausible because of the time at which the Catesby project was first announced. It is even more likely that Sherard had already planned to use the services of his new friend in America. Albin's rejection of the proposal probably provided the destination and made available at least some of the subscribers who were necessary to finance a return to any part of America other than Virginia.

On October 19, 1720, Samuel Dale wrote to Sherard that he had forwarded a letter to Catesby which contained materials relating to the latter.[55] This must have been the communication in which the proposal was definitely made. On the day following Dale's letter, the following notation was made in the *Council Minutes* of the Royal Society:

Colonel Francis Nicholson going Governor to South Carolina was pleased to declare that he would allow Mr. Catesby, recommended to him as a very proper person to Observe the Rarities of that Country for the uses and purposes of the Society the Pension of Twenty Pounds per Annum during his Government there, and at the Same time to give him Ten pounds by way of advance for the first half Years payment and so for the future a Years pay beforehand.[56]

[51] For the Temple Coffee House Club see Pasti, *Sherard,* 48-55. Professor Pasti is the discoverer of the group.

[52] The summary above is taken from Stearns, "James Petiver," *passim.*

[53] *MS Radcliffe Trust,* C. IV, fol. 19; also in *Richardson*

Extracts, 156; and Nichols, *Illust. Lit. Hist.,* I, 370-71.

[54] *Richardson Extracts,* 156.

[55] *Sherard Letters,* II, No. 218.

[56] *R.S. Council Minutes,* II, 324.

This declaration by the first Royal Governor of South Carolina is significant both in fixing the approximate time the project was conceived and in showing the place of the Royal Society in it. Clearly, Catesby's proposed work in America was approved "for the uses and purposes of the Society," and, although the Society, as such, contributed no funds to the enterprise, its stamp of approval — wholly in keeping with its policies —[57] lent great prestige to the undertaking, and induced other patrons the more readily to loosen their purse strings.

Financial assistance, then, came from individual patrons. William Sherard appears to have taken over the task of soliciting and organizing contributors, but it did not move forward speedily. On November 12 Sherard wrote to Dr. Richardson:

Mr. Catesby a Gentleman of small fortune, who liv'd some years in Virginia with a relation, pretty well skill'd in Natural history who designs and paints in water colours to perfection, is going over with General Nicholson, Governor of Carolina; that Gent. allows him 20£ a year and we are indeavouring to get subscriptions for him, viz. Sir Hans, Mr. Dubois, and myself, who are all that have yet subscribed to him but I'm in hopes to get the Duke of Chandos, which will be a good help.[58]

The names of these men, Sherard, Sir Hans Sloane, Charles Dubois, and James Brydges, first Duke of Chandos, were on the final list of patrons of the

enterprise.[59] The first three apparently provided the principal support. Sir Hans, Court Physician and collector par excellence, whose mammoth collections were to form the basis of the British Museum, was always a ready patron for anyone likely to swell his hoard.[60] Despite previous disappointments, he remained undiscouraged, as was indicated in his letter to Richard Richardson a year later:

There are two or three people, well qualified, going abroad, to Guinea, Maryland, and the Canaries or East Indies, from whose travels there may reasonably be expected observations of considerable Consequence to Natural Historians; and though by Mr. Vernon and Mr. Jones in such undertakings my friends and self have been very much disappointed and losers, yet I intend to encourage all of these undertakings, notwithstanding they cannot promise better than they did.[61]

Aside from Sloane, and possibly Dr. Richard Mead, the other subscribers to Catesby's American undertaking had not hitherto distinguished themselves as patrons of natural history. Charles Dubois, Nabob and Treasurer of the East India Company, had a transitory reputation as a collector of exotics.[62] James Brydges, the heir to a minor barony, attained financial power and a dukedom through a successful career as a war profiteer. He is remembered more as a patron of the arts, for his support of Handel particularly, however, than for his contributions to scientific enter-

---

[57] See Raymond P. Stearns, "The Royal Society of London, Retailer in Experimental Philosophy, 1660-1800," *Dargan Historical Essays* (William C. Dabney and Josiah C. Russel, eds., Albuquerque, N.M., 1952), 39-44, and esp. 51-52. The financial position of the Royal Society was never very secure, and the Society rarely contributed funds directly to scientific expeditions — though it could and did often persuade others to subscribe to them. See R. K. Bluhm, "Remarks on the Royal Society's Finances, 1660-1768," *Notes and Records of the Royal Society of London,* XIII (1958), 82-103, for the financial status of the Society in this period.

[58] *MS Radcliffe Trust,* C. IV, fol. 23; also in *Richardson Extracts,* 157-58; and Nichols, *Illust. Lit. Hist.,* I, 371-72.

[59] The list of patrons as given in *Carolina,* I, vi, is:
"His Grace the Duke of Chandois
The Right Honourable Thomas [Robert Harley?] Earl of Oxford
The Right Honourable John Lord Percival
Sir George Markham, Bart, F.R.S.
Sir Henry Goodrick, Bart.

Sir Hans Sloane, Bart. President of the Royal Society, and of the College of Physicians
The Honourable Colonel Francis Nicholson, Governor of South Carolina
Richard Mead, M.D. and F.R.S.
William Sherard, L.L.D. and F.R.S."

[60] Sloane, who deserves better biographical treatment than he has received, has been treated in two recent books, which should be read together: Gavin Rylands de Beer, *Sir Hans Sloane and the British Museum* (London, 1953), and Eric St. John Brooks, *Sir Hans Sloane the Great Collector and His Circle* (London, 1954).

[61] Sloane to Richardson, Nov. 28, 1721, quoted in Nichols, *Illust. Lit. Hist.,* I, 278-79. William Vernon collected in Maryland in 1698. The Rev. Hugh Jones, not to be confused with the author of *The Present State of Virginia,* collected there from 1698 to 1702. See Stearns, "James Petiver," 292-310.

[62] *D.N.B.*

prise.[63] His name ostentatiously appears first on the list in *The Natural History of Carolina,* as was befitting both to his rank and the hopes of Mark Catesby.[64]

The Duke, it appears, had become convinced of the ability of the naturalist, but he was at first unwilling to send him to America. Indeed, during the early months of 1721 he toyed seriously with other plans. In February Sherard wrote: "Mr. Catesby is going for Africa in the Companie's service where he will do our business as well if not better than in Carolina, which is better known to us."[65] Six weeks later this plan had advanced further, as the Consul again informed Richardson that "Mr. Catesby is not yet fixt with the African Company, but will be, I believe this week." But Sherard was not wholly pleased with the project, and he added: "Tis a Sickly place and I could wish he had held to his resolutions of going to Carolina, but I think he's now too far engaged with the Duke of Chandos to think of it."[66]

Ultimately, however, the African adventure was abandoned and the original plan was restored. Evidently an important factor in its restoration was the dissatisfaction expressed by Governor Nicholson, who complained in March (1721) from Plymouth, where he was preparing to leave for his new post, that he neither had "Mr. Keatesby" with him nor had he heard from him.[67] By November the Governor had learned of the African plans promoted by the Duke and, after expressing regret, requested that the ten pounds which he had already advanced to Catesby

be repaid to the Treasurer of the Royal Society. However, Nicholson still approved the plan, and he renewed his offer to anyone else the Society might choose to send in Catesby's stead.[68]

While all of this activity was going on in his behalf, Catesby was not inactive. Although he probably spent a good share of his time in Castle Hedingham and Sudbury, he also frequently made journeys to London by way of Braintree. In the course of these trips, he often acted as letter carrier between Samuel Dale and William Sherard and as a sort of man of all work for both of them. Dale had many plant specimens which his eager correspondent wished to see, and Sherard had a number which the apothecary lacked as well, and the former had a greater familiarity with the identities of plants.[69] Catesby, as their go-between and assistant, was placed in a good position to continue his education in botany.

Finally on December 7, 1721, well over a year after the plan had originally been formulated, the voyage to Carolina seemed a near certainty. Sherard believed that Catesby would embark within a month, as he had secured nearly enough subscriptions to satisfy the would-be traveler.[70] But Catesby delayed further, and not until January 27, 1721/22, could the Consul say with certainty to Dr. Richardson: "Mr. Catesby goes next week for Carolina. He has put off his going till the last ship. I have got sufficient subscriptions without putting you or Dr. Uvedale to charges and as his obligations are more to me than to all the rest, I hope he'll make me suitable returns that I may furnish all my friends."[71] The voyage to Charles Town began, then, sometime early in February of 1722.[72] With it

[63] See Charles H. Collins Baker and Muriel I. Baker, *The Life and Circumstances of James Brydges First Duke of Chandos, Patron of the Liberal Arts* (Oxford, 1949).

[64] *Carolina,* II, vi.

[65] Sherard to Richardson, London, Feb. 14, 1720/21, *MS Radcliffe Trust,* C. IV, fol. 27; also in Nichols, *Illust. Lit. Hist.,* I, 373.

[66] Same to same, London, March 28, 1721, *M.S. Radcliffe Trust,* C. IV, fol. 33; also in *Richardson Extracts,* 165; and Nichols, *Illust. Lit. Hist.,* I, 374.

[67] Francis Nicholson to Alban Thomas, Plymouth, March 8, 1720/21, *Guard Books* (MSS in the Library of the Royal Society of London), N-1, 89.

[68] Same to same, Charles Town, Nov. 16, 1721, *R.S. Guard Book,* N-1, 90.

[69] See letters of Dale to Sherard, Dec. 12, 1720, to Dec. 26, 1721, *Sherard Letters,* II, Nos. 220, 221, 223, 224, 226, 227.

[70] Sherard to Richardson, *MS Radcliffe Trust,* C. IV, fol. 57; also in Nichols, *Illust. Lit. Hist.,* I, 377.

[71] *MS Radcliffe Trust,* C. IV, fol. 63; also in Nichols, *Illust. Lit. Hist.,* I, 378.

[72] See Catesby to Elizabeth Cocke Pratt, Charles City, June 22, 1722, *Jones MSS,* I, No. 149; also in Jones, *Capt. Roger Jones,* 218.

went the blessings of the Royal Society of London, which, spurred on by the energetic Dr. Sherard and others of its Fellows, exhibited a lively and continuing interest in Catesby's new discoveries among the flora and fauna of British North America.

Actually, in the view of the Royal Society and of Catesby's patrons, the project soon developed into a pincers movement. Shortly after Catesby embarked for America, Consul Sherard began to solicit subscribers for one Thomas More, who proposed to canvass the colonies north of Virginia for rarities in all of the branches of natural history. More had advanced grandiose schemes — he once proposed "to give us an account of the whole creation from an Angell to an Attome" —[73] but his achievements were a great disappointment to his sponsors, and they paled into insignificance when placed alongside Catesby's work.[74] Actually, soon after he arrived in New England, More became so incensed at the colonists' disregard for the interests of His Majesty's Navy (by felling trees marked for masts on naval vessels) that he set out to seek appointment as Royal Forester. And his search for preferment replaced his search for specimens in the natural life of the northern colonies.[75]

Catesby, however, persevered. He was, as Richard Pulteney said, "one of those men, whom a passion for natural history very early allured from the interesting pursuits of life" —[76] only such was Catesby's zeal for natural history that for him it *was* the most interesting pursuit of life. His extraordinary accomplishments in this pursuit form the principal topics of the succeeding chapters.

[73] Jacob Bobart to James Petiver, Oxford, Nov. 10, 1704, *Sloane* 3321, fol. 157.

[74] See Appendix below for an account of Thomas More's barren expedition to New England.

[75] Pasti, *Sherard*, 216-18.

[76] *Pulteney*, II, 219.

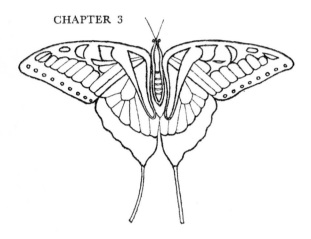

CHAPTER 3

The Naturalist in the Field

Mark Catesby returned to America in the late winter and early spring of 1722 with a definite commission to perform for his patrons, a commission which gave him ample opportunity to indulge in his passion for natural history and one which he accomplished, as subsequent events demonstrated, with far greater success than any of his predecessors assigned to the English colonies. This time he went to a newer and rawer land than Virginia. South Carolina, even with the leaven of its little metropolis at Charles Town, was essentially a frontier country. Its culture had had but little more than fifty years to grow, while that of Virginia was now well into its second century. Carolina was a buffer standing against the Spanish and Indians on both the south and west. In 1722 the memories of the Yamasee War (1715 to 1718) were still fresh in the minds of Carolinians. Internally, too, the colony had but recently undergone severe strain. The revolution of 1719, the last in a series of revolts against the proprietors, had, in essence, only really

been completed with the arrival, in May, 1721, of Francis Nicholson to govern for the Crown.[1]

The voyage, which was made to the south to avoid the storms of the North Atlantic, was an easy one, even though it took three months. While on board ship, the naturalist was able to busy himself with the usual diversions, such as watching the porpoises playing alongside. Three hundred leagues from the Canary Islands, he pondered the endurance of land birds when he saw an owl hovering over the vessel. He was prepared for this, too, as he had armed himself with Willughby's *Ornithology* against such emergencies.[2] This was fortunate, for, some distance nearer his destination, he used this ornithological "bible" to identify a "Turnstone or Sea Plover" which was taken aboard.[3] Although he found little other than the gulfweed to gratify his desire for botanizing, there were other compensations. As the vessel approached the coasts of America, Catesby found fish as well as birds to describe. He had a rather extended opportunity to capture these creatures which inhabited the air and water near the shore. Around

[1] David Duncan Wallace, *The History of South Carolina* (3 vols., New York, 1934), I, 67-81, 203-20, 235-54.

[2] John Ray, *The Ornithology of Francis Willughby . . . in Three Books . . .* (London, 1678). All of the references in *Carolina* are to this English edition of this work.

[3] "Turnstone" — ruddy turnstone, *Arenaria interpres morinella* (Linnaeus).

April 19 the vessel was within sounding distance of the coast, but an opposing wind sent it back into the Gulf Stream. It took two weeks to make up the lost distance; and not until May 3 did Catesby land in Charles Town, where Governor Nicholson, mollified by a letter from Sherard, received him cordially.[4]

Sponsorship by Nicholson was a great boon to the visitor. The relations of the Governor with the South Carolinians were still in a "honeymoon" stage, and Catesby, as a protégé of Nicholson, was accorded cordial entrée to the homes of the best people in the colony, both those in the proprietorial and antiproprietorial factions. *The Natural History of Carolina* contains a number of references to items collected on the plantations of the lowland gentry. The names, Moore, Blake, Bull, Johnson, Waring, and Skene, constitute a respectable roster of the more important families of the South Carolina Tidewater.[5] This easy access to their holdings near Charles Town was important in Catesby's early trips from the city and supplied him, as in Virginia, ready bed, board, and helpful information.

Catesby made his first journey soon after his arrival. On June 22 he informed Sherard that he had just returned "from 40 miles up the Country" and would soon go a greater distance in another direction.[6] The letter had the sound of a man anxious to be about his work.

In these early expeditions, Catesby soon confronted problems in the field, and particularly those which concerned his patrons in England. He wondered if Sir Hans and Mr. Dubois wanted separate collections. If they did — and it appears that this was the case — the mere problem of transportation would be very

serious. "The more specimens I collect," Catesby wrote, "the more time it takes and consequently prevents my collecting as many kinds as I should. Especially when I am several hundred miles off, it will increase their bulk." This conflict between the desires of his insatiable patrons and the broader objectives of their agent, who was eager to be about his own work, would continue throughout his stay in America.

While he was thus concerned about his supporters in England, Catesby did not forget his friends and relatives in America. He wrote his niece, Elizabeth Cocke, who had become Mrs. William Pratt, that he had intended sending some things to her mother, but unfortunately they had spoiled while waiting for the ship to sail.[7] Of Sherard he inquired: "If Sir you can spare a few common Roots such as Lillys (except the White Lilly), Martagons, Daffodils, or any bulbose root, I shall be glad of them to gratify some Gentlemen at whose houses I frequent. For many of them are desirous of such improvements and here is little either for use or ornament, tho' the Country is productive of everything."[8] The bulbs were sent, too, and subsequently they bloomed.[9] Obviously, the exchange of botanical specimens between the continents worked both ways.

Catesby continued his collections in the low country for the rest of the summer.[10] Apparently he had planned originally to go to the Bahamas in November, but near the middle of September he was unfortunately "seized with a swelling" in his cheek which was treated by being cut open twice and by "injections every day." The result of this surgery was to confine him indoors until well into December.[11] To further complicate matters,

[4] Catesby to Sherard, Charles Town, May 5, 1722, *Sherard Letters*, II, No. 163. In *Carolina*, I, vi, he says that he arrived May 23. This was probably a typographical error.

[5] *Carolina*, I, 31, 35, 43.

[6] Catesby to Sherard, Charles City ["City" written over "Town"], June 20, 1722, *Sherard Letters*, II, No. 164. Charles Town was incorporated as Charles City and Port on June 23, 1722. This brief period of self-government, the last until after the Revolution, only endured until Nicholson announced the disallowance of the act in November, 1723.

Wallace, *Hist. S.C.*, I, 286-87.

[7] *The Papers of the Jones Family* . . . (MSS in the Library of Congress), I, No. 149.

[8] *Sherard Letters*, II, No. 164.

[9] Catesby to [Sherard], Charles Town, April 6, 1724, *Sherard Letters*, II, No. 176.

[10] *Carolina*, I, viii.

[11] Catesby to Sloane, Charles City, May 10, 1723, *Sloane* 4046, fol. 353; Catesby to Sherard, Charles City, Dec. 10, 1722, *Sherard Letters*, II, No. 166.

About the middle of September here fell the greatest floud attended with a Hurricane that has been known since the country was settled. Great numbers of Cattle, Horses, Hogs, and some people were drowned. The Deer were found frequently lodged on high trees. The wind was so violent that it tore up by the roots great numbers of Trees, and disrobed most others of their leaves, Cones, and seed; so that had I been well, the collection would have fallen short of other Years. Perticularly it dispersed all the Laurels, Umbrella, and many other things I sent out for, but none to be found.[12]

By this time, and especially because of his prolonged illness, Catesby realized that he could not go on without assistance. He wrote to Sherard asking if he might draw twenty pounds against him in order to buy a "Negro Boy." The request, made first in December, was repeated in February. Unfortunately, communications across the Atlantic were slow (Catesby had not heard from Sherard since he left England), and finally in March, on his way upcountry, he advised Sherard that he had drawn the bill on his correspondent.[13]

Before he purchased his slave, however, he resumed his work in the area near Charles Town. For better than a month following his illness, he collected in the region near the Ashley River. On January 4, 1722/23, he was at the home of Alexander Skene, located south of the river across from the old town of Dorchester.[14] His host, a sturdy Scotsman who had been one of the leading figures in the revolt of 1719, was a member of the Council of the colony. Apparently Skene was at home and received his guest in person.[15] Early in February, Catesby was still in the same area, but north of the stream, at Newington, the seat of Joseph Blake.

Blake had inherited one of the principal fortunes in the colony from his father, who had been both Governor and one of the proprietors.[16] Nature, however, was no respecter of rank, for at Newington the naturalist encountered an uncommon number of rattlesnakes. Here he saw (whether on this visit or a later one is impossible to say) a rattler eight feet long.[17] Also, he had a frightening experience which illustrates still another problem which confronted him in Carolina:

. . . a Negro Woman making my bed, a few minutes after I was out of it, cryed out a Rattle Snake. We being drinking Tea in the next Room, which was a ground flore, and being Surprised with the vehemence of the wenches bauling, went to see the cause, and found, as the wench had said, a Rattle Snake actually between the Sheets in the very place I lay, vigorous and full of ire, biting at every thing that approach't him. Probably It crept in for warmth in the Night; but how long I had the company of [the] charming Bedfellow I am not able to say.[18]

Had Mark Catesby been a less tenacious man, occurrences like this in the low country might have driven him to seek higher ground. This he did, soon after, but for better reasons. On March 19 he was "80 Miles from Charles City" on his way to "Fort Moor a frontier garrisson 140 miles up the Country."[19] The outpost was located on the Carolina side of the Savannah River on the bend just below the future site of Augusta.[20] The little detachment, which was stationed there to guard against the Indians and to regulate the trade with them, was commanded by Captain Gerard Monger, whose men declared loyally "that they would as soon serve under him as any

[12] Same to same, Charles City, Dec. 9, 1722, *Sherard Letters,* II, No. 165.

[13] *Sherard Letters,* II, Nos. 165, 168, 169.

[14] Catesby to Sherard, "from Mr. Skeins," Jan. 4, 1722/23, *Sherard Letters,* II, No. 168.

[15] Wallace, *Hist. S.C.,* I, 240-41; *South Carolina Upper House Journal,* Jan. 22, 1722/23 (microfilm of MS in the South Carolina Historical Commission, Columbia), No. 2, 153.

[16] Langdon Cheves, "Blake of South Carolina," *South Carolina Historical and Genealogical Magazine,* I (1900), 158-

59; Henry A. M. Smith, "The Upper Ashley, and the Mutation of Families," *ibid.,* XX (1919), 159-65.

[17] *Carolina,* II, 41.

[18] Catesby to Sherard, Charles Town, Jan. 16, 1723/24, *Sherard Letters,* II, No. 174. The story is repeated in *Carolina,* II, 41.

[19] Catesby to Sherard, "Carolina 80 Miles from Charles City," March 19, 1722/23, *Sherard Letters,* II, No. 169.

[20] Fort Moore is shown on most eighteenth-century maps of the area, including Catesby's. For a convenient reference see William R. Shepherd, *Historical Atlas* (New York, 1911), 193.

commander in the Province."[21] Catesby, who reached the command of the popular captain early in April, was pleased with what he saw. He rhapsodized to Consul Sherard:

The inhabited part of the Country is a Sink in comparison of it. It is one of the Sweetest Countrys I ever saw. The Banks of the River, perticularly where the fort stands, is 200 foot perpendicular in most places, from whence are seen large Prospects over the tops of the trees on the other side of the river, which is generally low but prodigious rich land. Most part of the Country hereabouts is composed of moderate hills and valleys like the best part of Kent. Aboundance of little Rivulets fall into the great one and form delicious places for habitations.[22]

The enchanted naturalist spent but five days in this "sweet country" on this occasion. While he was there, he encountered still another of the hazards of the area. While on a buffalo hunt with several companions, he met a band of sixty Indians. Fortunately, the tribe was at peace with the English, and the party returned safely to the fort. Catesby's relations with the Indians, however — in sharp contrast with those of his recent predecessor in Carolina, John Lawson, who was killed by the redskins[23] — were generally pleasant. While he was in the region above the fort — though probably on later visits — he made good use of them:

In these excursions I employ'd an Indian to carry my Box, in which besides Paper and Materials for Painting, I put dry'd Specimens of Plants, Seeds, etc. — as I gather'd them. To the Hospitality and Assistance of these Friendly Indians, I am much indebted, for I not only subsisted on what they shot, but their First Care was to erect a Bark Hut, at the Approach of Rain to keep me and my Cargo from Wet.[24]

This, of course, raises the question of what happened to the slave which Catesby purchased. Nowhere did Catesby mention the Negro boy again.

In May of 1723, after his return from Fort Moore, Catesby finally received word from William Sherard.[25] By this time the Consul had read the accounts of the illness of his friend, and, if we are to judge from a letter to Dr. Richardson written about the same time, Sherard was well satisfied with the specimens Catesby had sent.[26] These related, however, only to Catesby's principal patron. Catesby had depended on Sherard to share his surplus with other patrons and friends. Finally, in May, the naturalist sent a miscellaneous group of shells, birds, snakes, and a few seeds to Sir Hans Sloane. Unlike Sherard, whose interest was in botanical items, Sloane was concerned with zoological specimens as well.[27]

Shipping specimens to England involved a great many problems. Dried plants (and drying was often difficult in the humid climate of Charles Town) were best sent in books or in quires of paper, and fresh ones were sometimes shipped in tubs of damp earth. Seeds were transported in gourds or, lacking these, in small wooden boxes.[28] Snakes, and occasionally other small animals, were preserved in wide-mouthed bottles filled with rum or other spirits, but even these were inadequate for the larger specimens.[29] Birds were occasionally kept in alcohol, but the preferred method was to dry them gradually in an oven and then to stuff and cover them with tobacco dust.[30]

[21] S.C. Upper House Journ., Feb. 11, 1722/23, No. 2, 184.
[22] Catesby to Sherard, Charles City, May 10, 1723, Sherard Letters, II, No. 171. This is probably the same story which Catesby embellished in Carolina, II, viii-ix.
[23] Vincent H. Todd, ed., Christoph von Graffenried's Account of the Founding of New Bern (Publications of the North Carolina Historical Commission, Raleigh, 1920), 263-70.
[24] Carolina, I, viii-ix.
[25] Sherard Letters, II, No. 171.
[26] Sherard to Richardson, London, Feb. 23, 1722/23, MS Radcliffe Trust, C. V, fol. 4.
[27] Catesby to Sloane, Charles City, May 10, 1723, Sloane 4046, fol. 353. Unfortunately for the ornithologists, there is no indication as to where he found these birds.
[28] Catesby to Sherard, Charles Town, Aug. 16, 1724, Sherard Letters, II, No. 178. One of the best expositions of the methods used is James Petiver, "Brief Directions for the Easie Making and Preserving Collections of All Natural Curiosities . . . ," printed in Raymond P. Stearns, "James Petiver, Promoter of Natural Science," Proceedings of the American Antiquarian Society, n.s., LXII (1952), 363-65.
[29] Sloane 4046, fol. 353.
[30] Catesby to John Bartram, n.p., [1741], in Darlington, Memorials, 321-22; Peter Kalm, Kalm's Visit to England on His Way to America in 1748 (Joseph Lucas, tr., London, 1892), 51-52.

Catesby was continually in need of preservatives and containers. Paper, pasteboard, and bottles had to be sent from England. The gourds and boxes could be supplied in Charles Town, but the naturalist found that the cost was excessive. For such small boxes, the "Makannics" of the city charged him "20 *d.*, that is 4 *d.* sterling, besides being obliged to them for working at any rate."[31]

Once specimens were prepared for shipment, their safety depended on the whims of the captains of the vessels on which they were sent, and these gentlemen could scarcely appreciate the value of items which lay outside the normal bounds of trade. Even when the precious cargoes, carefully packed and labeled, were undisturbed by sea water or rain, they were sometimes rifled by inquisitive but unskilled hands and rendered almost useless for their receivers. Even the wide-mouthed bottles, which carried snakes, birds, or insects, did not escape thirsty sailors, who did not mind the animal contents, provided that they got the spiritous preservatives.[32] Catesby's problems were made worse by the fact that he was away from the port so much of the time that he could not get to know which shipmasters could be depended upon to put plants where they would not be damaged. Some of these mariners, too, were "surly Fellows" who could not be prevailed upon at all.[33]

Even when these shipments were cared for in good faith, they might be damaged. A case in point involved items destined for Sloane and Sherard, which were sent with Captain Robinson on the *Dolphin,* on May 16, 1723. Unfortunately, the *Dolphin* met with pirates, was damaged, and forced to return to South Carolina to refit. Buccaneers were a common hazard in these waters; Catesby himself had met the victims

of one attack at the time of his arrival on the Carolina coast. In the case of the *Dolphin,* it stayed in port for such a short time on its return that Catesby had no opportunity to check his shipment, which went on to England as it was.[34]

Near the end of June, Catesby wrote Sherard that he intended again to go to "the remote part of the Country. . . ."[35] This time he planned to supplement the collections which he had made around Fort Moore in the spring: "My method is never to be twice at one place in the same season. For if in the spring I am in the low Country, in the Summer I am at the heads of Rivers, and the Next Summer in the low countrys, so I visit the two different parts of the Country."[36] This was the ideal scheme, although the naturalist could not always carry it through completely. It did mean, though, that he attempted to be in each particular section, either in the piedmont or in the lowlands, at different stages of plant development during the growing season, even if it were in different years.

He appears to have worked in the area around and above Fort Moore for most of July and August and to have returned to Charles Town in the middle of September.[37] Toward the end of August, in addition to gathering specimens and drawing illustrations of them in color, he witnessed a run of sturgeon up the Savannah: "Twenty Miles above Savannah Fort [Fort Moore], on the Savannah River, where the Cataracts begin, three of us in two days killed sixteen, which to my Regret was left rotting on the Shore, except that we regaled our selfes with at the Place, and two we brought to the Garison."[38]

On this occasion, unlike the expedition of the previous spring, he returned with a staggering number of items, especially in view of the distance and the pre-

[31] *Sherard Letters,* II, No. 165.

[32] See Stearns, "James Petiver," 289-90, for some of these transportation problems.

[33] Catesby to Sherard, Charles Town, Oct. 30, 1724, *Sherard Letters,* II, No. 179.

[34] Catesby to Sloane, Charles Town, Nov. 15, 1723, *Sloane* 4047, fol. 90; *Sherard Letters,* II, No. 163; Catesby to Sherard, Charles City, May 16, 1723, *ibid.,* No. 172; same

to same, Charles City, June 26, 1723, *ibid.,* No. 185.

[35] *Sherard Letters,* II, No. 185.

[36] Catesby to Sherard, Charles Town, Jan. 16, 1724, *Sherard Letters,* II, No. 174.

[37] Same to same, Charles Town, Nov. 13, 1723, *Sherard Letters,* II, No. 170; *Sloane* 4047, fol. 90.

[38] *Carolina,* II, xxxiv.

carious state of the trails. This time he had three or four specimens of each variety of plant which he sent to Sherard, asking the Consul to share his abundance with Dubois and Dale. He had another collection for Sloane and, in addition, he had items for Isaac Rand, the demonstrator at the Apothecaries' Garden in Chelsea; for Thomas Fairchild, the gardener of Hoxton; and for Peter Collinson. Collinson, in fact, received an extra portion, in recognition of some new subscriptions he had raised for Catesby.[39]

Yet, although Catesby's subscribers and friends fared well in some specimens, they received few of some other important items. Mark Catesby himself, as is shown in his *Natural History of Carolina* and in the posthumous *Hortus Britanno-Americanus*,[40] was strongly interested in domesticating the flora of North America in English gardens. Several of his sponsors shared this interest in addition to their desire to add to their collections of dried plants. In consequence, then, both the naturalist and his patrons sought to introduce the more spectacular plants, the forest trees and shrubs of Carolina, into Britain. In some cases Catesby had been successful in procuring seeds, but this was not true for many of the nuts, the oaks, and the pines. To some extent, also, these omissions were attributable to the illness which Catesby had suffered during the fall of his first year in Carolina (1722), as he had been unable to search the forests when mature seeds were plentiful.[41] Quite possibly, too, the hurricane of September, 1722, had so "disrobed" the trees, as Catesby had put it, that well-matured nuts, acorns, and cones were in very short supply in 1723. In any case, Catesby began his search for them soon after his return from the upper reaches of the Savan-

nah. By mid-November his attempts had been unsuccessful, but he still had hopes of finding pine cones.[42]

He did not want for local assistance in his quest. Robert Johnson, who was to be of considerable aid in supplying material for *The Natural History of Carolina,* searched for seeds with the visitor from England. At this time Johnson might have been called an unemployed Governor, as he had served the proprietors in that capacity until the revolution of 1719. Later he held the post again, after the proprietors (save Lord Carteret) had surrendered their interests in Carolina to the royal government.[43] The ex-Governor, however, was no more fortunate in finding "pine apples, acorns, and other Forest Seed" than Catesby had been. Fortunately, though, Johnson was to leave in January for London, where he promised to see William Sherard and explain the lack of success to Catesby's anxious patrons.[44]

The latter, however, continued to be a cause for anxiety. The bulk of the collections were, of course, destined for Sherard, with a somewhat smaller number going to Sloane, and even fewer to Dubois. Thus the other patrons had to depend mainly on the largess of Consul Sherard or go without. Some of them asked for little. Sir George Markham requested a specimen of St.-Andrew's-cross, which had been reported by William Byrd to be a successful snakeroot.[45] Catesby sent some plants in January, 1723/24, along with several other examples of species which were reputed to be cures for snake bite. Careful man that he was, though, he cautioned, "Where a vein or Artery is pricked by the bite of a Rattle Snake no Antidote will avail anything, but Death certainly and Suddainly

[39] Catesby to Sherard, Charles Town, April 6, 1724, *Sherard Letters,* II, No. 176; *ibid.,* No. 170; *Sloane* 4047, fol. 90.
[40] *Hortus Britanno-Americanus: Or, a Curious Collection of Trees and Shrubs, the Produce of the British Colonies in North America; Adapted to the Soil and Climate of England* . . . (London, 1763).
[41] Catesby to Sherard, n.p., Nov. 26, 1724, *Sherard Letters,* II, No. 182.
[42] *Sherard Letters,* II, No. 170.
[43] Wallace, *Hist. S.C.,* I, 242-43, 324.

[44] *Sherard Letters,* II, No. 174; Gov. Nicholson to Lord Carteret, Charles Town, Jan. 26, 1723/24, *C.S.P., Col., 1722-1723,* XXXIII, 361.
[45] St.-Andrew's-cross — *Ascyrum hypericoides* Linnaeus. Byrd was an enthusiastic supporter of snakeroot for many years afterward. As late as 1739 he was still endorsing it as a cure not only for snake bite but also for pleurisies, gout, rheumatism, asthmas, dropsies, fevers, and nausea. Byrd to Peter Collinson, Viriginia, July 10, 1739, *R.S. Letter Book,* XXVI, 21-25.

ensues, sometimes in 2 or 3 minutes, which I have more than once seen."[46]

Some subscribers, however, were not so easily satisfied, and, unlike Sir George, they supplied no specific demands which might have served as a guide to Catesby in complying with their requests. Actually, Catesby was remarkably patient, understanding, and cooperative with his patrons, but, in April, 1724, he nearly lost his temper with them. His exasperation arose from a letter from Sherard, a letter which must have been written after the Consul had received the collections made at Fort Moore the previous spring but probably before the larger autumn shipments had reached England.[47] Catesby replied vigorously:

I shall not indicate my remissness in writing or anything else I am knowingly tardy of. But I protest before God I never can be more industrious in collecting whatever I could possibly meet with either those few days that I was at Savannah Garrison or Since.

Apparently, however, Sherard had not been the only subscriber to express disappointment in his returns. Catesby continued:

You say, Sir, several of my Subscribers complain, which surprises me. I could not learn by enquiery and asking those I saw that Collections would be acceptable to any but Sir Hans, your self, and Mr. Dubois. I wish I could know what you required and by whome. I hope it can't be expected I should Send Collections to every of my Subscribers, which is impracticable for me to doe.

However, I'le Doe to the best of my abilities, nor can I say or doe more. I should have thought abundance of my time lost if, at my return to England, I could show no more than the collections I send. Not that anything obstructed my collecting Plants and Seeds, which all gives place to when oppertunity offers.[48]

In the circumstances, it was remarkable that the busy naturalist was able to find time to make his drawings and water colors. By the summer of 1724

even these were being demanded by his supporters in England. Now he had to explain to Sloane:

My sending Collections of plants and especially Drawings to every of my Subscribers is what I did not think would be expected from me. My designe was Sir (til you'l please to give me your advice) to keep my Drawings intire that I may get them graved, in order to give a general History of the Birds and other Animals, which to distribute Separately would wholly Frustrate that designe, and be of little value to those who would have so small fragments of the whole. Besides, as I must be oblidged to draw duplicates of whatever I send, that time will be lost which otherwise I might proceed in the designe and consequently be so much short in proportion to what is sent. I beg Sir, if you (as I flatter myself you will) think this reasonable, that you will pleas, to satisfy Lord Persival, who no doubt but will be influenced with what you Say.[49]

Meanwhile, the work continued in spite of these complaints. Catesby apparently spent the winter of 1723/24 in and around Charles Town. It was an uneasy time, though. To Sherard he wrote: "Abundance of people has this winter been carried off by the pluricy." The naturalist kept his health, but appended the hope "God spare my life" to his promise to send certain elusive seeds to his principal patron.[50]

During this winter, also, Catesby began to lay plans to go beyond the lower piedmont region, which he had already visited, to see the "Cherikees, a numerous nation of Indians, inhabiting part of the Apalathean mountains about 400 miles from hence." This proposal, first formulated in a letter to Sir Hans in November, was repeated two months later to William Sherard.[51] On March 12, 1723/24, Catesby wrote that he was setting out for the Cherokees, who were then at war with another nation and would thus be diverted from injuring white travelers.[52] In less than a month, however, by April 6, he was back in Charles Town.[53] The short time which had elapsed

---

[46] Fragment of letter, Catesby to [Sir George Markham], Charles Town, Jan. 16, 1723/24, *Sherard Letters,* II, No. 173.

[47] This letter does not seem to have survived. Its contents are inferred from Catesby's reply.

[48] *Sherard Letters,* II, No. 176.

[49] Catesby to Sloane, Charles Town, Aug. 15, 1724, *Sloane*

4047, fol. 213.

[50] *Sherard Letters,* II, No. 176.

[51] *Sloane* 4047, fol. 90; *Sherard Letters,* II, No. 174.

[52] Catesby to Sloane, Charles Town, Aug. 15, 1724, *Sloane* 4047, fol. 147.

[53] *Sherard Letters,* II, No. 176.

makes it appear most unlikely that anyone burdened with the paraphernalia of a painter and collector could have gone as far as the Cherokee country. Only a few years later, according to the notes of George Hunter, it required twenty-nine days to travel from Charles Town to Keowee, the principal Cherokee town, and back, by way of the Congaree and Saluda Rivers.[54] Catesby, if past performances are any indication, would have gone from Charles Town to Fort Moore and then up the Savannah. This could hardly have taken less time. Indeed, it appears unlikely that he reached the mountains at all while in Carolina, as neither his letters nor *The Natural History of Carolina* gave any evidence of it. Some of his specimens came from this area, but they were probably sent to him by Indian traders and soldiers.[55]

Still, Catesby was not inactive during the spring and summer of 1724. He missed several opportunities to make shipments during April because he was in the field through this important month. In the early part of the summer, he again took his paints and paper to the piedmont area, probably to the region above Fort Moore. He had already made collections in this area during the spring and the late summer, and others had, at his request, sent items found there in October.[56] Now, with the expedition of this year, Catesby would have collected specimens in each of the important months, botanically speaking, in the upcountry. Only the winter season was left, and that would have afforded too few items for his botanist friends to compensate for the rigors of the trip.

By the middle of August he was back in the settlements, looking for new fields to which to extend his activities. By this time he had collected in the coastal plain in every season, and the collections which he made there in the late summer of 1724 largely duplicated his earlier work. In spite of this, Catesby wrote Consul Sherard of his willingness to stay there for another year or go to the Bahamas, even at his own expense. This did not exhaust the possibilities, though, because he had formulated a much more ambitious scheme with one of his principal friends in Charles Town.[57]

This was Thomas Cooper, a parson's son of Litton in Somersetshire, who had received a B.A. from Wadham College, Oxford, in 1720,[58] and had then gone to Charles Town, where he had set himself up as a physician. Apparently he was very successful, too, as Catesby credited him with having "extraordinary business in his profession."[59] It seems likely that Cooper was the "Doctor of Phisik" at whose house the naturalist often stayed while he was in Charles Town and in whose garden he planted the bulbs which Sherard had sent him.[60]

Dr. Cooper, like many another physician of his time, was also interested in experimental science, especially where it impinged upon his profession. In this role he came to the attention of Sir Hans Sloane and of the Royal Society. He was among a little group in the South Carolina capital who were experimenting with antidotes for rattlesnake bite, and who, in the course of their experiments, bade fair to denude the city of its canine population. One of his experiments found its way into the *Philosophical Transactions,* by way of Sloane, who communicated it. Dr. Cooper had a single snake bite three dogs. The first, which received most of the venom, died too soon for medication. The second was given a potion and recovered, but lost its hair within a month. The last animal, which was apparently used as a control, for-

[54] A. S. Salley, Jr., *George Hunter's Map of the Cherokee Country and the Path Thereto in 1730 (Bulletins of the Historical Commission of South Carolina,* No. 4, Columbia, 1917).

[55] Catesby sent Sloane a "black Fox," which he said was rare and caught only in the mountains. There is no indication that he himself caught it. *Sloane* 4047, fol. 213.

[56] *Sherard Letters,* II, Nos. 176, 179.

[57] Catesby to Sherard, Charles Town, Aug. 16, 1724, *Sherard Letters,* II, No. 178; *ibid.,* No. 179; *Sloane* 4047, fol. 213.

[58] Joseph Foster, ed., *Alumni Oxonienses . . . 1715-1886* (4 vols., Oxford, 1891), I, 325.

[59] *Sloane* 4047, fol. 213.

[60] *Sherard Letters,* II, No. 176.

tunately received nothing and recovered completely without treatment.[61]

Cooper must have impressed Governor Nicholson with his experiments, for the latter indicated his willingness to subscribe forty pounds per annum to further them in June, 1724. However, the good Governor was able to retain his reputation for generosity and his money as well, for he made his pledge contingent upon a similar grant by the colony, doubtless knowing full well that by this time the Assembly was of no mind to make such an appropriation, especially one arising at the Governor's suggestion.[62]

The project which Cooper and Catesby proposed followed shortly after this. It was principally the child of the ambitious Doctor; and the apparent failure of the first proposal may have hastened the genesis of the second. Quite conceivably, Dr. Cooper saw in Catesby a means of access to the patronage of the naturalist's wealthy friends in London, even though these worthy gentlemen were not pressed to subscribe. Catesby wrote both to William Sherard and to Sir Hans Sloane in the middle of August, 1724, to let them know of the new plan, which was to visit "the remoter parts of this Continent and perticularly Mexico in order to improve Natural knowledge." The scheme, as he outlined it, was quite ambitious:

As his [Cooper's] Natural Genius bends to the Mathematics, he proposes to communicate to the Royal Society what observations he makes in Astronomy and Perticularly in his way of Practice etc. The Principal Obstruction in such an Undertaking, I conceive, is the unsafe traveling amongst so treacherous and jealous a People as the Spaniards are. But it is conceived a pasport or Letter of protection might be procured from Old Spain to facilitate the designe with safety, which, if it could, would be a sufficient Obligation on him to gratify the learned in Such Observations as should be required of him.[63]

The part of Catesby would be, of course, to study and collect the flora and fauna of the Spanish colonies. His modesty and the sense of the immensity of the task forced Catesby to suggest to Sloane that he should have skilled assistance in "delineating Birds and other Natural Productions." He suggested that if no painter could be found in London, one could be procured from Paris or Amsterdam to accompany him on the proposed expedition.[64]

As Catesby could not sit idly in Charles Town to wait for an answer to his letters, he returned to the field. On September 3, while he was "gone a considerable way back into the Country," his friend, Cooper, wrote to Sir Hans to press their case further. The Doctor asked only for a pass from Spain, or, barring that, the use by the Baronet of his influence to screen the travelers in some Spanish settlement until they could insinuate themselves into the affections of the colonial authorities. He also wrote a similar request to Dr. Richard Mead, another of Catesby's patrons.[65]

This ambitious project, if it could have been carried out, might indeed have resulted in a great increase in knowledge of the natural history of North America. Unfortunately, though, it aroused much more enthusiasm in South Carolina than in England. Governor Nicholson apparently believed it was feasible, and urged Catesby to return home with him to plead the case in person.[66] But despite the continued concern of the naturalist for opinions from his well-connected patrons, they apparently gave no word and took no action. His letters to Sherard and to Sloane, which were sent aboard H.M.S. *Blandford,* must have been received in London around the end of October.[67] There is no record of an answer by either Mead or Sloane, and Sherard did not reply until January 27, 1724/25. This message, even if it were favorable,

[61] Capt. [Fayer] Hall, "An Account of Some Experiments on the Effects of the Poison of the Rattle-Snake . . . ," *Phil. Trans.,* XXXIV (1727), 314.

[62] *S.C. Upper House Journ.,* June 11, 1724, No. 2, 277.

[63] *Sherard Letters,* II, No. 178.

[64] *Sloane* 4047, fol. 213.

[65] Thomas Cooper to Sloane, Charles Town, Sept. 3, 1724,

Sloane 4047, fol. 229.

[66] Catesby to Sherard, Charles Town, Nov. 26, 1724, *Sherard Letters,* II, No. 182.

[67] Gov. Nicholson to Council of Trade and Plantations, Charles Town, Sept. 5, 1724, *C.S.P., Col., 1723-1724,* XXXIV, 218.

probably did not reach its receiver until well after he had left Carolina.[68]

The uncertainty regarding his future left Catesby in an unhappy position in the late summer and autumn of 1724. He continued his work in the settlements after August, even though he was turning up few new things. He explained to Sherard that he would have to "goe a great distance from the Settlements, at least 300 miles South," in order to find new varieties. In the meantime, he tried to fill whatever gaps existed in the collections sent to Sherard and his other major supporters. He began to inquire, also, what plants he might send alive to replace those that had not survived transportation.[69] This autumn, though the supply of pine cones was still not plentiful, he had much better success in finding forest seeds to send to the Consul.[70]

To Sir Hans, that indefatigable collector of anything and everything, Catesby sent an "Indian Apron made of the Bark of Wild Mulberry" and promised an Indian basket and tobacco pipe.[71] He could not find enough snakes to fulfill Sloane's demands for reptiles. The Baronet had not sent the necessary bottles for shipping them until the season was too far advanced. Even so, Catesby was able to send a few to Dr. Richard Mead, who had not already shared in his collections.[72] Still other subscribers were benefited by the shipments made in these last days in Carolina. The Earl of Oxford received a box of seeds, and Governor Nicholson, as befitted a professional public servant, directed that a similar package be sent where it might further his career — to Robert Walpole.[73]

Nor did Catesby neglect his family in England. His brother Jekyll, for instance, had managed his affairs in England and had sent him supplies as well. Although Jekyll Catesby had already been sent a few boxes from Carolina, he appears to have lacked the zeal for natural science which Mark possessed. Accordingly, he was rewarded with an Indian apron similar to that which had been sent to Sloane.[74] Nicholas Jekyll, who shared with his well-traveled nephew an interest in botany, was rewarded with seeds for his garden at Castle Hedingham and for those of his friends as well.[75]

Further, the naturalist lent aid to his friends in Carolina as well as to those across the Atlantic. In addition to items which he imported from England, Catesby also brought plants from the piedmont into the low country. He took the credit for having introduced the catalpa tree into the "inhabited parts of the country."[76] But he was too practical to be concerned solely with things of ornament. He shared the concern of his New World acquaintances to discover plants which would have commercial or medical value. In the summer of 1722, when he first arrived in the colony, Catesby found the Carolinians importing coffee trees, in an attempt to increase the number of staples which they could produce. Quite sensibly, he ventured his opinion as to their unsuitability for the Carolinian climate.[77] Now, late in 1724, Catesby tried to find products which would be well suited to the colony. At the behest of "a gentleman intent on the procuring and propagating things of this kind," Catesby asked Sherard if opium could be produced in Carolina from the true "Poppy from Turkey, and rhubarb and worm seed as well?" Answers to these queries, however, even if the learned Consul gave them, arrived too late for any immediate

[68] Sherard Letters, II, No. 178.

[69] Sherard Letters, II, No. 179.

[70] Catesby to Sherard, Charles Town, Nov. 24, 1724, Sherard Letters, II, No. 181; same to same, Charles Town, Nov. 26, 1724, ibid., No. 182; same to same, Charles Town, Nov. 27, 1724, ibid., No. 183; same to same, Carolina, Jan. 10, 1724/25, ibid., No. 184.

[71] Catesby to Sloane, Charles Town, Nov. 27, 1724, Sloane 4047, fol. 290.

[72] Sloane 4047, fols. 147, 213; Catesby to Sherard, Charles Town, Jan. 10, 1724/25, Sherard Letters, II, No. 183a.

[73] Sherard Letters, II, No. 183.

[74] Catesby to Sherard, Charles Town, October 30, 1724, Sherard Letters, II, No. 180; ibid., Nos. 170, 171, 174, 176.

[75] Sherard Letters, II, Nos. 183a, 184.

[76] Carolina, I, 49.

[77] Sherard Letters, II, No. 164.

benefit, because Catesby had gone to the Bahamas before they could have reached him.[78] But even if they came to nothing, the questions illustrated the range of interests held by the visitor and his friends in Charles Town.[79]

By January 5, 1724/25, Catesby felt that he had met his obligations, both to his friends at home and in America, and he was ready to resume his work in another place. He had waited long enough for a reply to his entreaties for help in the travels he had planned with Cooper. Now he abandoned this dream — for the moment, at least — in favor of something attainable. He wrote to Sir Hans:

I am, Sir, preparing to goe to the Bahama Islands to make a further progress in what I am about. This will add another year to my continuance in America. And though I doe not expect a continuance of my full Subscriptions, yet I hope, partly by your interest and continuance of your Favours, I may expect the greater part of it. This will, Sir, protract my proposed Mexico expedition, which I some time since wrote you concerning, for your advise and approbation. I promise my self great variety of Shells and animals not to be found here.[80]

Two more letters, written five days later to Consul Sherard, are the last which have survived from the trip to Carolina, or, for that matter, for the remainder of Catesby's entire stay in America. He wrote Sherard in a similar vein, hoping that his subscriptions would be continued. He would go ahead, however, even if they were not. Moreover, he had had enough of complaints from those "benefactors" who knew nothing of the conditions under which he worked. He seemed almost relieved when he wrote of the worst of these: "The discontent of Mr. DuBois and the trouble he gives my friends in receiving his Subscription is such that I had rather be without it."[81]

With these communications end the last reasonably detailed accounts of Mark Catesby's activities on his voyage to America, and, to some extent, for the rest of his life. The year or so which followed, while he was in the Bahamas, must have been a crowded time. Still, we lack information from letters to tell us exactly when he was there and where he went. For his stay, there are only a few hints from his *Natural History of Carolina,* although Catesby devoted a considerable portion of the book to the natural products of the Bahama Islands.

One of his primary purposes in going was to find and describe the marine life of the islands. He had collected a few shells and depicted a few fish in Carolina, but had largely deferred this work until he reached the Bahamas, where marine life abounded and where there were "but few Quadrupeds and Birds" to distract him. The fish offered a further attraction, "there being not any, or very few of them described by any Authors."[82] Such, indeed, was largely the case, except for those species which had figured in Sloane's account of Jamaica.

Catesby visited several of the significant islands of the Bahamas: Eleuthera, Andros, and Abaco; but he went first to New Providence and to Nassau, the capital. The town, as he decribed it, could hardly have been impressive. Its houses were "built of Palmetto leaves, a few being of stone. . . ." He did not, however, reside in one of these, but rather in the Governor's house, which stood on a steep hill overlooking the town.[83]

Again, as in Virginia and South Carolina, the visitor came with highly placed support. His first invitations to the islands, in 1722, had come from Woodes Rogers, who had leased the islands from their pro-

[78] *Sherard Letters,* II, No. 178.

[79] Apparently, though, these interests did not extend to such projects if they were put into unskilled hands. When a Dr. Sinclair arrived in the colony and claimed to have a patent for raising these and other drugs and spices, Catesby had only contempt for him and questioned how "such an Emperick and so ignorant a Person" could have imposed upon intelligent sponsors. *Sherard Letters,* II, No. 178.

[80] *Sloane* 4047, fol. 307.

[81] *Sherard Letters,* II, Nos. 183a, 184.

[82] *Carolina,* I, x.

[83] *Carolina,* II, xxxviii.

prietors, and who was twice Governor of the colony.[84] Now, in 1725, Catesby was the guest of George Phenney, who held the governorship between Rogers' terms of office.[85] The visitor left us but a few reminiscences of his stay with Phenney. On one occasion, he was able to indulge his entomological curiosity in watching the Captain General, Governor in Chief, Chancellor, and Vice-Admiral of the Bahama Islands — all of these eminent personages being combined in Phenney — search the gubernatorial feet for "Chegoes." In addition to this charming domestic scene, Catesby noted that on two days in December, 1725, it was so cold that they had to make a fire in the kitchen of the mansion in order to keep warm. It is a matter of speculation as to whether this information affected the tourist trade, which at that time consisted largely of ailing refugees from the malarial ricelands of Carolina.[86]

The governor probably introduced his guest to at least one kindred spirit in the islands, one William Spatches, a member of the Council and "a person of more than uncommon curiosity."[87] On New Providence Island the naturalist saw logwood trees grown from seed which Spatches had brought from Honduras.[88] Such an activity appealed to Mark Catesby, the gardener and the practical man, who was, as were nearly all the naturalists of his day, interested in the utilitarian aspects of botany.

In many ways Catesby's stay in the Bahamas must have been very pleasant after nearly three years on the mainland. The "most serene air" of the islands offered a welcome relief after summers spent in the low country of Carolina.[89] This mood of serenity is found in Catesby's account of "lying upon the deck of a sloop at Andros Island," in September, 1725, where for three nights he listened to the sounds of "rice birds" passing overhead.[90] His busy mind could not content itself with merely listening, but turned rather to an explanation of the migration in terms of the birds following the ripening rice from Cuba to Carolina, an explanation which was included in his fine paper, "Of Birds of Passage," which he later read to the Royal Society.[91] Not every experience was so pleasant, however, and his curiosity sometimes involved him in painful situations. Catesby did not appreciate fully the toxic qualities of the "Mancaneel Tree" until he helped cut one down on Andros Island.[92] Some of the sap spurted in his eyes. "I paid for my incredulity," he wrote, ". . . I was two days totally deprived of my sight, and felt a violent pricking pain. . . ."[93]

This sojourn in the Bahamas really was the last time Catesby would know either the pleasures or the pains of the field naturalist. When he returned to England in 1726, he exchanged this role forever for those of gardener, author, and scientific artist. Despite this fact, more than a fourth of his forty-three years had been spent searching the fields, forests, and waters of America. Now, with his notes, his specimens, and his drawings, he would cease to be merely an errand boy for the great and the wealthy and earn a greatness of his own.

Still, these years in America were the basis of any fame he won and, as such, are worth considering in some detail. Unfortunately, the principal sources for them, the letters to Sherard and Sloane, give a somewhat distorted picture. They emphasize too strongly

---

[84] *Sloane* 4046, fol. 353; Harcourt G. Malcolm, *A History of the Bahamas House of Assembly* (Nassau, 1921), 15, 41.

[85] Phenney was commissioned Aug. 17, 1721, and was superseded by Rogers on Dec. 26, 1728. Malcolm, *Bahamas House of Assembly,* 31, 41.

[86] *Carolina,* II, xxxix, *Appendix,* 10.

[87] This may have been either William Spatches senior or junior. Both of them served as councilors. See Malcolm, *Bahamas House of Assembly,* 21, 25, 39, 44, 82.

[88] Logwood — *Haematoxylon campechianum* Linnaeus; *Carolina,* II, 86.

[89] *Carolina,* II, xxxix.

[90] "Rice birds" — the bobolink, *Dolichonyx oryzivorus* (Linnaeus).

[91] *Carolina,* I, 14; *Phil. Trans.,* XLIV, pt. 2 (1747), 438.

[92] "Mancaneel Tree" — the manchineel, *Hippomane mancinella* (Linnaeus).

[93] *Carolina,* II, 95.

the work of Catesby as a collector, the results of which were largely ephemeral, and ignore his activity as a painter and descriptive naturalist, which constituted his permanent contribution to natural science. The lists of plants and animals, which many of these letters contained, revealed a thorough and discriminating scientist. Unfortunately, though, they tell us too little about such important problems as where the specimens were found. They are fragments only; and the whole is found, as best Catesby could see it, only in *The Natural History of Carolina, Florida, and the Bahama Islands.*

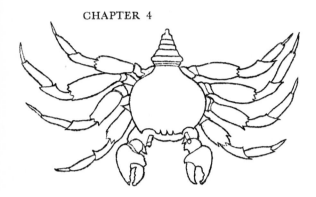

CHAPTER 4

The Natural History:
Twenty Years of Labor

In 1726, when Mark Catesby returned to the "Center of all Science," he left the rigors of the wilderness behind him forever. But the time which remained to him was not easy. He devoted it, in large part, to one object, the completion of his *Natural History.* Besides the magnificent folio pages of plates and text between the four covers of this work, Catesby bound — if we count the years in America — almost half his lifetime. He approached the task with the same determination that he had shown in the field. He was not the amateur that most of his friends were, but a man for whom science had become a vocation.

When he reached England, the naturalist had the satisfaction of having his "Labours approved of" by a number of his patrons. These gentlemen, "most skill'd in the Learning of Nature," not only favored his drawings but were "pleased to think them worth Publishing."[1] This must have encouraged him greatly, for he had hoped, probably from the beginning of the project and certainly while he was in Carolina,

that his illustrations would appear in print.[2] Unfortunately, however, his patrons had already been to considerable expense in his behalf, and they were not willing to go further. Catesby had hoped to take his drawings to Paris or Amsterdam to have them engraved, but his friends discouraged him. Sir Hans Sloane had gone to the artists and engravers of London, at least for the plates of his *Natural History of Jamaica,* the second volume of which had been published the year before, and he must have known the cost of this work. His opinions, then, and those of the others, forced Catesby to turn to his own resources.

For professional advice Catesby turned to a French-born water colorist and etcher, Joseph Goupy, by whose "kind Advice and Instructions" he was "initiated in the way of Etching. . . ." In many respects this rather informal schooling in the ways of working with acid upon copper was fortunate. Much of the

[1] *Carolina,* I, xi.

[2] Catesby to Sloane, Charles Town, Aug. 15, 1724, *Sloane* 4047, fol. 213.

charm of the plates in *The Natural History* and whatever accuracy they have as well comes from the fact that the artist chose not to do them in a "Graver-like manner" but to follow the "humour of the Feathers."[3]

This period of learning must have been extremely tedious, and it accounted in large part for the slow progress which Catesby made. During the two or three years which followed his return to England, the naturalist apparently isolated himself from his family and many of his old friends in Essex and Suffolk. George Rutherford, the husband of Catesby's sister Ann, wrote from Castle Hedingham to his niece, Elizabeth Cocke, who had married Thomas Jones after the death of her first husband, William Pratt, ". . . your Uncle Mr. Mark Catesby is now in London but I can't tell you where he lodges."[4] Mrs. Jones, who was in England at this time, probably did see her Uncle Mark while she was there. At any rate, she had instructions from her husband, Catesby's gardening friend of Virginia days, to greet the naturalist and to get flowers "for all the seasons" from him.[5]

While his work continued, Catesby needed financial help. He was, in the words of William Sherard, "a gentleman of small fortune."[6] He could ill afford the time spent in engraving plates, and was unable to meet the costs of publication without assistance. At this point Peter Collinson, always the friend of American science, stepped in. The Quaker merchant lent him "a considerable amount of money without interest" to prevent the work from falling "prey to the book sellers." Thus did Collinson, who later made it possible for John Bartram to make a living from botany, enable Catesby to support himself by the sale of his two large volumes.[7]

William Sherard also helped the busy author in these years. Catesby credited this "learned and accurate Botanist" with supplying the Latin names for the plants in *The Natural History*.[8] Most of the long polynomials which grace the text were probably the work of Sherard, at least for those plants which were collected on the trip or which Catesby received from America within the year or two after his return. Much of this classification probably was done from the specimens sent to his great sponsor before Catesby returned to England. That which remained had to be done soon after Catesby again met his friend, as William Sherard had but little time left in 1726 either to help others or to work on his *Pinax*. He had been feuding with Sir Hans Sloane since 1725, when Catesby was in the Bahamas, but composed the quarrel after the death of Sir Isaac Newton, in order to prevent the antiquary Martin Folkes from succeeding Sir Isaac in the presidency of the Royal Society. Sherard himself was elected to the Council of the Society for a second term, on November 30, 1727, as a member of the group which was led by Sloane. Whatever aid he gave Catesby must have been terminated within the next three months. Sherard attended his last meeting of the Council early in February 1727/28. Within a month he was at Eltham, the home of his brother James, and already was in his final illness. While Dillenius, his assistant, attended him at Eltham, and again in London, whatever they accomplished before his death in August probably was done on the *Pinax*.[9]

So ended the relationship between Catesby and Consul Sherard. Had it not been for this man and his *Pinax*, the author of *The Natural History of Caro-*

---

[3] *Carolina*, I, xi; *D.N.B.*

[4] Rutherford to Mrs. Jones, "Att Mr. Randalls in Manner Street in Chelsea, In Middlesex," June 27, 1728, in Jones, *Capt. Roger Jones*, 217. Rutherford must have married Anne Catesby, Mark's sister, though L. H. Jones calls her Rachel.

[5] Thomas Jones to Mrs. Jones, July 8, 1728, "Jones Papers," *Va. Mag.*, XXVI (1918), 173; same to same, Sept. 30,

1728, *ibid.*, 173.

[6] Sherard to Richard Richardson, Nov. 12, 1720, *MS Radcliffe Trust*, C. IV, fol. 23.

[7] Manuscript statement by Peter Collinson in his copy of *Carolina*. See the note to Chapter 5 below, pp. 50-51.

[8] *Carolina*, I, xii.

[9] George Pasti, Jr., *Consul Sherard; Amateur Botanist and Patron of Learning* (unpublished Ph.D. dissertation, University of Illinois, 1950), 212, 219-20.

lina might either have gone back to Virginia to become an almost nameless collector of plants or have stayed in London in the anonymity of one of the nurseries.

Catesby was invited to attend the Royal Society as a visitor on May 22, 1729.[10] It was his first visit to a meeting of his patrons' famous organization and he seized the opportunity to exhibit the first part of his *Natural History of Carolina.* The first section contained the first twenty plates of the work, together with proposals for its completion; obviously Catesby hoped to win additional subscribers among the wealthy Fellows of the Society.

The book was published in this way, in sections, each of which held twenty plates and their descriptive texts. The reasons for this serial publication were twofold. The first, of course, was that the transition from rough drawings to the finished pages was extremely slow, and the second lay in the dearness of the volumes. As originally projected, with a total of two hundred illustrations, they cost twenty guineas. Catesby realized that few copies would sell at such a price, and he enhanced his income by selling a part at a time at two guineas each.[11]

The cost was not surprising in view of the labor which went into each of the volumes. According to Cromwell Mortimer, Catesby's friend, who was Secretary to the Royal Society, the author not only engraved the plates of the early parts but also colored the finished pages himself.[12] Quite likely this was the case at first when money needed to hire colorists was scarce. Even after many sets had been sold, though, Mortimer noted that "all the illuminated sets were colour'd under his Directions, and all touch'd up and finish'd by his own Hand."[13]

During this period of intense activity Mark Catesby apparently lived and worked in Hoxton, which, though it has now been swallowed by metropolitan London, was still, in the early eighteenth century, an essentially rural village with green fields where a naturalist might follow his bent for the observation of the local flora.[14] Among the basically agricultural enterprises of Hoxton was the nursery of Thomas Fairchild with its fine collection of American exotics, to which Catesby had contributed even while he was in Virginia. In view of his early acquaintance with Fairchild, and his interest in domesticating American plants in England, Catesby probably went to work in Fairchild's establishment before the death of its owner in 1729. This served two probable purposes: in augmenting the income of the struggling author and artist and also in providing him with live specimens of American plants which he may have drawn inadequately in the field. At any rate, he was in Hoxton on March 1, 1729/30, from whence he wrote to his niece, Mrs. Elizabeth Jones, in Virginia, sending her an unpainted copy of the first part of his book and asking for seeds in return.[15] A number of the plants shown in the first volume were growing in the Hoxton nursery, and they passed on to Stephen Bacon after Fairchild's death in 1729. These, Catesby noted, had "withstood the Rigours of several Winters without Protection."[16] It is difficult to say how long Catesby stayed in Hoxton. He was at the nursery in 1731 or 1732 when the title page to the first volume of *The Natural History* was printed.[17] In all likelihood, he lived there until around the middle of the decade.

In view of the work involved and the fact that Catesby divided his time by growing exotics, it is

[10] *R.S. Journal Book,* XIV, 336.

[11] Catesby to John Bartram, London, May 20, 1740, in Darlington, *Memorials,* 319-20.

[12] Cromwell Mortimer, "An Account of Mr. Mark Catesby's Essay Towards the Natural History of Carolina . . . ," *Phil. Trans.,* XXXVI (1730), 425.

[13] Cromwell Mortimer, "A Continuation of an Account . . . ," *Phil. Trans.,* XLV (1748), 173.

[14] This can be seen from any of the eighteenth-century maps of London even well beyond Catesby's time. See R. Horwood, *Plan of the Cities of London and Westminster the Borough of Southwark and Parts Adjoining . . .* (London, 1799).

[15] In Jones, *Capt. Roger Jones,* 218-19.

[16] *Carolina,* I, ix, 53, 57, 62, 66; *Pulteney,* II, 239.

[17] The title page noted that the volume was sold ". . . by the Author, at Mr. Bacon's in Hoxton."

remarkable that his book reached the public as quickly as it did. By the end of 1730 he had finished the first three parts. On November 19 he attended a meeting of the Royal Society as a guest of Dr. Mortimer and presented his third part.[18] More than a year later the author completed still another twenty pictures. He wrote again to Mrs. Jones on December 30, 1731, sending her the second, third, and fourth parts, which, he said, "are all I have yet published."[19] The fifth and last section of the first volume took still a year more and was not ready for presentation to the Royal Society until November 23, 1732.[20] Thus, despite the fact that the volume bore the year 1731 on its title page, it appears that it was neither started nor finished in that year. These hundred plates had taken six years to complete, and the second volume would take even longer.

Publication of the first volume brought Catesby more attention from men of science in London. He was, of course, already known to the circle of botanists of which Sherard, while he lived, and Sloane were the most prominent members. By the continued favor of these men, Catesby made his way into the honored ranks of the Royal Society. After his first visit to the Society in May, 1730, Catesby was present at a number of meetings, probably to allow the nonbotanical members to appraise him. On these occasions he was several times the guest of friends or protégés of the President, Sir Hans Sloane, such as Cromwell Mortimer and the young Swiss-born physician, Johann Amman.[21] At the same time, the long uncritical reviews of *The Natural History of Carolina*, which Mortimer was to read from time to time over a period of some seventeen years, were begun in

December, 1730, and must have helped to increase the number of Fellows who knew its author.[22] As a further indication of the quality of Catesby's friends, he also attended meetings of the Society through the good offices of John Martyn, one of the better English botanists of the time who would shortly hold a chair in the subject at Cambridge; Philip Miller of the Apothecaries' Garden; and that most active patron of early science in America, Peter Collinson.[23]

Finally, when a guest of Collinson, on February 1, 1732/33, Catesby was formally nominated Fellow of the Royal Society with the presentation of the following certificate:

Mark Catesby a Gentleman well Skill'd in Botany and Natural History who travell'd for Several years in Various parts of America where he Collected Materials for a Natural History of Carolina and the Bahama Islands which Curious and Magnificent Work he has presented to the Royal Society Is desirous to become a Member thereof and is proposed by us

> R. Gale
> H. Sloane
> Rob. Paul
> John Martyn
> P. Collinson[24]

Except the obscure Robert Paul, who has left little trace other than a long membership of some forty-six years in the Society, and Roger Gale, who was an antiquary, the remainder of the sponsors of Catesby were botanists.[25] As required by the statutes of the Society, a copy of the proposal was then displayed "in the common meeting room of the Society at ten several ordinary meetings,"[26] and, on the eleventh, that of April 26, 1733, Mark Catesby was elected

[18] *R.S. Journal Book*, XIV, 516. He probably gave the Society the second when he attended Jan. 8, 1729/30, *ibid.*, 393. *Gentleman's Magazine* noticed the publication of the third part in January, 1730/31, and again in February. Vol. I (1731), 46, 91.

[19] Printed in Jones, *Capt. Roger Jones*, 219-20. Cf. *Gentleman's Magazine*, II (1732), 635.

[20] *R.S. Journal Book*, XV, 190.

[21] *R.S. Journal Book*, XIV, 393; XV, 190, 206.

[22] *R.S. Journal Book*, XIV, 535.

[23] *R.S. Journal Book*, XIV, 393; XV, 230; *D.N.B.*

[24] *Certificates* (MSS in the Library of the Royal Society of London), I, 41.

[25] Thomas Thomson, *History of the Royal Society . . .* (London, 1812), Appendix IV, xxxiv; *D.N.B.*

[26] *The Record of the Royal Society of London* (ed. 4, London, 1940), 91.

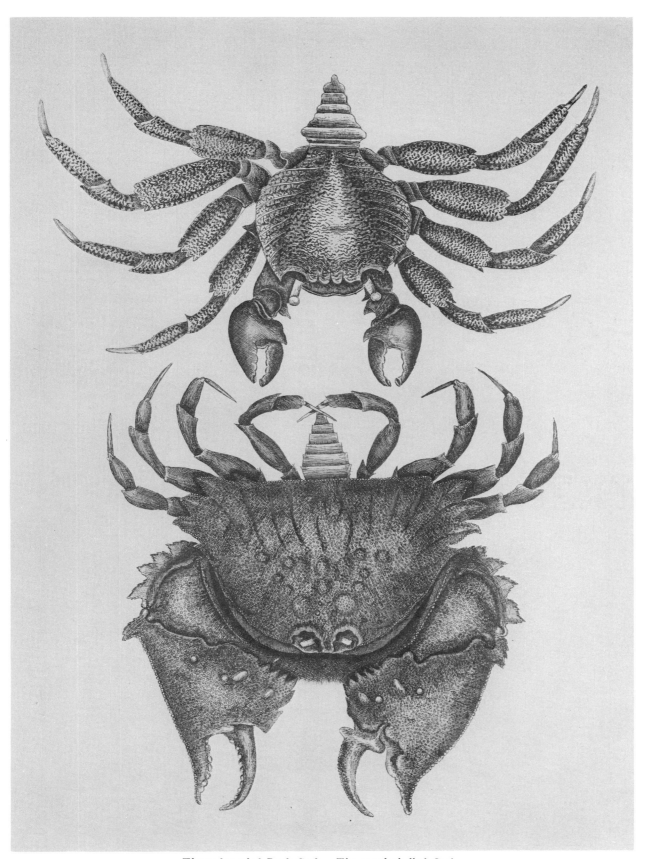

The red motled Rock Crab · The rough-shelled Crab

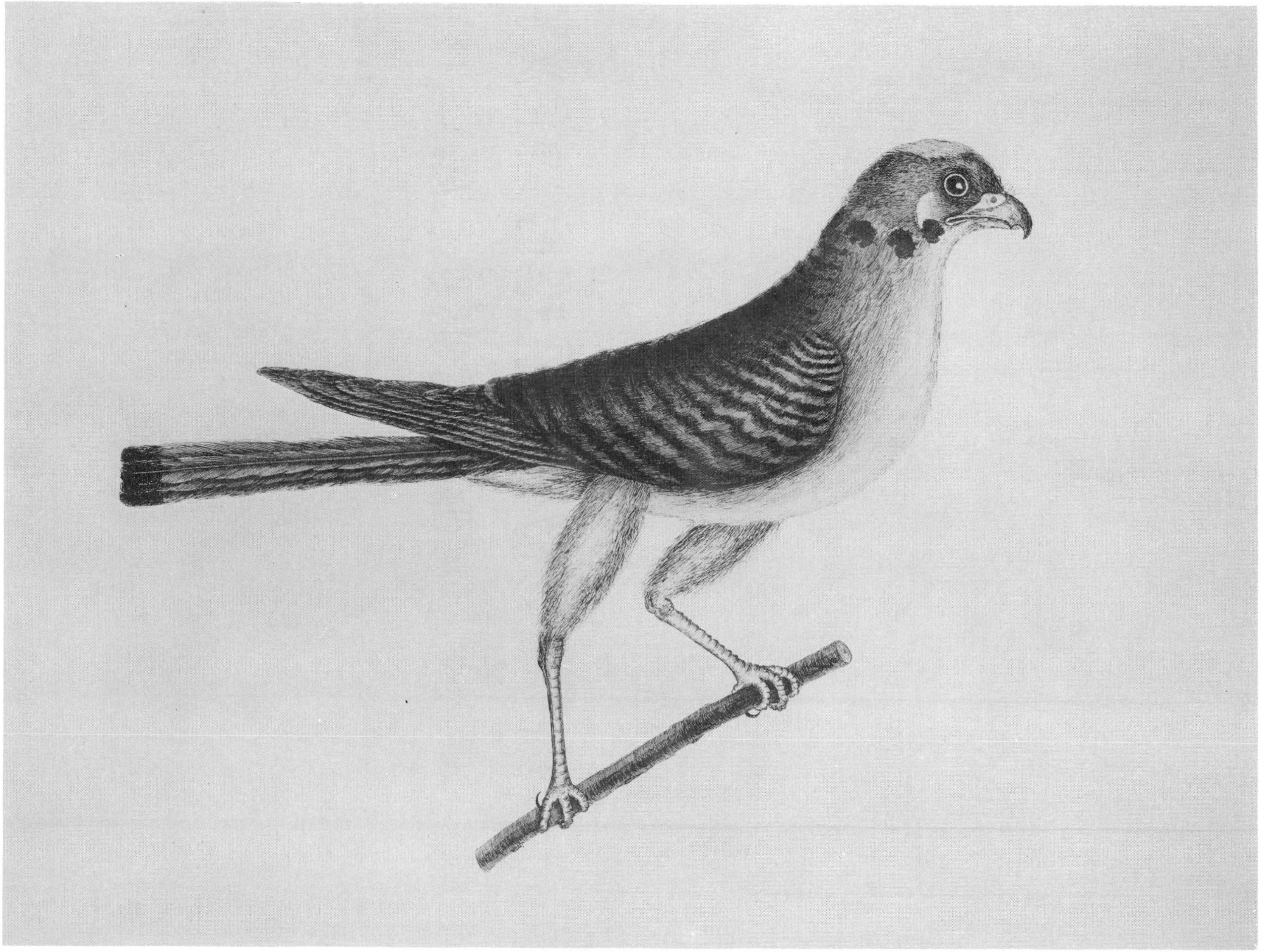

The Little Hawk

The Blew Jay · The Bay-leaved Smilax

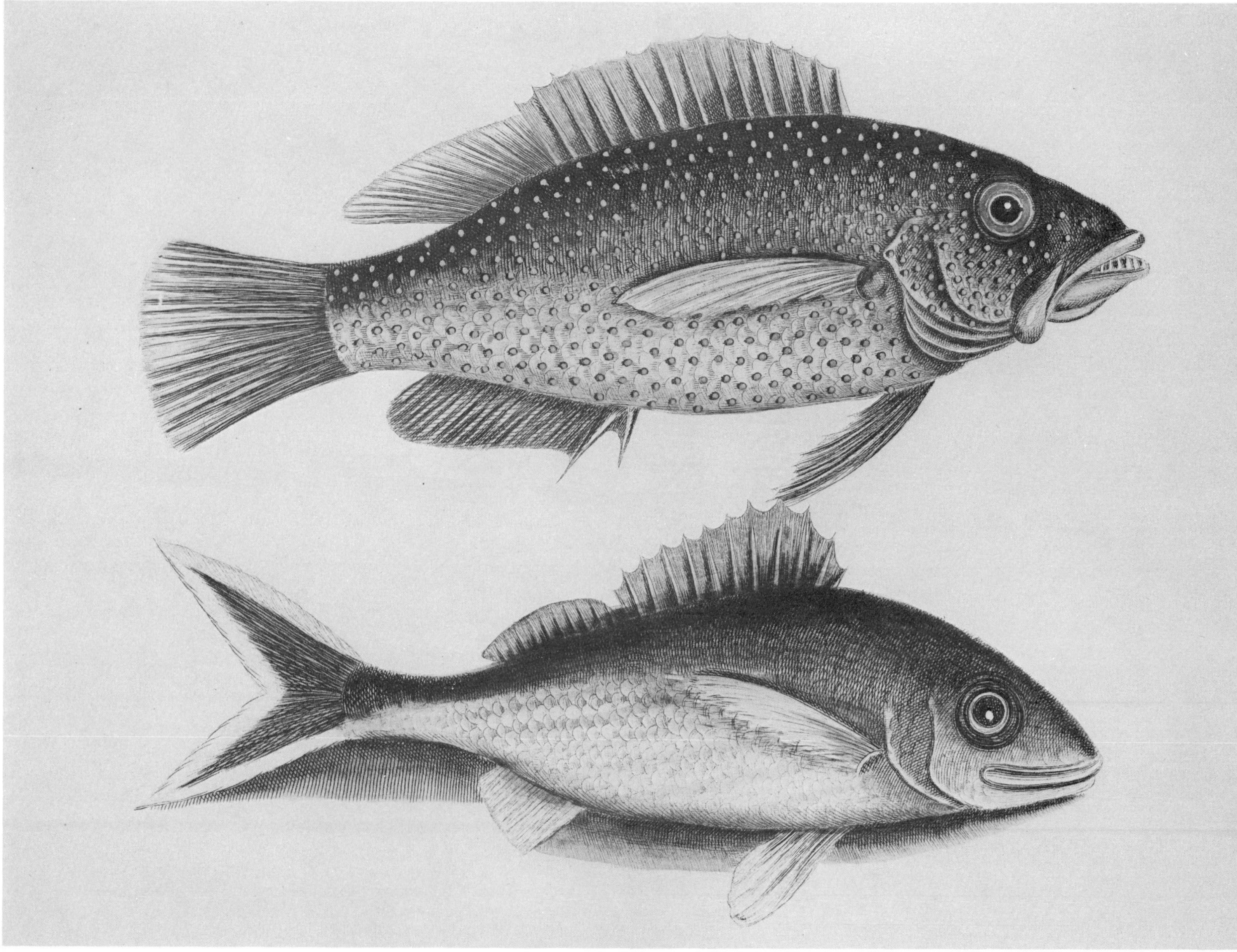

The Negro Fish · The Black-Tail

A Tooth.

The Section
of a Rattle

A Rattle of
Twenty four
Joynts.

The Rattle-Snake

The Little Owl

The large Lark · The little yellow Star-Flower

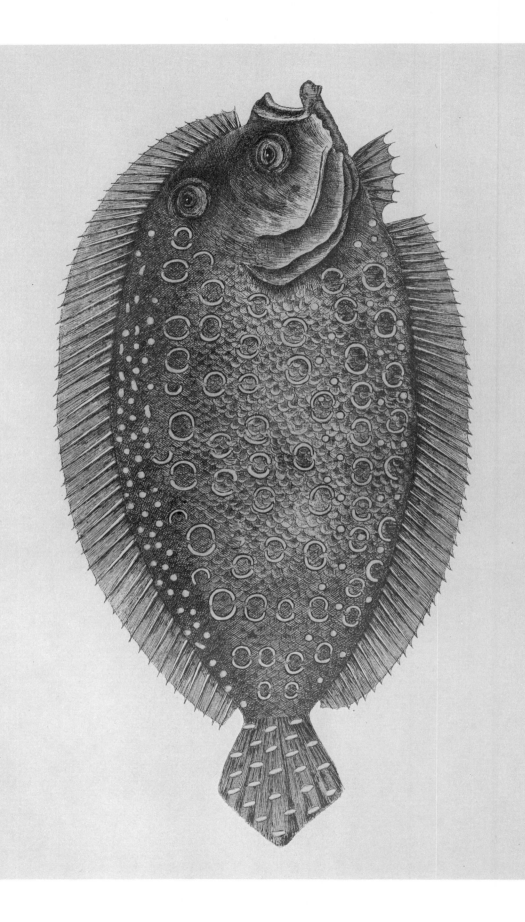

The Porgy

The Wood Pelican

The Swallow-Tail Hawk

The Parrot of Carolina · The Cypress of America

The Bald Eagle

Frutex virginianus trifolius · Papilio caudatus maximus

The red Bird · The Hiccory Tree · The Pignut

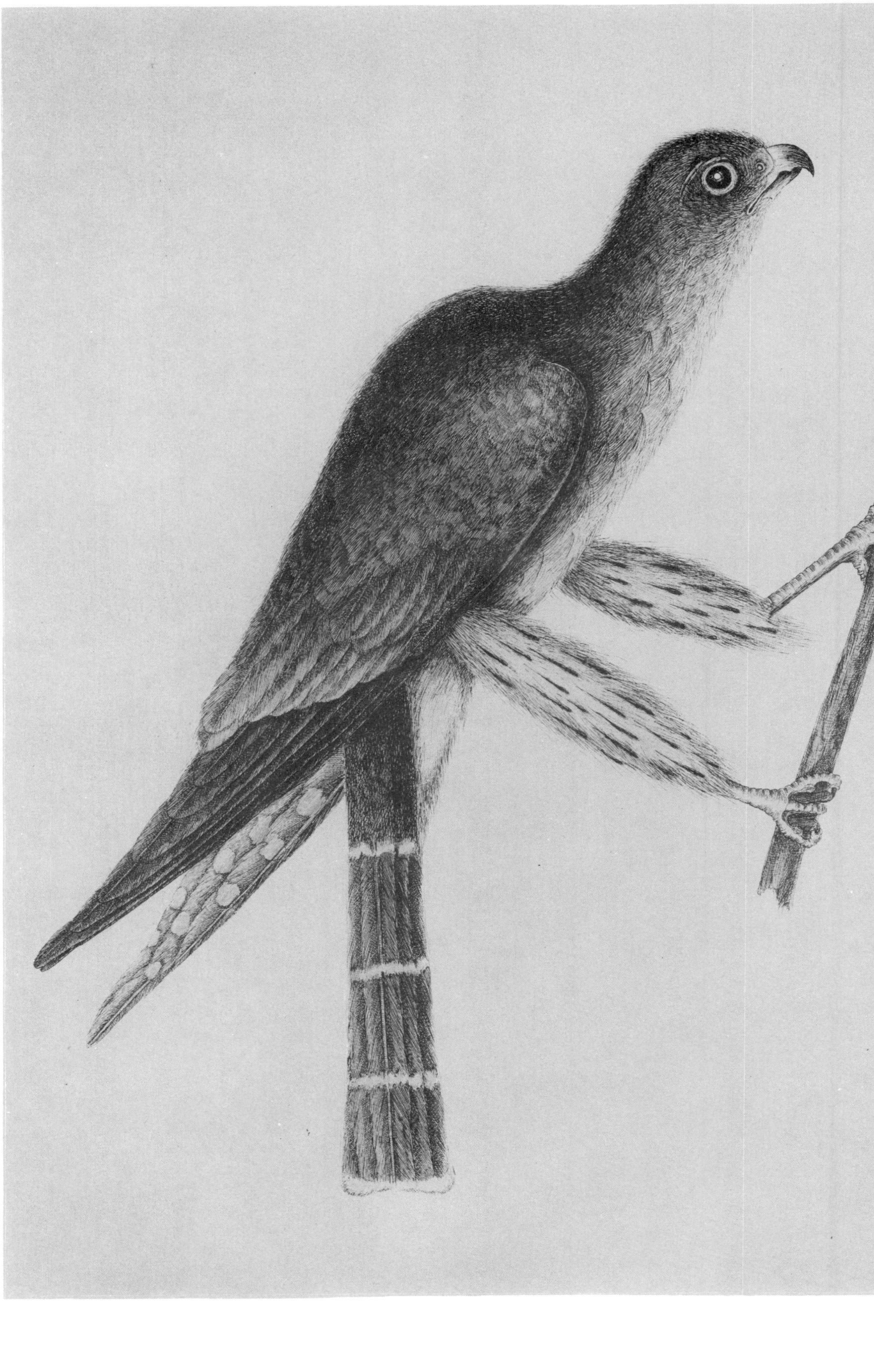

The Pigeon-Hawk

Fellow. One week later, he signed his obligation and was admitted to the Society.[27]

During the years that followed, Catesby became a reasonably active member of the Society — unusually so in view of the amount of work required to publish the successive parts of his book. In an age when many of the Fellows were not scientists at all, it might have been expected that a man who supported himself by his science should have been a more interested participant in the activities of the body than many of the members. Indeed, Catesby was able to support his membership in the Society as a scientific artist. Even before his election, the Council of the Society, at the suggestion of Dr. Mortimer, on November 10, 1732, had "Resolved that Mr. Catesby be employed" to draw cuts for the *Register Book* with the proviso that he "submit to such rates as on examination should appear reasonable."[28] There the matter stood for some time until, on April 30, 1734, Mortimer showed the Council several items which Catesby had drawn for the book. The rates which the artist demanded were reasonable: only that his bond for future payments to the Society be given to him.[29] In 1735 this right to be free of the ordinary payment of fifty-two shillings a year, paid quarterly, was made equivalent to the "composition fee" of twenty-one pounds.[30] The struggling naturalist saved more than that in the weekly shillings, no longer due, shillings which he could ill afford but which the thrifty councilors did not have to appropriate immediately for his work.

The busy artist served the Society in other ways as

well. He was called upon by the group to help disseminate foreign scientific items among its members. On January 16, 1734/35, the Society referred the first volume of Réaumur's *History of Insects* to him for his judgment.[31] Certainly this indicates the confidence which men of science in London had in Catesby. It also says something for the state of his education, as apparently he was able to read French. Despite the demands which the second volume of *The Natural History of Carolina* made on his time, Catesby studied Réaumur and gave his reviews, although two years passed before he was ready to read them. His account of the first volume was presented in four parts at several meetings of the Society between March and November, 1736. In March and April of the next year he reviewed the second volume for the Society, and followed this with the third in 1738 and the fourth in 1740.[32] Apparently the reviews ended there, without any word on the two remaining volumes. The manuscript versions of these accounts which have survived are detailed descriptions of the books but lack any critical comment.[33] In all likelihood, Catesby lacked the scientific background necessary to do this even if it had been expected of him; and probably it was not, for few of the "reviews" presented to the Society were critical accounts. Indeed, the reviews of Catesby's own work by the good Secretary Mortimer were mere lists of the contents coupled with short condensations of Catesby's descriptions of the plants and animals.[34]

While he was still occupied with Réaumur, Catesby was asked (December 18, 1735) to review the first

---

[27] The certificate quoted above gives the election as February 26, 1733, but the *R.S. Journal Book,* XV, 283, shows it correctly as April 26.

[28] *R.S. Council Minutes,* III, 118.

[29] *R.S. Council Minutes,* III, 142.

[30] *R.S. Record,* 94-95.

[31] *R.S. Journal Book,* XVI, 60; René Antoine Ferchault Réaumur, *Memoirs pour servir a l'histoire des insectes* (6 vols., Paris, 1734-42).

[32] *R.S. Journal Book,* XVI, 295, 345, 358, 391; XVII, 80,

83, 338; XVIII, 107.

[33] "Catesby's acct. of Reaumur's 1st vol. of Insects," endorsed, "Reading finished Nov. 18, [17]36," *Add. MS* 4437 (British Museum), fols. 3-24; "Catesby's acct. of Reaumur's 2d volume of Insects," endorsed, "April 21, 1737; Entered in R[ecord] B[ook]," *ibid.,* fols. 25-32.

[34] See *Phil. Trans.,* XXXVI (1730), 425-34; XXXVII (1731-32), 174-76, 447-50; XXXVIII (1734), 315-18; XXXIX (1735-36), 112-17, 251-58; XL (1738), 343-50; XLIV (1747), 599-608; XLV (1748), 157-73.

edition of Linnaeus' *Systema naturae*.[35] He had received this volume from Johann Friedrich Gronovius, the co-author with John Clayton of the *Flora Virginica*, which, excepting Catesby's own book, was the greatest work on the plants of British North America published during the colonial period.[36] But Catesby declined to review the book by the young Swedish doctor whose writings would do so much in the next half-century to change the naturalist's profession. Catesby was not a systematist, nor, for that matter, even a consistent follower of a system. It would have been difficult, if not impossible, for him to appraise the writings of a man who would one day be the king of systematists.

It is interesting to speculate as to what Catesby's impressions of Linnaeus' book might have been. Certainly many of his scientific friends did not accept Linnaeus' botanical classification, based, as it was, on the sexual system. Johann Amman wrote from St. Petersburg to his — and Catesby's — friend and former patron, Sir Hans Sloane, that animals might as well be arranged according to their penises as plants by their reproductive organs.[37] Many of Catesby's English friends, schooled as they were in the system of John Ray, were at first unwilling to accept the work of this Scandinavian upstart. In the summer of 1736, a little more than half a year after Catesby received the *Systema,* Linnaeus visited England and melted some of the hostility of the English botanical circle. Although there is no evidence that he met the author of *The Natural History of Carolina,* a work with which he was already acquainted,[38] there is a strong possibility that Linnaeus met Catesby in the course of the former's visits to British gardens

and museums. Linnaeus did meet Sir Hans Sloane, Cromwell Mortimer, Philip Miller, J. J. Dillenius, G. D. Ehret, John Martyn, and Peter Collinson, a roster of British botanists which, without Catesby's name, would hardly have been complete.[39]

The fact that Linnaeus' book was brought to the attention of the Society because of the correspondence between Catesby and Gronovius illustrates in part, at least, the importance of letter writing to the dissemination of scientific information in the early eighteenth century. At a time when there were few learned journals, other than the memoirs of the various academies, private correspondence was the principal means of keeping abreast of discoveries in foreign parts. Almost from its foundation the Royal Society had encouraged this communication; and, while Mark Catesby could not help in the grand manner of his friends, President Sloane and Peter Collinson, he could, nevertheless, contribute an occasional word from his acquaintances abroad.[40] On September 4, 1735, Catesby read to the Society a letter which he had received from Johann Amman, who had left London in 1733 for St. Petersburg, where he held a chair in botany.[41] Dr. Amman's letter brought word of the animals of Russia and particularly those of the Kamchatka Peninsula.[42] Catesby was thus able to help inform the Society of the results of Russian explorations, which, in many ways, paralleled his own work in America. On January 12, 1737/38, he brought word to the Society from one of its long-time American Fellows and his botanizing companion of Virginia, William Byrd. Contrary to Catesby's opinion, Byrd still held to the hope that good wine might be made in Virginia. He

[35] *R.S. Journal Book,* XVI, 219; Carl Linnaeus, *Systema naturae sive regna tria naturae systematice proposita per classes ordines, genera, & species* . . . (Leyden, 1735).

[36] (ed. 1, 2 vols., Leyden, 1739-43). The second edition, published at Leyden in 1762, was much improved, principally by the hand of Clayton.

[37] *Sloane* 4054, fol. 298.

[38] Linnaeus used it extensively in *Hortus Cliffortianus* (Amsterdam, 1737).

[39] Benjamin Daydon Jackson, *Linnaeus: The Story of His Life, Adapted from the Swedish of Theodor Magnus Fries* (London, 1923), 155-58.

[40] Raymond P. Stearns, "Colonial Fellows of the Royal Society of London, 1661-1788," *Notes and Records of the Royal Society of London,* VIII (1951), 179-80, 190-95.

[41] Sir Hans Sloane to Richard Richardson, Aug. 7, 1733, in Nichols, *Illust. Lit. Hist.,* I, 287.

[42] *R.S. Journal Book,* XVI, 201-2.

also wrote Catesby in favor of Dr. William Tennant's fabulous cure-all, the senega snakeroot, a remedy which found a firm supporter in the many-sided but credulous Byrd.[43]

In this same period, Mark Catesby also lent his good name to certificates which recommended two new Fellows for the Society. In neither case was the person recommended prominent; and Catesby's signatures were probably given more as favors to friends than as considered opinions of the abilities of the proposed Fellows.[44] The first of these, Dr. Thomas Stack, who was elected January 26, 1737/38, was the more noted of the two. Stack later served the Society as Foreign Secretary, but was known principally as the friend and protégé of Dr. Richard Mead, whose Latin medical works he translated into English.[45] Catesby knew Stack, but he also owed a debt of gratitude to Mead, who had subscribed to the trip to Carolina and apparently had been an undemanding patron at that. The motive for Catesby's second recommendation at about this time, that of John Maud, is less easily fathomed. Maud's scientific interests, as indicated by two contributions on chemistry in the *Philosophical Transactions*, were hardly those of the American traveler.[46] Neither of them coincided with Catesby's own predilections as well as did his later sponsorship of Dr. John Mitchell, the botanist and cartographer of Virginia.[47]

Mark Catesby was able on occasion, however, to enlighten the assembled Fellows with items which fell within his particular province, the flora and fauna of North America. A year after he was admitted to the Society, he presented the Society with the skin of an animal from South Carolina, which, he said, was called a black fox there but was actually a polecat.[48] This specimen was, in all probability, the model for the animal which he figured in his second volume.[49] The picture, at least, has the appearance of being drawn from a stuffed pelt rather than from a living animal. Again, in 1741, he showed the Society a Virginian plant, the poison ivy, which he had raised near Fulham, and gave an account of it.[50] Obviously Catesby's interest in the flora and fauna of the New World was primarily scientific, without the strong utilitarian bent of many of his contemporaries. Eleven years before, the hardy nurserymen of London had offered a number of toxic plants for sale, presumably to customers who preferred scientific observation to comfort.[51]

During the period in which he was writing his second volume, Catesby continued his work in the domestication of American plants. At some point during these years, however, as the place of growth of the poison ivy indicated, he transferred his activities from Bacon's garden in Hoxton to that of Christopher Gray in Fulham. This move probably occurred around the middle of the decade of the 1730's. In 1737 Gray published, on a single sheet, *A Catalogue of American Trees and Shrubs That Will Endure the Climate of England.*[52] The picture at the center of the sheet was an excellent drawing by Catesby of the *Magnolia altissima*[53] from his *Natural History of Carolina*, surrounded by a list of plants many of which bore references to pages in Catesby's work. This catalog, which probably provided the

[43] Part of a letter, Byrd to Catesby, Virginia, June 27, 1737, *R.S. Letter Book*, XXIV, 115-18.

[44] Allen, *Am. Ornith.*, 476, cites the appearance of Catesby's name on the certificates for both Stack and Maud. See *R.S. Record*, 404, for dates.

[45] *R.S. Record*, 343; John Nichols, ed., *Literary Anecdotes of the Eighteenth Century* . . . (9 vols., London, 1812-15), VI, 113.

[46] *Phil. Trans.*, XXXIX (1736), 282; XL (1738), 378.

[47] *R.S. Journal Book*, XX, 527.

[48] *R.S. Journal Book*, XV, 422.

[49] *Carolina*, II, 62; polecat — Alleghenian spotted skunk, *Spilogale putorius* (Linnaeus).

[50] *R.S. Journal Book*, XVIII, 269.

[51] [Philip Miller?], *Catalogus plantarum* . . . (London, 1730).

[52] This rare piece is reproduced in Gordon Dunthorne, *Flower and Fruit Prints of the 18th and Early 19th Centuries* . . . (Washington, D.C., 1938).

[53] *Magnolia altissima* — *Magnolia grandiflora* Linnaeus. See *Carolina*, II, 61.

basis for his *Hortus Britanno-Americanus,* shows that the artist was working for (and possibly with) Gray at the time of its publication. In the year following this, according to *The Natural History of Carolina,* one of the varieties brought from America by Catesby bloomed in this nursery.[54] By 1740 and 1741 he was certainly living in Fulham, where he noted several varieties bearing blossoms in his own garden.[55] It may well be, as Daniel Lysons, the topographer of the London area, wrote, that this garden lay within Gray's nursery. According to Lysons, trees which Catesby had planted were growing there at the end of the eighteenth century.[56]

This gardening activity by Catesby was, in part, at least, related to his more important efforts on the second volume of *The Natural History of Carolina,* as these and other references to it in the book indicated. While he was engaged with his plants, Catesby did not neglect to publish the succeeding sections of the work. The sixth part, which contained the first twenty plates of the second volume, was printed and colored within two years after the completion of the first. At any rate, Cromwell Mortimer was ready, on January 20, 1734/35, to read his account of the fishes contained in these pages.[57] The Secretary's summaries of the three parts which followed were printed in the *Philosophical Transactions* for the next four years.[58] Then, quite inexplicably, the accounts stopped, not to be renewed until late in 1747. It is possible that Mortimer merely forgot that he had not finished his task and did not remember the "last part" of the volume until after Catesby had presented him with the *Appendix.*[59]

Catesby progressed rather slowly between 1738 and 1743. Probably his gardening activities in Ful-

ham, even if they supplied the subjects for some of his plates, accounted for the tardy appearance of the introduction to this second volume, "An Account of Carolina and the Bahama Islands," and of the final score of plates. Then, in 1743, Catesby gave indications to his friends in the Royal Society that he was reaching the end; though, as it later proved, more would follow. On May 5 and 12 of this year he read a paper on the "State and Conditions of the Indians in America" to the Society.[60] This paper later appeared as part of the "Account," in his second volume of *The Natural History,* as did the other papers which he read in subsequent meetings. On May 19 he favored the Society with "The Manner of Making Tarr and Pitch in Carolina";[61] and on June 23 he "communicated an account of the method used in Carolina for the striking of Sturgeon according to the practice of the Indians and also two Receipts he obtained from his Excellency, Mr. Johnson, late governor of South Carolina: one for the Pickle for Sturgeon, the other for making Caviar."[62] The "Account" was thus well on its way. Then, a little less than six months later, on December 15, 1743, Catesby showed the Society the "last part" of his book, which ended with his blushing presentation of the *Catesbaea,* named for him by his friend J. F. Gronovius.[63]

In 1743 Mark Catesby had reached the rather advanced age — for the day, at least — of sixty, and probably thought that his great work was finished. Still, less than three years later, he delivered the twenty plates of the *Appendix* to their home in Crane Court. However, this final effort on *The Natural History of Carolina* bore less relationship to his own work in America than had the preceding parts. It was essentially the work of a compiler who worked

[54] *Carolina,* II, 78.
[55] *Carolina,* II, 98.
[56] Daniel Lysons, *The Environs of London . . .* (ed. 2, 2 vols., London, 1810-11), II, 829.
[57] *R.S. Journal Book,* XVI, 68. See *Phil. Trans.,* XXXVIII (1734), 315-18. This was apparently printed out of order.
[58] *Phil. Trans.,* XXXIX (1735-36), 112-17, 251-58; XL (1738), 343-50.
[59] *R.S. Journal Book,* XX, 307, 349-51.
[60] *R.S. Journal Book,* XIX, 98-99, 101. See *Carolina,* II, viii-xvi.
[61] *R.S. Journal Book,* XIX, 106. The full transcript is given in *Sloane* 4438, fols. 71-72. See *Carolina,* II, xxiii-xxiv.
[62] *R.S. Journal Book,* XIX, 130.
[63] *R.S. Journal Book,* XIX, 172; *Carolina,* II, 100.

from specimens which had been sent by John Bartram and other correspondents in the New World. Very possibly, had Catesby lived a few years longer, he might have turned out more things of this sort, as was the case of his friend George Edwards, whose *Natural History of Uncommon Birds* and *Gleanings of Natural History* contained pictures of animals from around the world, frequently drawn without the benefit of having seen the originals in their natural surroundings.[64]

Obviously, too, Catesby devoted part of these last years to work on his *Hortus Britanno-Americanus,* although parts of it could not have been completed much before his death in 1749,[65] as is evidenced by his reference to a catalpa tree blooming as late as 1748. The pages of this smaller book, though, when placed beside the magnificent *Natural History,* appear to have been hardly better than hack work. Superficially, the *Hortus* was little more than a catalog for Catesby's friend, Christopher Gray.[66] It treated a subject in which Catesby had repeatedly shown a lively interest, namely, the domestication of American trees and shrubs in England; but it was hardly a major contribution to botany. Indeed, Catesby had dealt with the subject, to some extent, in his larger book; and as most of the plants had already appeared in *The Natural History,* the *Hortus* was surely an effort to extend both his materials and his income. Unhappily for the latter consideration, the book did not appear in print until after his demise.

While he was engaged with his engraving and writing, Catesby continued to be an active participant in the business of the Royal Society. On April 12, 1744, he joined Collinson, Sloane, Mortimer, and others in sponsoring George Edwards for membership. For some reason, though, the application was withdrawn two weeks later, and Edwards did not become a Fellow until 1757, long after Mark Catesby had died.[67] Catesby also brought other guests to meetings of the Society, as, for example, Emanuel Mendez da Costa on March 6, 1745/46, and afterward — although this proved to be an unintentional disservice to the Society when, later, da Costa betrayed the Society's trust.[68] Still later in the same year, on December 6, 1746, he brought his fellow student of American flora, Dr. John Mitchell, to a meeting at Crane Court.[69]

Catesby also contributed more directly to the scientific objectives of the Royal Society. On the same occasion that he brought da Costa as his guest, he allowed Peter Collinson to read a letter he had received from the gardener, Thomas Knowlton of Lonesborough, Yorkshire. Knowlton's communication, concerning "the Situation of the ancient Town, Dogovicia, and . . . two Men of an extraordinary Bulk and Weight,"[70] was one of those strange combinations of antiquarian information and oddity which found their way so often into the pages of the *Philosophical Transactions.* One week later, though, on March 13, 1745/46, Catesby was apparently sufficiently interested to read still another letter from Knowlton. This one concerned "Two extraordinary Deers Horns, found under ground in different Parts of Yorkshire. . . ."[71] These bits were very insignificant, however, in comparison with the paper of his own composition which he read a year later, on March 5, 1746/47.[72] This was the end product of his thoughts on the migration of birds, "Of Birds of

[64] (4 pts., London, 1743-51); (3 pts., London, 1758-64).

[65] *Hortus Britanno-Americanus* . . . (London, 1763); republished as *Hortus Europae Americanus* . . . (London, 1767), 25.

[66] *Hortus,* iii.

[67] *R.S. Certificates,* I, 286; *R.S. Journal Book,* XXIII, 521, 611, 620-21.

[68] *R.S. Journal Book,* XX, 60; Sir Henry Lyons, *The Royal Society 1660-1940* . . . (Cambridge, 1940), 169.

[69] *R.S. Journal Book,* XX, 171.

[70] *R.S. Journal Book,* XX, 66. See *Phil. Trans.,* XLIV, pt. 1 (1746), 100-102.

[71] *R.S. Journal Book,* XX, 70-71. See *Phil. Trans.,* XLIV, pt. 1 (1746), 124-27.

[72] *R.S. Journal Book,* XX, 218-23.

Passage," which was, by all odds, his most important contribution to the deliberations of the Society. With its faults — and its chief one was, in Catesby's words, "the want of occular testimony" — it was, nevertheless, a rational view which rejected the commonly held belief that swallows hibernated in caves or hollow trees or at the bottoms of ponds.[73]

This paper was the outgrowth of the work of Mark Catesby in ornithology which had filled the pages of the first volume of his *Natural History of Carolina* and which would soon be concluded in the nine birds figured in the *Appendix* to the book. These plates, along with the other eleven of the final section, were finished a little more than a year after Catesby had read his paper. On April 16, 1747, Peter Collinson wrote Linnaeus, "Catesby's noble work is finished."[74] Possibly only the uncolored sheets were

ready though, because the proud author did not take this concluding section of his life's work to Crane Court for presentation to the Society until July 2.[75]

It had taken Catesby twenty years from the time of his return to England until his great project was completed; and, while he still had almost thirty months of life left to him after he gave the *Appendix* to the Society, these remaining two and a half years were almost anticlimactic. *The Natural History of Carolina, Florida, and the Bahama Islands* had occupied most of his time and his thought since he left England for Charles Town. Even though he was married during these last years of his life and though he continued his work as a naturalist, his great task, the thing for which he would be remembered, was finished.

[73] *Phil. Trans.*, XLIV, pt. 2 (1747), 435-44. See below, pp. 63-64.

[74] In Smith, *Corresp. Linnaeus*, I, 18; see also John Mitchell

to Linnaeus, London, April 16, 1747, *ibid.*, II, 443. The *Appendix* was not officially published until one year later. *Gentleman's Magazine*, XVIII (1748), 192.

[75] *R.S. Journal Book*, XX, 307.

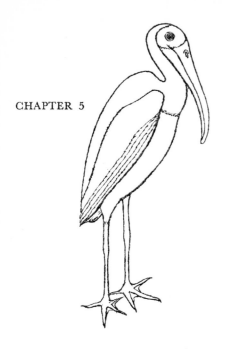

CHAPTER 5

Catesby's Last Years

In July of 1747, when Mark Catesby signaled the completion of *The Natural History of Carolina* to the world of science and learning by presenting its *Appendix* to the Royal Society, his most fruitful years had passed. At the age of sixty-four, he was beyond the point of beginning a major new project and could content himself with reading, with the less arduous work involved in the *Hortus Britanno-Americanus,* and in coloring additional copies of his *Natural History*.[1]

In these, his latter years, Catesby was a respected elder, an ornament to British natural history, whose pronouncements on North America were listened to carefully by his Fellows at the Royal Society, who was introduced with pride to visiting naturalists, and who impressed the "curious" with his zeal in domesticating American plants to the British climate.[2] Other and more specific honors came to him as well. During these last few years he was elected an honorary

member of the Gentlemen's Society at Spalding in Yorkshire.[3] This organization, founded in 1710 by the barrister, Maurice Johnson, was primarily a society of antiquaries, but included also an interest in the arts and sciences. Sir Isaac Newton and Alexander Pope had been honored earlier by the group, and, within the natural history circle, Sir Hans Sloane, Richard Mead, Thomas Stack, John Mitchell, George Edwards, and Emanuel Mendez da Costa were listed on its rolls.[4]

It is from these later years, too, that we find the only surviving evidence regarding Mark Catesby's person and demeanor. The painter of birds and flowers left no self-portrait; and he and his family lacked sufficient means to have it done by a professional portrait painter. However, his friend, Emanuel Mendez da Costa, left a verbal sketch of the author of *The Natural History of Carolina*. Da Costa remembered him as "tall, meagre, hard favoured, and [with]

[1] Peter Kalm, *Kalm's Visit to England on His Way to America in 1748* (Joseph Lucas, tr., London, 1892), 119.

[2] *Kalm's Visit to England*, 17; *Phil. Trans.*, XLIV, pt. 2 (1747), 575; Thomas Knowlton to Richard Richardson, July 18, 1749, *MS Radcliffe Trust*, C. XI, fol. 57.

[3] John Nichols, ed., *Literary Anecdotes of the Eighteenth*

Century . . . (9 vols., London, 1812-15), IV, 78. The date of Catesby's election was not given; but he was listed as being of "St. Luke's, London." He did not move to the Parish of St. Luke's until sometime after 1742.

[4] Nichols, ed., *Literary Anecdotes*, 4-7, 80, 83, 97, 98, 106, 111, 113.

a sullen look . . ." and that he "was extremely grave or sedate, and of a silent disposition; but when he contracted a friendship was communicative and affable."[5] To this might be added that Catesby was rather nearsighted — or so Peter Kalm found him in May, 1748.[6] These notes square well with the accomplishments of the man. It would have taken a grimly determined — and rather introverted — man to have spent lonely years in the American wilderness, only to follow these with two decades more of solitary labor on the plates of *The Natural History,* a labor which may well have sapped his vision.

During his later life, Mark Catesby lived in London "behind St. Luke's church in Old-street."[7] The date of his removal is not clear, but it was sometime between 1742, when he recorded plants growing at his garden in Fulham, and the fall of 1747, when the record of his marriage gave his residence as being in the Parish of St. Luke's, Middlesex.[8] It is reasonable to suppose that the move was made just before his marriage, as this must have necessitated larger quarters. Thus Catesby spent his last years in a poor section of London not far from Hoxton, where he had lived and worked over twenty years before.

Mark Catesby's marriage at the age of sixty-four is surprising for a man who had presumably spent the whole of his life a bachelor; and it was accomplished under rather unusual — or at least irregular — circumstances. On October 2, 1747, he married Mrs. Elizabeth Rowland, who was apparently a widow with a grown daughter, at the chapel of the Reverend Alexander Keith in May Fair.[9] The chapel was one of those at which so-called clandestine marriages were performed without banns, license, or the consent of parents — the last of which was hardly necessary in this case. These weddings, though contrary to ecclesiastical law, were considered valid and binding at the time.[10] Mr. Keith's chapel was one of the most popular of such establishments in London — he was reputed to have a veritable "bishopric of revenue" — and probably the most fashionable.[11] Its proprietor, who enjoyed his revenues from Fleet Prison, where he had been sent for his misdeeds, advertised a year after Catesby's marriage:

The Way to Mr. Keith's Chapel is thro' Piccadilly by the End of St. James' Street, and down Clarges — Street, and turn on the Lefthand. The Marriage (together with a Licence on a Five Shilling Stamp, and Certificate) are carried on for a Guinea, as usual, any time till Four in the Afternoon, by another regular Clergyman, at Mr. Keith's Little Chapel in May-Fair, near Hyde Park Corner, opposite the great Chapel and within Ten Yards of it. There is a Porch at the Door like a Country Church Porch.[12]

Mark Catesby and Elizabeth Rowland passed through the "Country Church Porch" on October 8, 1747. Two years, two months, and fifteen days later, at the time of Catesby's death, the couple had two children, Mark and Ann. Young Mark was reputed to have been eight years old at the time his father died; of Ann's age we know nothing.[13] It is possible that both children were the issue of a previous marriage, although there is no indication that Elizabeth Rowland Catesby was not their real mother, nor does there seem to be any record of a previous marriage by

[5] Emanuel Mendez da Costa, "Notices and Anecdotes of Literati, Collectors, Etc., from a MS by the Late Mendez da Costa, and Collected Between 1747 and 1788," *Gentleman's Magazine,* LXXXII, pt. 1 (1812), 206.

[6] *Kalm's Visit to England,* 119.

[7] *Gentleman's Magazine,* XX (1750), 31.

[8] *Carolina,* II, *Appendix,* 13; George J. Armytage, ed., *The Register of Baptisms and Marriages at St. George's Chapel May Fair (Publications of the Harleian Society, Registers,* XV, London, 1889), 92.

[9] All of the women listed in the register at this period were denominated "Mrs.," but it is reasonable to assume her

widowhood on the basis of the mention of her daughter, also Elizabeth Rowland, in her will dated Jan. 4, 1753, and proved Aug. 29, 1753, *P.C.C. Searle* [5 *Searle* 803: 240] (Principal Probate Registry, London), 327.

[10] Armytage, ed., *Register . . . St. George's Chapel,* viii; John Southerden Burn, *The Fleet Registers* (London, 1833), 1-2. Their validity was on the basis of common law, which would not have required the presence of a clergyman.

[11] Burn, *Fleet Registers,* 97.

[12] *The London Gazetteer* (Dec. 30, 1748) and later issues.

[13] *P.C.C. Searle;* George Edwards to [Thomas Pennant], London, Dec. 5, 1761 (MS in the Pierpont Morgan Library, New York).

the naturalist.[14] Mark and Ann may well have been natural offspring of Catesby and Elizabeth Rowland, with possibly both of their births preceding a marriage which added a certain solemnity — if little more legality — to an existing relationship.[15]

Mark Catesby did not permit his new bride to keep him from his usual "philosophical" haunts. On October 22, less than two weeks after the ceremony, he attended a meeting of the Royal Society at Crane Court. On this occasion he heard an archeological paper read which concerned the body of a woman and an "antique Shoe found in a Morass in the Isle of Axholm in Lincolnshire." Catesby was able to contribute something to comparative anthropology, as he told the Fellows that "this Shoe or Sandal was exactly like what the Indians in Virginia wear at this Day, and call Mokasin."[16] Catesby's word carried great authority when he spoke on America. His little comment was deemed sufficiently important to be printed in the *Philosophical Transactions,* where such trivia seldom found a place.

In all probability, Catesby continued to attend the meetings of the Society faithfully during these last years of his life as often as his health would allow. On April 21, 1748, he met Peter Kalm, the young professor from Åbo in Finland, whom Peter Collinson had taken to hear the deliberations of the Society.[17] The young Swedish Doctor wrote: "A little after 7 o'clock the meeting was concluded, when the Fellows went home by degrees. Mr. Collinson at once introduced me to Dr. Mortimer, secretary of the Royal Society, and to Mr. Catesby, author of the precious and costly work on the Flora and Fauna of Carolina in America."[18] Collinson, who so assiduously promoted the study of American natural history, quite obviously felt that Catesby was someone that Kalm, who was then on his way to America, should know.

Kalm, too, was quite obviously impressed by this man who had preceded him to the New World. A little more than a month after their first encounter, on May 23, he called on Catesby at his home and had the good fortune to see Dr. John Mitchell there as well.

Nearly the whole afternoon was spent in the house of Mr. Catesby, a man who is very well known for his *Natural History of Carolina* in America. In this work he has incomparably well represented with lifelike colours, the rarest trees, plants, animals, birds, fishes, snakes, frogs, lizards, painted-toads, which are there found, so that no one can see that they are not living where they stand with their natural colours on the paper.[19]

Kalm found his host in an expansive — even discursive — mood, quite willing to prepare his younger guest for what he would find in America. Kalm's desire for information was not confined to natural history, however. He inquired of Catesby and Mitchell whether punch was "a useful or baneful drink," and was told that it was useful or harmful according to how it was prepared. Catesby's answer, though based, he said, on his experience in Virginia, could hardly have persuaded his young friend to sample the drink. He told Kalm that in Virginia a punch had formerly been made which was strongly laced with brandy or rum and sugar but which contained relatively little lemon juice. This concoction in due time caused a paralysis of the fingers so that the drinker was forced to hold his glass with his wrists (Catesby was not above generalizing on the basis of scanty evidence or hearsay when natural history was not concerned).

[14] Elizabeth Rowland Catesby's will refers to them as "my loving children."

[15] Another reason for such an irregular marriage may have included its cheapness. Mr. Keith, this "Marryin' Sam" of eighteenth-century London, averred that "many have come to me to be married when they have had but half-a-crown in their pockets, and sixpence to buy a pot of beer. . . ." Even so, it was a place of fashion and this consideration may have dictated its choice by Elizabeth Rowland. Martha Smith, the Martha Arther to whom Elizabeth left a bequest, followed her friend to this chapel a few months later. Burn, *Fleet Registers,* 99; *P.C.C. Searle; Armytage, ed., Register . . . St. George's Chapel,* 96.

[16] *Phil. Trans.,* XLIV, pt. 2 (1747), 575; abstracted in *Gentleman's Magazine,* XIX (1749), 204.

[17] *R.S. Journal Book,* XX, 490.

[18] *Kalm's Visit to England,* 17.

[19] *Kalm's Visit to England,* 118-19.

He continued by saying that this mixture had given way to one containing less brandy and more lemon. This made it a much less debilitating drink, but the consequence for the frequent drinker, even of this version, was a palsied old age.[20] Kalm did not say what he drank in America, but presumably he was thoroughly forewarned. The warning was also apparently in keeping with the best American medical opinion, as Dr. Mitchell, who had long practiced medicine in Virginia, said nothing to contradict it.

The conversation drifted to other topics. Catesby expatiated on the introduction and prevalence in England of "Wall lice." Like all bad things, they had come from abroad, and had become so common within two decades that hardly a house in London was free of them. More to the point, Catesby gave Kalm careful instructions for the preservation of the specimens which he might send from America.[21]

This afternoon meeting in London of three of the leading figures in American natural history of the eighteenth century was a further indication of the friendship which had grown between Catesby and Mitchell, since Mitchell's return to England less than two years before. Soon afterward, Catesby was able to make a concrete gesture of his friendship in helping to advance the ambitions of John Mitchell. On June 9, 1748, Catesby's name appeared on the certificate which recommended Mitchell's election as Fellow of the Royal Society, an election which was accomplished on December 15.[22]

Catesby apparently continued his active attendance at the meetings of the Society, although the records of that body contain but one more reference to his participation in its work. It again involved his recommendation for membership of a man closely connected with America. This was Lieutenant General James Oglethorpe, the leading "trustee" of the young colony

of Georgia, and the founder of Savannah, whose certificate was dated April 6, 1749.[23] Although Oglethorpe was said by his sponsors to be "well versed in Natural History, Mathematicks, and all branches of Polite Literature," his was a candidacy based largely on attainments other than "philosophical." He had brought botanical specimens from Georgia — indeed, Catesby had seen them — but his major concerns at this time lay outside natural history.[24] Possibly his sponsors, who included the President of the Society, Martin Folkes, and the past President, Sir Hans Sloane, erred in recommending the General, as he later defaulted in his payment of dues and was dropped from the Society rolls.[25]

With this action — if indeed he were physically present to attest to Oglethorpe's qualifications — Catesby's relationship with the Royal Society was all but concluded. Early in the summer of 1749 he lay in what was apparently his final illness. His old friend, Thomas Knowlton, who once had served as gardener to Catesby's patron, William Sherard, visited Catesby at his house near Old Street, during the early weeks of July.[26] Knowlton wrote Dr. Richard Richardson on July 18: ". . . poor Mr. Catesby's legs swell and he looks badly. Drs. Mead and Stack said there were little hopes of him long on this side of the Grave."[27] Probably there was no better prognosis available in London than this one by Catesby's friend and benefactor, Richard Mead, and Thomas Stack, Mead's assistant, whose election as F.R.S. Catesby had sponsored. A tired heart, worn by years of exertion in the cause of natural science, was giving way; and Catesby's dropsy was symptomatic of weaknesses which would lead shortly to his end.

The end did not come yet, for by December Catesby was able to walk about. On one of these walks with his son, he fell "Crossing the way" in Holborn. Mark Catesby never again recovered consciousness. He was

[20] *Kalm's Visit to England,* 119-20.

[21] *Kalm's Visit to England,* 51-52.

[22] *Certificates* (MSS in the Library of the Royal Society of London), I, 372; *R.S. Journal Book,* XX, 527.

[23] *R.S. Certificates,* I, 396.

[24] *Carolina,* II, 75.

[25] *R.S. Council Minutes,* IV, 184; *R.S. Journal Book,* XXII, 587 (copy).

[26] *Pulteney,* II, 239.

[27] *MS Radcliffe Trust,* C. XI, fol. 57; also in *Richardson Extracts,* 400-402.

placed in a coach and carried home to his wife. There he lingered two or three more days, and then, two days short of Christmas, 1749, he died and was buried in St. Luke's Churchyard.[28] His funeral was attended by George Edwards, his fellow delineator of birds, and doubtless by many other members of the natural history circle of which he had been such an honored member. A month later, the *Gentleman's Magazine* announced to its readers:

On Saturday morning the 23rd of December died at his house, behind St. Luke's church in Old-Street, the truly honest, ingenious, and modest Mr. Mark Catesby, F.R.S. who, after travelling through many of the British Dominions, on the continent, and in the islands of America, in order to make himself acquainted with the customs and manners of the natives, and to collect observations on the animals and vegetables of those countries, which he very exactly delineated, and painted on the spot, he returned with these curious materials to England, and compiled a most magnificent work, intitled, A natural History of Carolina, Florida, and the Bahama Islands, which does great honour to his native country, and perhaps is the most elegant performance of its kind that has yet been published; since not only the rare beasts, birds, fishes, and plants etc. were drawn, engraven, and exquisitely coloured, from his original paintings, by his own hands, in 220 folio copper plates but he has also added a correct map and a general history of that world. He liv'd to the age of 70, well known to and much esteemed by, the curious of this and other nations, and died much lamented by his friends, leaving behind him two children and a widow, who has a few copies of this noble work, undisposed of.[29]

This notice was the last tribute of the British natural history circle to their "truly honest, ingenious, and modest" friend, and may well have been written by the prime mover of that circle, Peter Collinson,

Catesby's patron and friend, who, a few months later, repeated some of it in a letter to Linnaeus.[30] Save for some exaggeration of the unique qualities of *The Natural History of Carolina*, this obituary was, after all, an act of love and an attempt to aid the widow and her fatherless children; and if we except the fact that Mark Catesby was four years younger than seventy, this was as good and as accurate an account of his life as his contemporaries could give.

Mark Catesby had survived the completion of this elegant book only by a little more than thirty months. It had so consumed his energies and his own inheritance that when he died his plates and the few finished copies he had left were virtually his only estate. His widow and two children were able to live for two more years on the sale of these copies, although Elizabeth Catesby was forced by her need of money to reduce their price by one-fourth.[31] Even this did not suffice. She was compelled to do what her husband had tried so hard to avoid: she sold what parts she had left, along with the plates, to the booksellers for four hundred pounds.[32] Even this modest sum quickly disappeared. When Elizabeth Catesby died, a victim of consumption, in February, 1753, much of it was gone. She was able to leave a bequest of ten pounds to her daughter, Elizabeth Rowland, and a guinea to her friend, Martha Arther. To her "loving cousin, Jekell Catesby," she left "a second volume of Mr. Catesby's Natural History to make his sett compleat." Young Mark and Ann were to receive all the rest, "whether money, Goods, Plate and all that I may be possessed of or entitled unto. . . ."[33] The money was only about half of what she

[28] See the account of Catesby's death by George Edwards in G. F. Frick, "Mark Catesby . . . ," *Papers of the Bibliographical Society of America*, LIV (1960), 172-75.
[29] *Gentleman's Magazine*, XX (1750), 30-31. This corrected an earlier notice which had given his death date as Dec. 24, *ibid.*, XIX (1749), 573.
[30] Dated May 8, 1750, in Smith, *Corresp. Linnaeus*, I, 23-24.
[31] John Mitchell to Linnaeus, London, May 1, 1750, in Smith, *Corresp. Linnaeus*, II, 451.
[32] See the note to Chapter 5 below.
[33] *P.C.C. Searle.* Jekyll Catesby, who was also executor of the

estate, was apparently the son of Catesby's brother Jekyll. He lived in the Parish of St. Paul's, Covent Garden, in the 1750's and 1760's, and seems to have died there, a pauper, in 1786. In April, 1766, he was noted as "Haberdasher in Henrietta street, Convent Garden. . . ." His copy of Catesby's *Carolina*, purchased from him by Thomas Pennant, is now in the Pierpont Morgan Library. See the note in the hand of Thomas Pennant in the Morgan copy of *Carolina*, I, recto of front flyleaf. *The Registers of St. Paul's Church, Covent Garden, London (Pub. of the Harleian Society, Registers, XXXIII-XXXVII*, London, 1906-9), XXXV, 191, 198-99; XXXVII, 12, 144.

had received from Mark Catesby's literary remains. He left his children little more than his art; and this they shared with the world.

Mark Catesby was not a great naturalist: his training was meager, his talents were of a secondary order, and, as if to compound these handicaps, he did not begin his work in Carolina until he was nearly forty. Still, he accomplished a great deal. He wrote and illustrated a magnificent book, and did so almost unaided. A less tenacious man might have given up and have been reduced to a mere collector when, in the wilderness, his patrons had pressed him with unreasonable demands. Catesby, however, had chosen the hard, seemingly impossible way. He had gone to America with little more than a critical mind, a love of nature, and the hand of an untrained artist; but he returned to England with his precious drawings, his notes, and his vision of a great natural history. A less persevering man might have quailed at devoting more than two decades to engrave and color more than two hundred plates; but Catesby did, and, adding nearly three hundred pages of descriptive data in two languages, produced *The Natural History of Carolina, Florida, and the Bahama Islands.* This was his accomplishment. Through his efforts, the Old World discovered much more of the New, and the New World learned to know itself better. Upon the foundations laid by Mark Catesby and his sometimes nameless co-workers, the great systematists of an age of systems built their grand taxonomic structures. More than that, Mark Catesby was both an artist, who grounded his art in a knowledge of nature, and an innovator, who developed a new genre of ornithological illustration. By presenting his birds, plants, and animals amidst their own natural environments, Catesby prepared the way, as did almost no one else, for his ninteenth-century successor, John James Audubon. This *Natural History of Carolina,* though a pioneer effort in its field, was unquestionably one of the finest works of its kind in the eighteenth century, a fitting monument to Mark Catesby's pertinacity, imagination, artistry, and scientific accomplishments.

Even its faults were long perpetated by those who imitated it and plagiarized so greedily from it. To assess this extraordinary work in the light of contemporary knowledge and to note its impact upon the continuum of natural science are the principal objects of the remainder of this book.

Note: *Some Statements by Peter Collinson Concerning Mark Catesby*

The following is a manuscript note in the British Museum copy of Pulteney's *Historical and Biographical Sketches of the Progress of Botany in England,* Vol. I, in the blank pages before the title page, writer unknown:

"The following is copied from the blank leaf preceding the Title page in Vol. 1 of Catesby's *Carolina.* It is in the hand writing of Collinson with his signature, but without a date.

[1] The ingenious author, Mr. Mark Catesby, was born of a gentleman's family at Sudbury in Suffolk. Some of his family being settled in Virginia, and having himself a turn of mind to Natural History, went over there to see his sister, and to prove his genius. From thence he travelled to Carolina, Bahama Islands, etc., and painted all the subjects from life. At his return the subscription being at an end, he was at great loss how to introduce this valuable work to the world, until he met with a friend* to assist and promote his views. He lernt to engrave and coloured all himself, yet it proved so very expensive that he was many years in accomplishing the work, being himself the principal operator. So noble, and so accurate a performance, begun and finished by one hand is not to be parallelled; but it afforded a subsistence to himself, his wife, and two children to his death, and his widow subsisted on the sale of it for about two years afterwards. Then the work, plates, etc., sold for £400, and about £200 more left by the Widow was divided between the two children a son and a daughter.

Peter Collinson

---

* Peter Collinson referred to in this manner in the original.

"At the bottom of the Titlepage of the same work, are the following words, also written and signed by Peter Collinson.

[2] This edition of the noble work is very valuable, as it was highly finished by the ingenious Author, who in gratitude made me this present for the considerable sum of money I lent him without interest to enable him to publish it for the benefit of himself and family, else of necessity it must have fallen a prey to the book sellers.

Peter Collinson (F.R.S., R.A.S., S.A.S.) Soc Suecias"

In his *Extracts from the Literary and Scientific Correspondence of Richard Richardson,* Dawson Turner noted (101-2): ". . . the very fine library of the late Mr. Charles Collinson of the Chantry, Ipswich, has been dispersed by auction. The sale took place 21st July, 1834. The library was principally that of Peter Collinson, Esq.; and among other works of high price, it included Catesby's *Carolina,* in which Mr. Collinson had made the following remarks: —

[3] Mr. Mark Catesby, the author of this book, was born at Sudbury in Suffolk. This copy of this noble work is very valuable; as it was highly finished by the ingenious author, who, in gratitude, made me this present for the considerable sum of money I lent him without interest, to enable him to publish it, for the benefit of himself and family; else, through necessity, it must have fallen a prey to the booksellers.

"— Another note, also in Mr. Collinson's handwriting, says,

[4] On Saturday morning, the 23rd of December, 1749, died at his house behind St. Luke's Church, in Old Street, the truly honest, ingenious, and modest Mr. Mark Catesby, F.R.S., who, after travelling through many of the British Dominions on the Continent and in the Islands of America, in order to make himself acquainted with the customs and manners of the natives, and to collect observations on the animals and vegetables, which he there very exactly delineated and painted on the spot, with these materials returned to England, and compiled a most magnificent work, entitled, *A Natural History of Carolina,* with two hundred and thirty copper-plates, which does great honour to him and to his native country, and perhaps is the most curious and elegant performance of the kind that has any where appeared in Europe; wherein not only the rare beasts, birds, fishes, and plants were drawn, engraved, and exquisitely coloured after the life, from the original paintings by his own hands, but he has also added a map, and general history of those countries. He lived to the age of seventy, well known to and much esteemed by the curious of this and other nations, and died much lamented by his friends; leaving behind him two children and a widow, who has a few copies of this noble work undisposed of. — P. Collinson, F.R.S., F.S.A., A.R.S., *Sueciae Socius.*

"For the lovers of Bibliography, it may be well to add, that this precious work . . . was purchased at the sale by a London bookseller for £15.10s., and is now placed in the excellent botanical library of my friend, Aylmer Bourke Lambert, Esq."

Statements 1 and 2 seem, without the originals, to be more accurate than Turner's published note (statement 1 is copied also in the hand of A. B. Lambert in the Collinson papers in the Linnaean Society of London). Of the latter, 3 is a version of 2, with possibly a line from 1; 4 is a near approximation of the death notice which appeared in the *Gentleman's Magazine.* This hardly proves Collinson's authorship of the notice, as he may merely have copied it. He did use very similar language in a letter to Linnaeus, May 8, 1750, where he wrote: "Our ingenious friend Mr. Catesby died the 23rd of December last, aged 70, much lamented" (Smith, *Corresp. Linnaeus,* I, 23-24). Again, this is not conclusive proof, as he may have had the notice in front of him when he wrote the letter; but it makes his authorship more probable. It is even more probable in view of the fact that Collinson was Catesby's close friend, his frequent sponsor in scientific circles and financially, and that he was demonstrably concerned for Catesby's widow (he was a witness to her will).

If Collinson were the author, then the death date as given, December 23, 1749, was undoubtedly correct. Even if he were not, his letter to Linnaeus would confirm it, as he, of all people, should have known. Elsa G. Allen, however, has found the will of a Mark Catesby indicating that he was "going to the seas" aboard the East Indiaman *Portfield,* and the record of his having been buried at sea on April 20, 1750 (*Am. Ornith.,* 477). It is obvious that this is not the Mark Catesby of the present study. Collinson's letter to Linnaeus; George Edward's description of Catesby's death, even though he recalled it as being in 1747 or 1748 (see n28 above); and the *Gentleman's Magazine* obituary provide overwhelming evidence in favor of the December, 1749, date.

PART II | CATESBY THE NATURALIST

CHAPTER 6

Catesby as a Naturalist: Ornithology and Botany

The first volume of *The Natural History of Carolina, Florida, and the Bahama Islands* was and is, without a doubt, the more important of the two, since in it, and in a few pages of the *Appendix,* Mark Catesby figured his birds. Although Catesby considered himself to be first of all a botanist, and although his pictures of plants provided the continuity of the work, his lasting fame has depended principally on his contributions as an ornithologist. His pre-eminence here was owing in large part to the fact that the *Natural History* contained more plates of birds than of any other form of fauna:

There being [as Catesby wrote] a greater Variety of the feather'd Kind than of any other Animals (at least to be come at) and excelling in the Beauty of their Colours, besides having oftenest relation to the Plants on which they feed and frequent; I was induced chiefly (so far as I could) to compleat an Account of them, rather than to describe promiscuously, Insects and other Animals; by which Method I believe very few Birds have escaped my Knowledge, except some Water Fowl and some of those which frequent the Sea.[1]

[1] *Carolina,* **I,** ix.
[2] For a discussion of Catesby's predecessors see Allen, *Am.*

This was Catesby's own explanation for the predominance, in numbers, of the birds. Probably, too, the same concern which made him, and has made almost every other naturalist, something of an ornithologist (and almost every nature lover a bird watcher) has accounted for the wide popularity and influence of this volume.

A second and perhaps still more important reason for Catesby's considerable impact on American ornithology is that he was a pioneer in the field. There had been a number of bird lists before his time, probably the best of which was that of his immediate predecessor, John Lawson, in *The History of Carolina;* and as early as the time of Sir Walter Raleigh's ill-fated colony at Roanoke, John White had made paintings of American birds.[2] Still, up to the time Catesby began his work, no one had combined pictures with reasonably accurate descriptions in — what was all-important — published form. Catesby's accomplishment, then, in the words of one of his more recent successors, Witmer Stone, "forms the basis of the ornithology not only of the Southern States, but

Ornith., 443-63.

of the whole of North America."[3] Little wonder, then, that he has been called the "founder of American ornithology,"[4] and that he has become a sort of patron saint of American bird study. In their official list of American birds, recent practitioners of this science have honored Catesby primarily (together with a few other pre-Linnaean writers) by indicating the debt of the great Swedish taxonomist, Linnaeus, to these precursors in the field.[5] This is quite unusual in a science where lists of synonyms are ordinarily limited only to binomials, and these only if they were coined after the publication of the first volume of the tenth edition of Linnaeus' *Systema naturae* in 1758.[6]

Catesby began his first volume with a dedication "To the Queen," as these tomes "contain an Essay towards the Natural History of that Part of Your Majesty's Dominions, which are particularly honoured by bearing your August Name, Carolina, this and your great Goodness in encouraging all Sorts of Learning, hath emboldened me to implore Your Royal Protection and Favour to my slender performance. . . ."[7] Such an invocation to the patronage and protection of the mighty was customary in Catesby's day, and these words to the much-beloved Queen Caroline were followed by a Preface which summarized the author's early life, related his travels to Virginia and Carolina, and set forth the aims and methods followed in the book.[8] This brief introductory section, as was the case with the rest of the text, was printed in parallel English and French columns. The translation was by a modest gentleman, "a Doctor of Physic, a French-man born,"[9] whose wall of anonymity remains unbreached today as none of Catesby's known associates fit his description. Until recently, when the letters of Sherard and Sloane were searched for materials relating to Mark Catesby, these few pages provided most of what was known about their author.[10] Even today they remain an important statement, in Catesby's own words, of his years of struggle and of his aspirations.

On the page following the Preface, "The Bald Eagle"[11] appears boldly as the first of the one hundred thirteen birds which Catesby figured in his work.[12] The arrangement of the species, which thus began with the diurnal birds of prey, was hardly systematic. The general pattern was that of John Ray in Willughby's *Ornithology*, which is not surprising, as Catesby cited the English edition of this great text more often in his synonyms than any other.[13]

[3] Witmer Stone, "Mark Catesby and the Nomenclature of North American Birds," *The Auk,* XLVI (1929), 447-54.

[4] Allen, *Am. Ornith.,* 463.

[5] American Ornithologists' Union, *Check-List of North American Birds* (ed. 5, [Baltimore, Md.], 1957), *passim.*

[6] Carl Linnaeus, *Systema naturae* (ed. 10, 2 vols., Stockholm, 1758-59).

[7] The second volume was dedicated to Augusta, Princess of Wales and mother of the future George III.

[8] *Carolina,* I, v-xii.

[9] *Carolina,* I, xii.

[10] The other major source was an obituary note in *Gentleman's Magazine,* XX (1750), 31. Richard Pulteney, whose summary of Catesby's life was the standard secondary source, based his material chiefly on the above and a few biographical items scattered in the text of *The Natural History of Carolina.* Pulteney, II, 219-30.

[11] Southern bald eagle, *Haliaeetus leucocephalus leucocephalus* (Linnaeus). The Linnaean designation was based on this plate. In the notes below, Linnaean names based on Catesby's work will be indicated by an asterisk. All identifications of North American birds are from the A.O.U. Check-List.

[12] There are one hundred bird plates in the first volume. Two of these (73, 74) are of the flamingo, *Phoenicopterus ruber* Linnaeus, and five of them depict two species. The *Appendix* — really a part of Vol. II, but its birds will be considered here — contains nine more birds. Four plates, however, contain either immature examples of species already figured (77, 83) or females of varieties which Catesby illustrated (98, 99). The total number of species is thus one hundred nine. See Allen, *Am. Ornith.,* 465-67, and W. L. McAtee, "The North American Birds of Mark Catesby and Eleazer Albin," *Journal of the Society for the Bibliography of Natural History,* III, pt. 4 (1957), 177-94, for the identification of most of Catesby's birds.

[13] John Ray, *The Ornithology of Francis Willughby . . . in Three Books . . .* (London, 1678). The long controversy

Even where he credited other authors, the reference was usually also found in Ray-Willughby. Catesby was, therefore, quite familiar with this greatest of all ornithologies which had been published by his time, and he used it consciously or unconsciously in arranging his own plates. He was fairly consistent in his arrangement of land birds through approximately the forty-eighth plate. But there was some divergence from Ray-Willughby's pattern. He placed his "Turkey Buzzard" after the hawks rather than before them, where it should have been according to Ray-Willughby, regardless of whether he considered it a vulture or a buzzard.[14] Similarly, he saved the kingfisher until the beginning of the water birds, rather than placing it after the woodpeckers, as he should have done had he followed Ray-Willughby consistently.[15] After the forty-eighth plate, the arrangement of land birds was rather haphazard, and the water birds, although grouped at the end, as in Ray-Willughby, were not in the same order.

Willughby's *Ornithology* was also probably the source of the Latin designations for most of the birds in *The Natural History of Carolina*. According to Catesby, "Very few of the Birds having Names assign'd to them in the Country, except some which had Indian Names; I have call'd them after European Birds of the same Genus, with an additional Epithet to distinguish them."[16] His Latin designations ordinarily took their initial nouns from the Latin names given in Ray-Willughby and modified these with a word or words translated from the "additional Epithets" of the English versions. The Latin nouns with which Catesby began his

names hardly could be considered generic designations in a modern sense, because of the way in which they were assigned. For example, he placed his purple grackle, "The Purple Jack-Daw, *Monedula purpurea*,"[17] in the relative position assigned to the crows in the scheme of Willughby and Ray, because the European jackdaw, which it resembled, belonged there.[18] Catesby followed it with a plate of the eastern red-winged blackbird,[19] which he thought belonged to the same genus as the grackle, but which, because of its superficial resemblance to a European bird, he named "The red wing'd Starling, *Sturnus niger alis superne rubentibus*." If *Sturnus* had any real force as a designation of kind, it would have belonged, according to Ray-Willughby, with the thrushes.[20]

Even though his names were devised on the basis of resemblance — this was, after all, the way in which the colonists themselves named many birds — in some cases Catesby's designations were better than the popular names which have survived. His excellent plate of a young though very dead robin he called "The Fieldfare of Carolina,"[21] probably on the basis of its mottled breast, which made it resemble the European fieldfare. This helped to place it among the thrushes, where it belonged, as it has no kinship with the European robin. Many of Catesby's names have, moreover, been kept in popular usage. "The Red-bellied Wood-pecker" is perhaps the least apt of these.[22] More appropriate,

over the principal authorship of this book has been settled in favor of Ray by Charles E. Raven, *John Ray, Naturalist* (Cambridge, 1942), 334-36.

[14] "Turkey Buzzard" — turkey vulture. The plate probably represents the northern subspecies, *Cathartes aura septentrionalis* Wied. Catesby was cited by Linnaeus for the *Vultur aura*, which subsequently became *Cathartes aura aura*. As the Linnaean name was based primarily on the southern subspecies, Catesby's rather poor figure played no part in either designation. *Syst. nat.* (ed. 10), I, 86-87.

[15] Eastern belted kingfisher, *Megaceryle alcyon alcyon* (Linnaeus); *Carolina*, I, 69; *Willughby*, 146.

[16] *Carolina*, I, xii.

[17] *Carolina*, I, 12; *Quiscalus quiscula quiscula* (Linnaeus).

[18] *Willughby*, 125.

[19] *Carolina*, I, 13; *Agelaius phoeniceus phoeniceus* (Linnaeus).

[20] *Willughby*, 196.

[21] *Carolina*, I, 29; eastern robin, *Turdus migratorius migratorius* (Linnaeus).

[22] *Carolina*, I, 19; *Centurus carolinus* (Linnaeus).

and just as enduring, were such names as "The Blew Jay,"[23] "The Hairy Wood-pecker,"[24] "The Red-headed Wood-pecker,"[25] "The Ground-Dove,"[26] and "The Blew Bird."[27] Some of these names have been retained because they were already in popular usage when Catesby was in America, as was the case with "The Bald Eagle," for which he preferred, and indeed named his plate, the more accurate "White headed Eagle." Others, however, must have been coined by Catesby.

As to the question of who supplied the Latin polynomials for Catesby's birds and other fauna, the most likely answer is that he invented most of them himself. It has been suggested that William Sherard was responsible, but this is unlikely, as Catesby credited Sherard only with naming the plants.[28] Consul Sherard had collected a few specimens of birds while he was in the Levant,[29] but by the time Catesby knew him, he was almost entirely concerned with botany and with the *Pinax*. Sir Hans Sloane may have helped in this matter, as the great physician and collector had dealt with birds in his *Natural History of Jamaica*. Catesby had written Sir Hans from Carolina suggesting that he name the "Tricolor" which he sent him.[30] The specimen appeared in the pages of *The Natural History of Carolina* as "The Painted Finch, *Fringilla tricolor*."[31] The learned Baronet may have placed it among the finches; but, considering the extent of his hoard, his busy practice, and his activities with both the Royal Society and

the College of Physicians, he probably left this to Catesby.

Catesby's Latin designations were rendered obsolete by Linnaeus' extension of the binary nomenclature to birds and animals in 1758, but traces of Catesby's names lived on in the Linnaean system. The robin, for example, which Catesby had called *Turdus pilaris, migratorius,* became the *Turdus migratorius*.[32] Catesby's "Blew Jay, *Pica glandaria caerulea cristata,*" appeared in the tenth edition of the *Systema naturae* as the *Corvus cristatus*.[33] Occasionally one of Catesby's names was adopted without change. His "Purple Finch, *Fringilla purpurea*" passed unchanged into Gmelin's edition, the thirteenth, of the *Systema*.[34]

Indeed, the principal factor which prevented *The Natural History of Carolina* from becoming merely an elegant, if dated, picture book is that Linnaeus based so many of his classifications of North American birds on Catesby's work. It remained a necessary ornithological reference work in spite of its antiquated nomenclature and pictures which were later surpassed in excellence. The American Ornithologists' Union *Check-List of North American Birds* lists seventy-five species, the designations of which were based by Linnaeus and his successors in whole or in part upon Catesby's *Natural History of Carolina*.[35] Three more Bahaman species may unquestionably be added to this total, which included only birds which are found on the continent itself. These

---

[23] *Carolina*, I, 15; northern blue jay, *Cyanocitta cristata cristata* (Linnaeus).

[24] *Carolina*, I, 19; *Dendrocopos villosus villosus* (Linnaeus).

[25] *Carolina*, I, 20; *Melanerpes erythrocephalus* (Linnaeus).

[26] *Carolina*, I, 26; eastern ground dove, *Columbigallina passerina passerina* (Linnaeus).

[27] *Carolina*, I, 47; eastern bluebird, *Sialia sialis sialis* (Linnaeus).

[28] *Carolina*, I, xii.

[29] See Eleazer Albin, *A Natural History of Birds* (3 vols., London, 1731-38), I, 52; III, 26.

[30] Catesby to Sloane, Charles City, May 10, 1723, *Sloane* 4046, fol. 353.

[31] *Carolina*, I, 44; painted bunting, *Passerina ciris* (Linnaeus).

[32] Carl Linnaeus, *Systema naturae* (ed. 12, 3 vols., Stockholm, 1766-68), I, 292.

[33] *Syst. nat.* (ed. 10), I, 106.

[34] Carl Linnaeus, *Systema naturae* (ed. 13, 3 vols., Johann Friedrich Gmelin, ed., Leipzig, 1780), I, 923; *Carolina*, I, 41; eastern purple finch, *Carpodacus purpureus purpureus* (Gmelin).

[35] Elsa G. Allen lists only seventy-four. Here she let her ability as an ornithologist stand in the way of making the list complete, as she ran into the confusion surrounding Catesby's two *Caprimulgidae*. Allen, *Am. Ornith.*, 465-67. See below, pp. 59-60.

are the western red-legged thrush, which was based on Catesby's "red leg'd Thrush;"[36] the Bahaman bullfinch, Catesby's "Purple Gross-beak;"[37] and the striped-headed tanager, Catesby's "Bahama Finch."[38]

A few other species can perhaps be added to the list. If the name *Phaethon lepturus catesbyi* is allowed to stand for the yellow-billed tropic bird, then it must have been so considered from Catesby's plate and named in his honor. Johann Friedrich Brandt, who made the designation as late as 1838 — and who placed a question mark after it — did so on the authority of *The Natural History of Carolina*, although he did not cite it as such.[39] Then, too, in the case of the smooth-billed ani, Catesby's "Razor-billed Blackbird of Jamaica,"[40] Linnaeus' identification may have been taken largely from Sloane's description in *The Natural History of Jamaica*, but Catesby was cited with him, and both followed the reference to Patrick Browne's *History of Jamaica*.[41]

One rather serious problem which this use of Catesby by Linnaeus and others raised for later ornithologists was that for many of these birds there were several subspecies, usually northern and southern races.[42] The matter was further complicated by the fact that both northern and southern varieties had been observed in South Carolina, and, indeed, birds there were often intermediate between the two. These facts have led to much confusion, and successive revisers have decided that the Linnaean name should belong first to one and then to another form. Catesby can hardly be held responsible for this. He

was a pioneer, he was in Carolina but for a relatively short time, and he had few references other than his own observations. Actually, it is somewhat astonishing that he did so well. The solution to these problems has been, to date, one which a practical man like Catesby probably would have approved. This was the suggestion by Witmer Stone, subsequently accepted by the American Ornithologists' Union, that the work of the first reviser of a species be accepted as final; which was a pragmatic, if perhaps inexact, settlement.[43]

No doubt one of the causes of this confusion was that some of Catesby's figures were composites of subspecies and some, indeed, of species — his was, after all, an age which sought uniformity in nature. This was the case with his figures of the *Caprimulgidae*.[44] The first, "The Goat-Sucker of Carolina," became the basis of Gmelin's *Caprimulgus carolinensis*, which is considered the first designation of chuck-will's-widow, but Catesby's plate combined some elements of the eastern nighthawk with this bird, and his text referred to the noises of the nighthawk.[45] Catesby's "Whip-poor-Will" was another case of a similar confusion. He had not seen the bird in America but had heard of it and perhaps had heard its call. Around 1741 he had written John Bartram: "There is a bird in Virginia and Carolina, and I suppose in Pennsylvania, that at night calls Whipper Will, and, sometimes, Whip Will's widow, by which names it is called (as the bird clinketh, the

[36] *Carolina*, I, 30; *Syst. nat.* (ed. 10), I, 169; *Mimocichla plumbea plumbea* (Linnaeus). For this and the next two notes, the technical names are those given in James Bond, *Check-List of Birds of the West Indies* (Philadelphia, 1950).

[37] *Carolina*, I, 40; *Syst. nat.* (ed. 10), I, 176; *Loxigilla violacea violacea* (Linnaeus).

[38] *Carolina*, I, 42; *Syst. nat.* (ed. 12), I, 320; *Spindalis zena zena* (Linnaeus).

[39] J. F. Brandt, "Monographiae Genaris Phaeton," *Bulletin scientifique publie par l'Academie Imperiale des Sciences de Saint Petersbourg*, IV (1838), cols. 97-99. W. L. McAtee, "Catesby's Tropic Bird," *The Auk*, LXII (1945), 137-40, casts reasonable doubt on this identification. If this

is the case, then Catesby probably should receive some credit for *Phaethon aethereus*, the red-billed tropic bird, as Linnaeus cited him first in his synonymy. *Syst. nat.* (ed. 10), I, 134.

[40] *Carolina*, II, *Appendix*, 3; *Crotophaga ani* (Linnaeus).

[41] *Syst. nat.* (ed. 10), I, 105; Patrick Browne, *The Civil and Natural History of Jamaica* (London, 1756).

[42] The material which follows is taken from Stone, "Nomenclature."

[43] A.O.U. *Check-List* (ed. 4, Lancaster, Pa., 1931), xi-xii.

[44] The following material is based on W. L. McAtee, "Confusion of Eastern Caprimulgidae," *The Auk*, LXV (1948), 128-29.

[45] *Carolina*, I, 8.

fool thinketh). I have neglected to describe it, and therefore should be glad of it. I believe it is a kind of cuckoo."[46] The letter indicates that Catesby confused the whippoorwill with its relative, chuck-will's-widow. The figure in *The Natural History* was drawn from several specimens sent later from Virginia, probably by John Clayton, whose description Catesby quoted.[47] This description was largely of the whippoorwill, but the figure was principally of the nighthawk, modified somewhat to conform with the text. The plate, however, became the sole basis of Johann Reinhold Forster's *Caprimulgus minor*, and as such has been accepted as the earliest designation of the eastern nighthawk.[48] Here, of course, Catesby was not wholly at fault, as he had been misled by his correspondent in Virginia, and, moreover, the members of this family of birds are confused by the bird-watching public today.

Classification and nomenclature are not ultimate goals of natural science, being, at best, only necessary tools. Certainly Mark Catesby was himself very little concerned with them. *The Natural History of Carolina* was significant in other ways, particularly in the development of ornithological illustration. Here again Catesby's position was that of a pioneer. Few of his birds were drawn in stiff profile, as was the case with the drawings of most of his predecessors — and even many of his near contemporaries, such as those by John Savage and Michael Vander Gucht for Sloane's *Natural History of Jamaica* or those of Eleazer Albin in *A Natural History of Birds,* a work which was almost completely contemporary with Catesby's own.[49]

Catesby's break with the past was further accentuated by his use of plants as backgrounds for most of his birds. Quite likely this was dictated by the need of including both flora and fauna in such an expensive work. Had Catesby confined himself to only one subject, as he did for the first eight plates, the work would have been impossibly long. Whether by necessity or by intent, Catesby initiated a style of bird painting which would reach its fulfillment in the work of John James Audubon a century later.

Catesby's backgrounds consisted of plants, too, and not the stylized grass and foliage which his friend George Edwards used as stage settings for the pretty but environmentally incorrect plates of *A Natural History of Uncommon Birds.* Such accuracy was, of course, to be expected from a man whose background was largely botanical. Moreover, Catesby's backgrounds were not only reasonably accurate but also they were usually ecologically correct. In many instances Catesby's text indicated that he had observed the birds eating the seeds or berries of plants with which they were pictured, or, as in the case of "The red leg'd Thrush" and "The Gum-Elimy Tree," had found the berries in the birds' stomachs.[50] Other trees and shrubs Catesby noted as being the favorite nesting or breeding places for the birds drawn with them.[51] Occasionally the combinations were dictated by lack of space rather than a concern for scientific accuracy. Thus Catesby did not hesitate to picture a Mexican bird with a Carolinian plant, or, on at least one occasion, to mix Virginian and Bahaman specimens.[52] He had also to overreach himself in various backgrounds for shore and water birds. However, none of his ornithological plates (save perhaps those of the flamingo, where marine products seem to grow on dry land) are as absurd as the final drawing in *The Natural History of Carolina,* in which a

[46] Catesby to Bartram, London, [1741?], in Darlington, *Memorials,* 321-22.

[47] *Carolina,* II, *Appendix,* 16.

[48] *Chordeiles minor minor* (Forster).

[49] Savage was an engraver and printseller (fl. 1690-[?]). Vander Gucht was an Antwerp-born portraitist and engraver (d. 1725). Albin's work was published between 1731 and 1738.

[50] *Carolina,* I, 30, *et passim;* gum elemi, *Elaphrium simaruba* (Linnaeus). Modern technical names of plants are those given in Nathaniel Lord Britton and Charles Frederick Millspaugh, *The Bahama Flora* (New York, 1920), and John Kunkel Small, *Manual of the Southeastern Flora* (New York, 1933).

[51] See *Carolina,* I, 48-55.

[52] *Carolina,* I, 58, 68.

rather delicate locust branch completely overshadows a buffalo.[53]

Catesby's choice and scale of backgrounds was usually, though not consistently, good. The same was true of the total arrangement of bird and plant on the page. In some cases, however, the bird almost appears to have been added as an afterthought, as if Catesby had begun a purely botanical plate and later added ornithological details. His painted finch perched upon the petal of a flower of the loblolly bay tree[54] is one of the more notorious examples of this, as is his *Regulus cristatus* lost against an impressive background of *Stuartia*.[55] In the latter case, however, the concept was good even though the bird in this case was simply too small to illustrate it adequately. Audubon used this plant in a similar way for his plate of the mourning dove, even to the extent of posing one of the figures in the same way as Catesby's kinglet.[56]

Though in a strict sense their works are not comparable — a century of ornithological experience as well as vast degrees of artistic competence separated the two men — still, there is always a temptation to try to find a greater similarity between the drawings of Catesby and Audubon than mere form. There is little doubt that the nineteenth-century artist was familiar with the work of his eighteenth-century predecessor. And occasionally this familiarity may have resulted — whether inadvertently or not — in the parallel treatment of subjects, as in the case

of the *Stuartia*. Audubon's use of smilax in his plate of the loggerhead shrike shows a strong resemblance to its use by Catesby with his crested flycatcher.[57] So, too, is the background of the leaves and blossoms of the sweet bay tree used with the warbling vireo in *The Birds of America* reminiscent of its utilization with the blue grosbeak in *The Natural History of Carolina*.[58] These resemblances may have been purely coincidental or they may simply have been due to Audubon's frequent use of other hands in supplying the incidental material for his paintings.[59] Probably the use by both artists of the yellow poplar with the Baltimore oriole lay in the realm of coincidence.[60] In most of the birds themselves there is little resemblance between the often inaccurately detailed drawings of Catesby and the minutely defined work of the later ornithological artist. It is a tribute to Catesby, though, that one of his better plates, that of the blue jay, is very much like one of Audubon's figures of the same bird.[61] The same holds true of the red-wing, which both artists drew similarly in order to display the wing markings, but in a way which does not redound particularly to the credit of either.[62]

Aside from his pioneer work in this genre of bird art, Catesby's ornithological illustrations had other elements of both strength and weakness. At his best, with his plate of the blue jay, for example, he was able, even in a stationary pose, to convey a sense of power and motion, a sense present also in his very similar drawing of "The Razor-billed Black-bird of

[53] *Carolina*, I, 73, 74; II, *Appendix*, 20.

[54] *Carolina*, I, 44; loblolly bay, *Gordonia lasianthus* (Linnaeus).

[55] *Carolina*, II, *Appendix*, 13; golden-crowned kinglet, *Regulus satrapa satrapa* Lichtenstein; *Stuartia malachodendron* Linnaeus.

[56] John James Audubon, *The Birds of America* (Elephant Folio, 4 vols., London, 1829-38), pl. 17. See Robert Henry Welker, *Birds and Men; American Birds in Science, Art, Literature, and Conservation, 1800-1900* (Cambridge, Mass., 1955), pl. 3.

[57] Audubon, pl. 57; *Carolina*, I, 52; Welker, pl. 3; southern crested flycatcher, *Myiarchus crinitus crinitus* (Linnaeus). Catesby's smilax is *Smilax bona-nox* Linnaeus; Audubon's

is *Smilax rotundifolia* Linnaeus.

[58] Audubon, pl. 118; *Carolina*, I, 39; eastern blue grosbeak, *Guiaraca caerulea caerulea* (Linnaeus); sweet bay, *Magnolia virginiana* Linnaeus.

[59] Welker, 85.

[60] *Carolina*, I, 48; Baltimore oriole, *Icterus galbula* (Linnaeus); yellow poplar, *Lireodendron tulipfera* Linnaeus.

[61] Audubon, pl. 102; *Carolina*, I, 47.

[62] Audubon, pl. 67; *Carolina*, I, 13. They are also both similar to one of Alexander Wilson's figures, as this was one of Audubon's famous plagiaries from Wilson. See Welker, pls. 9, 10.

Jamaica," the smooth-billed ani.[63] His conscious effort to portray motion often exceeded his skill as an artist and led, as in the case of the golden-crowned kinglet, where he apparently worked from a dried specimen, to a pose which was merely awkward.[64] The bulk of his illustrations, however, lay somewhere between these extremes.

If Catesby was, at times, successful in portraying movement, he was never able to render birds with a sufficient degree of accuracy to meet modern scientific requirements. Most of the birds in *The Natural History of Carolina* are recognizable, but only because of their gross details. In smaller matters — wing and tail markings — Catesby was inaccurate, if, indeed, he drew them at all. The errors here were occasionally those of commission as well as omission, as with the supposedly curly crest of the pileated woodpecker, an error which George Edwards attempted to correct with his brush in the second edition of Catesby's book.[65] These errors are understandable, however, as Catesby had almost nothing from which to make his finished engravings other than his field sketches. There simply were no other drawings with which he could compare his own, and preserved specimens, using the methods of the day, would have been of little help. Indeed, it must have been hard to tell from birds preserved in spirits whether feathers were curly or straight.

If we judge Catesby's birds in the light of work done by his contemporaries rather than by comparison with present-day artistic and scientific requirements, or even with the work of such later artists as Wilson and Audubon, they fare well. They were superior in all respects to those of Eleazer Albin, and, while they were perhaps slightly inferior in coloring and certainly inferior in attention to detail to those pictured by Edwards, their backgrounds frequently lent them a quality superior to those of the latter's "uncommon" birds (which, evidently, Edwards had never seen in their natural habitat). In addition, Catesby's plates have a certain virile quality not found in those of Edwards, whose illustrations have an almost undefinably feminine quality. It is perhaps too much to say that it is the difference between the work of a real field naturalist and that of a decorator, but this is the impression given when Catesby's folio is laid side by side with Edwards' quarto.[66] The difference is not merely in size. Certainly, in the later "revision" of *The Natural History of Carolina* done by Edwards and published in 1754, the changes, in colors at least, were inferior to the first edition.

The descriptive passages which Catesby wrote to accompany his drawings had, like the plates, their good and bad points. He gave relatively detailed accounts of coloration and size, frequently with reference to a similar European variety. These descriptions were ordinarily more complete for those birds where the limitations of the engraver and colorist made identification difficult, or where all of the identifying marks could not be shown in a single figure. The converse of this was, however, also true, and Catesby's dependence on pictorial rather than literary specification often led to descriptions which suffered from excessive brevity. In addition to supplying identifying characteristics, Catesby noted, where his observations permitted, details concerning migratory and feeding habits. Most of these he supplied from firsthand knowledge and depended but little, unlike his predecessor, the unfortunate John Lawson, on Indian lore or on the fanciful speculation of the white inhabitants. Possibly his note on the now-extinct "Parrot of Carolina," the Carolina parakeet, "Their guts are certain and speedy poison

[63] *Carolina,* I, 47; II, *Appendix,* 3.

[64] *Carolina,* II, *Appendix,* 13.

[65] *Carolina,* I, 17; (ed. 2, 2 vols., "Revis'd by Mr. Edwards," London, 1754); southern pileated woodpecker, *Dryocopus pileatus pileatus* (Linnaeus).

[66] Edwards' decorative tendencies are well illustrated in the unique copy of *The Natural History of Carolina* (ed. 1) owned by the Newberry Library, Chicago, which was colored by him. It has extra plants, done in water color (pls. 83, 84) and even added butterflies (pl. 84).

to Cats," belonged to one of these categories.[67] Still, this was exceptional. More often, if he made errors, they were due to his necessarily limited observations. For example, he saw the seasonal change in plumage of the male bobolink, his "Rice-Bird," but explained it incorrectly: "In September, when they arrive in infinite swarms to devour the Rice, they are all Hens, not being accompanied by any Cock." Thinking that they were perhaps the young of both sexes, Catesby dissected a number of birds, but unfortunately found only females.[68] Perhaps if he had opened one more bird, he would have come nearer the truth.

Most of Catesby's attempts at ornithological theory fell in his "Account of Carolina . . ." in the second volume rather than with the birds described in the first. He observed the common distinction between American and European varieties, that the former excelled in beauty of plumage while the latter were superior in song. Only the "Mockbird," among American species, could be called a songbird, though he allowed some ability to the "Virginian nightingale," the cardinal. Catesby pondered the occurrence of European fowl in the New World. All American birds, he thought, must have originally come from the Old World after the Flood. European waterfowl, natives of cold regions, probably passed between the continents in the far north, where the distance separating the land masses was not known in Catesby's day. Small land birds he thought might have made the passage in the same way, although this explanation did not altogether satisfy him.[69]

In this section, also, Catesby referred to one of his most strongly held beliefs, that "animals in general, and particularly Birds, diminish in numbers of species so much nearer they approach the Pole."[70] This, of course, was true enough, and, moreover, Catesby realized that water birds were an exception; but, by

applying the rule too stringently, he was led into error. He sought too great a uniformity in nature and apparently did not think that as more southerly species reached their northern limits, they might be replaced by others. Thus it was that because he included all he had seen or heard of between the thirtieth and forty-fifth degrees of north latitude Catesby thought he had figured nearly all North American birds. His ideas were probably reinforced by and perhaps originated in the fact that he had observed a greater number of birds in Carolina than in Virginia. During his years in the more southerly colony, however, he undoubtedly observed with greater care, and in Carolina he was also in an area where he might find both temperate and subtropical species.

The most advanced of Catesby's ornithological speculations, though, were his thoughts on bird migrations, which found brief expression in the introduction to the second volume of *The Natural History,* but which were presented more fully in the paper which Catesby read before the Royal Society in March, 1746/47. As this paper was published in full in the *Philosophical Transactions* and in a shortened form in the *Gentleman's Magazine,*[71] it had a much wider circulation than did those items which saw print in *The Natural History* alone. The immediate occasion for the paper was apparently the publication of a theory which held that birds of passage flew to their retreats by moving above the atmosphere. This Catesby found "as remote from Reason, as the Ethereal Region is free from the Aereal," through which latter region he could think of nothing to obstruct their passage. He also dismissed the more widely and dearly held belief that some birds, particularly swallows, hibernated in caves or hollow trees or beneath the waters of ponds. In this he was ahead of much

---

[67] *Carolina,* I, 11; Carolina parakeet, *Conuropsis carolinensis carolinensis* (Linnaeus).

[68] *Carolina,* I, 14; bobolink, *Dolichonyx oryzivorus* (Linnaeus).

[69] *Carolina,* II, xxxv-xxxvi.

[70] *Carolina,* II, *Appendix,* 16.

[71] *Phil. Trans.,* XLIV, pt. 2 (1747), 435-44; *Gentleman's Magazine,* XVIII (1748), 447-48. Allen, *Am. Ornith.,* 475, has confused the latter with an anonymous article which preceded it.

of the best opinion of his time, including both Jakob Theodor Klein, of Danzig, author of the *Historiae avium,* and even the great Linnaeus himself.[72]

Catesby's own explanation was less tradition-bound and much more naturalistic than that of his contemporaries. Yet, for a subject which is still not settled in our own day when the want of "occular testimony," which Catesby deplored, is no longer serious, his ideas were but common sense ruined by some misconceptions about climatology. Summer birds of passage flew to their new destinations in a normal way, urged south by cold and a diminished food supply. So much for common sense. Where Catesby erred seriously was in assuming a climatic uniformity depending upon the degree of latitude. These birds, then, he conjectured, must winter as far south of the equator as they had summered north of it, or, if barred by too great an expanse of water, at least to some other part of the southern hemisphere. Thus a passion for uniformity and symmetry, so dear to the Enlightenment, misled the explanations of this careful observer. Years later, Catesby's friend, George Edwards, with more material available to him from correspondents in many parts of the world, would correct these ideas. But Catesby was unable to comprehend these things.[73] Even the example of birds which wintered in the British Isles and flew to Scandinavia to breed offered no corrective. Catesby recognized them as separate cases.

Still different from these other migrants, in Catesby's mind, were those birds which remained but briefly to feed and then moved on. The ricebird was an example of this type. Birds would notice changes in the cultivation of grains, though it might take time to shake them from their habitual courses. This he illustrated by word from Dr. John Mitchell that more than half a century had elapsed between the time wheat, rice, and barley were first introduced in Virginia and the appearance of a foreign variety, the "Wheat-Bird."

In short all we can be said to know of the Matter, ends in this Observation that Providence has created a great Variety of Birds, and other Animals with Constitutions and Inclinations adapted to their different Degrees of Heat and Cold in the several Climates of the World (whereby no Country is destitute of Inhabitants) and has given them Appetites for the production of such Countries, whose Temperature is suited to their Nature, as well as Knowledge and Abilities to seek and find them out. From which we can only infer, that the Birds we have been mentioning could no more subsist in the sultry Climes of the *Molucca* Isles, than Birds of Paradise could in the frigid Regions of *Sweden* or *Lapland.*[74]

Thus, Catesby ended his considerations by admitting his inability to comprehend the Divine Plan. Considering that his ideas were superior to many of his contemporaries, and certainly no worse than many thoughts advanced long afterward, he need not have been so self-effacing.[75] This was even more the case because his reputation as an ornithologist did not have to rest on his theorizing. It was founded solidly on the plates and text of his *Natural History.*

The very prominence of the birds in the first volume of Catesby's great work has helped to obscure the fundamental fact that he was primarily a botanist. He went to Carolina as a botanical collector, and his plants, found on all of the plates except those of a few of the birds and more of the fishes, bound the diverse fauna pictured in the two volumes into a coherent whole.

Something more, though, than the prominence given to the fauna in *The Natural History of Carolina* accounts for its relative obscurity as a botanical work. Indeed, that same Linnaean revolution in natural history which helped to maintain the significance of

[72] Peter Collinson, "A Letter to the Honorable J. Th. Klein . . . Concerning the Migration of Swallows," *Phil. Trans.,* LI, pt. 2 (1760), 449-64; *Syst. nat.* (ed. 10), I, 191; Jakob Theodor Klein, *Historiae avium prodromus . . .* (Lübeck, 1750). See W. L. McAtee, "Torpidity in Birds," *American Midland Naturalist,* XXXVII (1947), 191-206.

[73] George Edwards, *A Natural History of Uncommon Birds* (4 pts., London, 1743-51), pt. III, 218-20.

[74] *Phil. Trans.,* XLIV, pt. 2 (1747), 442.

[75] See W. L. McAtee, "Unorthodox Thoughts on Migration," *The Auk,* LVII (1940), 135-36.

Catesby's birds contributed to the neglect accorded to his plants. Naturally again, as in the case of the fauna, the changes in nomenclature effected by Linnaeus rendered obsolete those who had come before him, Catesby included. More than that, however, the sexual system of classification, which was a less permanent contribution by the great Swede, helped to relegate Catesby's work to limbo. Catesby's botanical plates lacked sufficient detail in the parts of the flower to fit comfortably into the Linnaean system. This is not to say that Linnaeus did not make use of *The Natural History of Carolina* in his *Species plantarum* and other botanical works.[76] Probably the amazing thing is that he made as much use of Catesby's work as he did. The botany of the area which Catesby explored had been far more adequately treated than had its zoology. Father Plumier[77] and Sir Hans Sloane had dealt with the West Indian flora, while the correspondents of James Petiver had done their work on the North American mainland.[78] Gronovius had published the first edition of his Linnaean classification of plants sent by John Clayton in his *Flora Virginica,*[79] and Linnaeus' friend, Peter Kalm, had made his journey to North America before the publication of the *Species plantarum* in 1753.[80] It is important to note, however, that Catesby had contributed many of the exotic species of plants found in the garden of James Sherard at Eltham, the catalog of which, entitled *Hortus Elthamensis* and prepared by J. J. Dillenius, was frequently cited by Linnaeus in the latter's treatment of American plants.[81]

The main use made of Catesby's work by Linnaeus was as a secondary reference in his synonymy. The plates were useful references inasmuch as many of the plants were not illustrated elsewhere. In the same way, Linnaeus' requests for items from Alexander Garden, Catesby's great successor in South Carolina, were often made in terms of the figures in *The Natural History of Carolina.*[82] However, Linnaeus did base some of his classifications of American plants on Catesby alone. In at least twelve cases, Linnaean species which have been retained were based solely on Catesby's illustrations, and the genus *Zanthoxylum* was based on Catesby's "Pellitory, or Tooth-ach Tree." In addition, the genus *Catesbaea,* with which Gronovius honored his English correspondent, was retained by Linnaeus, and its type, the *Catesbaea spinosa,* was based on Catesby's plate.[83]

Again, as in the case of the birds, Catesby's greatest significance was as a collector and illustrator. If there was a smattering of system in his arrangement of birds, there was none in his plants, except perhaps for placing his oaks together. Catesby arranged the botanical illustrations of *The Natural History of Carolina* with a view toward providing a suitable environment for the zoological subjects, or merely for convenience. This is not to say that he did not owe a debt to some of the great systematists: to John Ray, to Joseph Pitton de Tournefort, and to Robert Morison; but the debt was chiefly for the names of the plants.[84] In the matter of names, Catesby most often used the works of Leonard Plukenet, who had published a good deal on Amer-

[76] (2 vols., Stockholm, 1753; ed. 2, Stockholm, 1762-63).

[77] Charles Plumier, *Description des plantes de l'Amerique* (Paris, 1693); *Nova plantarum Americanum genera* (Paris, 1703).

[78] See Raymond P. Stearns, "James Petiver, Promoter of Natural Science," *Proceedings of the American Antiquarian Society,* n.s., LXII (1952), 243-365.

[79] (2 vols., Leyden, 1739-43).

[80] See Adolph B. Benson, ed. and tr., *The America of 1750; Peter Kalm's Travels in North America* (2 vols., New York, 1937).

[81] Johann Jacob Dillenius, *Hortus Elthamensis* . . . London, 1732), 2.

[82] See Garden to John Ellis, Charles Town, Feb. 2, 1767, in Smith, *Corresp. Linnaeus,* I, 522-23; Garden to Linnaeus, Charles Town, June 2, 1763, *ibid.,* 310.

[83] *Carolina,* II, 100; *Syst. nat.* (ed. 10), I, 109. See the note to Chapter 6 below, p. 70.

[84] Catesby cited John Ray, *Historia plantarum* . . . (3 vols., London, 1686-1704); Joseph Pitton de Tournefort, . . . *Institutiones rei herbariae* . . . (3 vols., Paris, 1700-[1703]); and Robert Morison, *Plantarum historiae universalis Oxoniensis* . . . (2 vols., London, 1680).

ican botany, including some of John Bannister's materials,[85] and, of course, Sir Hans Sloane's *Natural History of Jamaica*. These tasted much more of collection than system.

The sources for these names were often eclectic in nature. Catesby was sometimes reduced to necessity — for American plants the sources were widely scattered — and even more to the work of William Sherard. In his famous *Pinax* Sherard had attempted to list all of the synonyms for all plants. In consequence, he was well acquainted with most published botanical works and with the major repositories of dried plants in England and Europe as well. As Catesby himself stated, Sherard had named many of the species figured in *The Natural History of Carolina*.[86] J. J. Dillenius, Sherard's protégé and first holder of the Sherardian professorship at Oxford, aided Catesby also, although his contributions were probably small inasmuch as he protested to Linnaeus that he could not be held responsible for Catesby's long polynomials, having supplied only some of the shorter names.[87] Possibly, too, Catesby contributed the names of some of the species which he figured after Sherard's death from plants growing in Hoxton, Fulham, or in the gardens of Peter Collinson at Peckham, although he could not have wanted for assistance from among his friends in the English botanical circle.

More to the point than any discussion of Catesby's place in the history of nomenclature is his place in the development of botanical illustration. Certainly, however, it can be said that his contributions in this area were not as great as was the case with his birds. Plant art had reached a higher stage of development than had its ornithological cousin. Still, Catesby's

accomplishment was not small in comparison with his better-trained contemporaries. Viewed from his own century, even a generation or more removed from Catesby's own time, Richard Pulteney could call *The Natural History of Carolina* "the most splendid of its kind that England had ever produced."[88] Only J. J. Dillenius' *Hortus Elthamensis* and Philip Miller's *Figures of the Most Beautiful, Useful, and Uncommon Plants Described in the Gardener's Dictionary*[89] could, according to Pulteney, rival it in its elegance.[90] In comparison, though, with the work of Georg Dionysius Ehret, the great German illustrator, Catesby's achievement as a botanical artist — considered in its parts rather than in its entirety — paled somewhat. Ehret's drawings for Patrick Browne's *History of Jamaica* and for Linnaeus' *Hortus Cliffortianus*[91] were far superior. The comparison between Catesby and Ehret can be made easily enough within *The Natural History of Carolina* alone, as Ehret supplied the two plates which were not Catesby's own.[92] The first of these, the *Magnolia altissima*,[93] was undoubtedly the most striking picture in the entire work. Larger than the rest, it presented a strong contrast of white, greens, and reds against a black background. In all probability, Catesby modeled his own very similar treatment of the *Magnolia, amplissimo*[94] on Ehret's plate. Though the two were similar, Ehret's was obviously superior. His lines were more delicate than those of Catesby, and such details as the veins in the leaves were truer. In almost all of Catesby's plates the veins were shown in a rather stylized manner. Catesby did gain something, though, from the technique of Ehret and other experienced engravers. In his later plates, for example, he often made use of crosshatching to give shading and depth to his figures, something which he

[85] John Bannister (d. 1692). See Stearns, "James Petiver," 330-32; Leonard Plukenet, *Phytographia* . . . (7 pts., London, 1691-1705); *Almagestum botanicum* . . . (London, 1696); *Almagesti botanici mantissa* . . . (London, 1700).

[86] *Carolina*, I, xii.

[87] Dillenius to Linnaeus, Oxford, Nov. 28, 1737, in Smith, *Corresp. Linnaeus*, II, 103-7.

[88] *Pulteney*, II, 226.

[89] *Pulteney*, II, 247.

[90] (London, 1760).

[91] (Amsterdam, 1737).

[92] *Carolina*, II, 61, 96.

[93] *Magnolia grandiflora* Linnaeus.

[94] *Carolina*, II, 80; *Magnolia tripetala* Linnaeus.

avoided at first, preferring to show them "in a flat tho exact manner. . . ." Perhaps it was this "flat tho exact manner" which led the nearly self-taught engraver into certain inaccuracies. Apparently Catesby engraved many plates directly from his drawings without reversing them, with the result that he sometimes depicted the stems and other parts of his plants twisting in the wrong direction.[95]

The scientific accuracy of Catesby's drawings varied considerably. In most of them he gave too little attention to details. The blossoms in almost all cases were done without the minute attention to their parts which would be necessary for a modern manual, and which Ehret often included. Many of the drawings in *The Natural History* also portrayed the plants as they could not have looked at any given moment, showing bud, blossom, and ripe seed together in a single plate. This inaccuracy was deliberate, however, and made the book more valuable for identifying these plants at various times throughout their growing season. The final judgment of Catesby's accuracy lies in whether his plants are recognizable to modern scholars, and nearly all are. Britton and Millspaugh in their *Bahama Flora* were able to identify all but one plant of those which Catesby cited as being Bahaman.[96]

The descriptions which accompanied the pictures of plants in *The Natural History of Carolina* suffered, as did those of the birds, from brevity. Again, Catesby depended too much on his plates and ordinarily described only that which could not be seen easily. In only three cases did he give an adequately detailed description of the plants he pictured. One of these, the *Catesbaea*, was written by Gronovius;[97] the second, the *Stuartia*, was contained in a letter from John Mitchell;[98] and only the third, the *Meadia*, was not credited to another author and may have been

written by Catesby.[99] The rest vary in quality. Where, as in the case of the shrubs and trees, the picture gave no indication of size, Catesby supplied length and girth. In some other cases, where it was not clear from the picture, he gave details of the blossoms, seeds, and leaves. Often, though, these were omitted. Catesby's botanical descriptions did have one advantage over his ornithological ones. He quite consistently included information about where he had found plants growing, including occasionally the kinds of soil in which they flourished. Of even more importance for Catesby's own day — when Englishmen on both sides of the Atlantic were seeking to increase the useful produce of their colonies — was the intelligence he supplied about the uses of American woods in carpentry and joinery, about the edible plants among those he figured, and about those berries, leaves, and roots which had found their way into the folk pharmacopoeia of the settlers and Indians.

This interest in the practical aspects of botany in no way detracted from Catesby's performance in the eyes of his contemporaries. The eighteenth century was one in which even the greatest theorists maintained lively interests in applied science. Catesby showed this same practical bent in his continual reference to those American plants which had survived the English climate in the nurseries of Stephen Bacon at Hoxton, of Christopher Gray at Fulham, of Peter Collinson at Peckham, and of those of various other "curious" growers of exotics. This aspect of Catesby's activities, the introduction and domestication of American plants, probably had as much immediate influence on English botany as did the publication of his works. J. C. Loudon, the nineteenth-century English botanist, credited Catesby with the introduction of some six American trees and shrubs into Eng-

[95] *Carolina*, I, xi. See H. A. Allard, "The Direction of Twist of the Corolla in the Bud, and Twining of the Stems in Convolvulaceae and Dioscoreaceae," *Castanea (Journal of the Southern Appalachian Botanical Club)* XII, No. 3 (Sept., 1947), 88-94.

[96] *Bahama Flora*, 646.

[97] *Carolina*, II, 100; *Catesbaea spinosa* Linnaeus.

[98] *Carolina*, II, *Appendix*, 13; *Stuartia malachodendron* Linnaeus.

[99] *Dodecatheon meadia* Linnaeus.

land,[100] and the *Catalogus plantarum,* possibly written by Philip Miller and published by a society of gardeners around London in 1730, listed some ten of these raised from seeds sent by Catesby from Carolina.[101] Actually, Catesby's total contribution was probably much larger, even if only trees and shrubs are considered, because he may well have supplied the seeds for plants whose introduction was credited to such of the gardeners around London as Thomas Fairchild, Stephen Bacon, Robert Furber, and Philip Miller, or to his patrons, James Sherard and Charles Dubois.[102]

In addition to the plants themselves, the end product of this interest was Catesby's *Hortus Britanno-Americanus: Or, a Curious Collection of Trees and Shrubs, the Produce of the British Colonies in North America; Adapted to the Soil and Climate of England. With Observations on Their Constitution, Growth, and Culture, and Directions How They Are to Be Collected, Packed up, and Secured During Their Passage.* This volume, which has occasionally been credited to its publisher, the bookseller John Ryall "at Hogarth's Head in Fleet-Street,"[103] was finished by Catesby shortly before his death in 1749 but was not published until 1763.[104] Apparently Ryall, who supplied only the dedication — to the amateur botanist, Henry Seymer of Handford, Dorsetshire — did not find this rather thin volume as popular as its larger and more expensive sister work. At any rate, the remainder of this printing appeared four years later under the auspices of still another bookseller, John Millan, with a more ambitious title, *Hortus Europae Americanus. . . .*[105] In spite of the appeal to a broader audience, this was merely a publisher's trick, and the only difference in these editions lay in their title pages.[106]

Catesby's Preface spoke of the variety of trees and shrubs afforded by the great forests of America "that may be usefully employed to inrich and adorn our woods by their valuable timber and delightful shade, or to embellish and perfume our gardens with the elegance of their appearance and the fragrancy of their odours. . . ." He hoped that the "opulent and curious" who possessed most of the specimens in England would "be excited to encourage their propagation and increase, as well for the benefit of our woods, as for ornaments to our gardens." There were, he wrote, few North American plants which could not be raised in England or in Europe, and he hoped that his observations would make the cultivation of these plants easier. Seeds and specimens were available at the nursery of Christopher Gray in Fulham, where the author had himself grown many of them.[107]

Yet, in spite of this advertisement for Catesby's friend, this volume was not merely another gardener's catalog. Catesby had, after all, devoted most of whatever time was left him, in addition to the work on his *Natural History,* in following what he advocated here in the *Hortus Britanno-Americanus.* The book itself dealt with eighty-five trees and shrubs, of which sixty-three were illustrated on seventeen plates. Four of the engravings ordinarily were shown on a single page, and the pages were considerably smaller than those of *The Natural History of Carolina.* Accordingly, they simply could not allow the bold conceptions which size permitted in the earlier and

---

[100] J. C. Loudon, *Arboretum et fruticetum Britannicum . . .* (ed. 2, 8 vols., London, 1854), I, 80-81.

[101] *Catalogus plantarum,* 3, 4, 13, 34, 55, 81, 82, 88. Some of these plants are the summer haw, *Crataegus flava;* the indigo bush, *Amorpha fruticosa;* the strawberry shrub, *Calycanthus floridus;* the catalpa tree, *Catalpa catalpa;* the *Stuartia malachodendron;* the water locust, *Gleditsia aquatica;* and the honey locust, *Gleditsia triacanthos.*

[102] See *Catalogus plantarum,* 34; and Loudon, *Arboretum et fruticetum,* I, 80-81.

[103] See note by A. B. Lambert in John Nichols, ed., *Literary Anecdotes of the Eighteenth Century . . .* (9 vols., London, 1812-15), VIII, 200-201; Loudon, *Arboretum et fruticetum,* I, 69.

[104] *Hortus,* 25.

[105] (London, 1767).

[106] Pages cited below apply to either edition. The Library of Congress has a copy which contains both title pages.

[107] *Hortus,* i-iii.

greater work. Most of the plants illustrated in the posthumous volume had been included in *The Natural History,* so that the later book contributed little new. And, though Catesby's engravings in the *Hortus Britanno-Americanus* were not merely miniature versions of his earlier ones, they were in most cases made from the same original sketches and paintings. This is especially noticeable in the seeds and blossoms, with which Catesby was more exact than with the leaves. Many of them were almost exact duplicates of those shown in *The Natural History,* though shown in slightly different positions.

Even though the plates of the *Hortus Britanno-Americanus* were much reduced from those of *The Natural History,* this was not the case with the text which accompanied them. Unlike the earlier work, in which the greatest attention was given to fauna, the *Hortus* was devoted only to plants. Added to this was the fact that it was designed to stimulate interest in growing American species and in providing the information necessary for their cultivation. Accordingly, the descriptive passages were generally much more detailed than those of *The Natural History.* Ordinarily these indicated the place of growth, the kind of soil in which the plants flourished, descriptions of the bark, leaves, and wood, and their uses for wood and for decoration — including the uses made of them by the Indians. To be sure, most of these things had been included in Catesby's *Natural History,* but they were neither so consistent nor at such great length as in his posthumous work.

In some cases, the time which had elapsed between the completion of the principal part of *The Natural History of Carolina* and Catesby's work on the *Hortus Britanno-Americanus* — that is, from about 1743 to 1748 or 1749 — wrought an improvement in his thoughts about some of these plants. A case in point was the cabbage tree or *Sabal palmetto.* Catesby's

original treatment of this tree (which he did not figure), in the introduction to the second volume of *The Natural History,* was greatly exaggerated.[108] In contrast to his usually careful observations based on his own experience, he apparently had accepted the observations of others to the effect that the range of this plant extended, though in a reduced stature, as far north as New England. The account of the tree in the *Hortus Britanno-Americanus* was much more accurate and it was accompanied by a plate which a twentieth-century botanist has described as "a good diagrammatic representation of the cabbage-tree."[109]

The *Hortus,* then, did correct a few errors of its more famous predecessor, and it gave Catesby the opportunity to picture a few trees and shrubs which, for lack of space or previous lack of knowledge, he had not included in his earlier work.[110] This monument, this self-composed epitaph to Catesby the gardener and to Catesby the experimental horticulturist — for he was more than a mere gardener — possibly deserved more than the oblivion to which it has been consigned. Had its author lived to oversee its publication as minutely as he had that of *The Natural History of Carolina,* perhaps the *Hortus* might have earned a wider reputation. There were other reasons, though, why the latter book remained unused except by antiquarians and a few botanical historians. It lacked the broad appeal which the wider choice of subjects gave to *The Natural History.* Its modest format made it a less desirable acquisition for the virtuosi who desired an elegant picture book. And, finally, Catesby's death broke the ties to the wider world of natural history which he and *The Natural History of Carolina* had had through the kindly offices of such great scientific entrepreneurs as Peter Collinson and Sir Hans Sloane. Sloane, along with most of Catesby's other patrons, had passed on to his eternal reward before the *Hortus* was set forth by mere profit-seeking booksellers.

[108] *Carolina,* II, xli.

[109] *Hortus,* 40; John K. Small, "The Cabbage-Tree–Sabal Palmetto," *Journal of the New York Botanical Garden,* XXIV (1923), 147-51.

[110] See *Hortus,* 19, 20. Some of the specimens included in the *Hortus* had been sent by John Bartram from Pennsylvania, and Catesby had seen them at the hand of Peter Collinson after the publication of his *Carolina.*

Note: *Some Plant Names Based by Linnaeus Solely on Catesby*

1. *Dendropemon purpureus, Species plantarum* (ed. 1), 1023; *Carolina,* II, 95.
2. *Phoradendron rubrum, Species plantarum* (ed. 1), 1023; *Carolina,* II, 81.
3. *Annona glabra, Species plantarum* (ed. 1), 537; *Carolina,* II, 67.
4. *Urechites lutea, Centuria plantarum* (2 vols., Uppsala, 1756), II, 12; *Carolina,* II, 53.
5. *Ipomoea carolina, Species plantarum* (ed. 1), 160; *Carolina,* II, 91.
6. *Zanthoxylum clava-herculis, Species plantarum* (ed. 1), 270; *Carolina,* I, 26.
7. *Jacuranda coerulea, Species plantarum* (ed. 1), 625; *Carolina,* I, 42.
8. *Catesbaea spinosa, Species plantarum* (ed. 1), 109; *Carolina,* II, 100.
9. *Plumiera obtusa, Species plantarum* (ed. 1), 210; *Carolina,* II, 93.
10. *Philadelphus inodorus, Species plantarum* (ed. 1), 470; *Carolina,* II, 84.
11. *Asimina triloba, Species plantarum* (ed. 1), 537; *Carolina,* II, 85.
12. *Mimusops emarginata, Species plantarum* (ed. 1), 512; *Carolina,* II, 87.

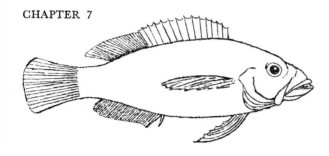

CHAPTER 7

Catesby as a Naturalist: Cartography, Geology, Anthropology, Zoology

The second volume of *The Natural History of Carolina* was a far more diverse publication than the first. Its contents approached those of a true natural history, whereas the first volume had been little more than an ornithology with botanical backgrounds. The more varied animal life pictured in this volume, and especially the "Account of Carolina and the Bahama Islands" with which it was prefaced, fulfilled the implications of the title.

This volume usually begins with "A Map of Carolina, Florida, the Bahama Islands and Parts Adjacent," though occasionally, depending on the whims of the binders, the map appears in the first. The more logical context for it, though, is with Catesby's "Account," and, further, it was completed only after the five parts of the first volume had been published. The map depicts what is now the southeastern United States, with Virginia on the north and Louisiana on the west, the West Indies as far south and east as Puerto Rico, Bermuda in the east, and the Yucatan Peninsula in the southwest. It was hardly an original work with Catesby. For all of his versatility in many branches of natural philosophy, cartography was not

one of them. Rather, the map was a good representation of the better English ideas about the geography of North America in the 1730's and early 1740's. Contrary to Catesby's usual practice, its obvious source was unidentified. This was a great "mother map," the origin of much cartographical plagiarism, Henry Popple's *Map of the British Empire in America with the French and Spanish Settlements Adjacent Thereto*.[1] Catesby's map was almost identical in detail, in its mainland portions at least, to Popple's much larger production. Each located Indian tribes in approximately the same position, each indicated "a fit Place for an English Factory" in the vague transmontane vastness of what is now Kentucky, and each distorted the Florida peninsula by widening its upper portions. Popple's map showed far more detail in the Bahamas — a region with which Catesby should have had greater acquaintance — and both maps located the infant settlements founded by James Oglethorpe in Georgia in 1733, the very year of Popple's map. There may have been some mutual aid between the two, as it seems likely that they knew each other. Popple (1705?-43) was a member of a family closely connected with America which had

[1] (London, 1733).

provided three secretaries to the Board of Trade, and Henry Popple himself was a subscriber to Catesby's work.[2] In addition, he was a Fellow of the Royal Society, though his election took place four years after his map was printed.[3] Catesby may have helped him locate some of the places in North America, but most of the help would seem to have gone in the opposite direction.

Catesby's "Account of Carolina and the Bahama Islands" followed hard upon the map. This preface to the second volume was much more than a mere introductory note to the plates which followed. Rather, it was a reasoned, if sometimes brief, account of the history, topography, geology, botany, zoology, and agriculture of the regions which Catesby had known in America. In short, it was a natural history. Viewed from the present, it displays an early eighteenth-century view of God's Creation, by a man reasonably well informed in most parts of natural philosophy but not particularly original. More than that, it provides a valuable — though little used — contemporary source for the economies both of Carolina and of the Bahamas.

The early section on the founding of Carolina was necessarily brief and gave way quickly to items more closely connected with Catesby's own interests, particularly to "Of the Air of Carolina."[4] This climatological section and the similar treatment of the Bahamas was the result of careful though unquantitative observation. As might be expected, with the exception of noting major weather phenomena such as hurricanes, Catesby was primarily concerned with the effects of climate on plants. Thus he noted the

moderating effects of water upon nearby areas, the fact that figs and oranges could be raised near the sea but not farther inland.[5] He was also fully aware that the North American continent had a much more severe climate than those parts of Europe which lay in the same latitudes, but he offered no explanation for it. This was strangely inconsistent with his theories on bird migration, however, for these assumed a world-wide uniformity of climate varying only in relation to the distance north or south of the equator.

The sections which followed, "Of the Soil of Carolina" and "Of the Water," contained most of Catesby's observations and speculations upon geological matters.[6] Much of this was very penetrating, tempered always by Catesby's own time and place. He clearly recognized that at least the lower part of the coastal plain was of marine origin, noting how the sea both built and destroyed the sandy shore and finding "innumerable Hills of loose Sand further within Land, in the Hollows of which, when the Water subsides, are frequently left infinite Variety of Shells, Fish, Bones, and other Refuse of the Ocean." Even some miles from the sea, Catesby recognized small hills which had once been like the dunes lying nearer the shore.[7]

His descriptions of the soil types of Carolina were concise: the rich, swampy "Rice Land"; "Oak and Hickory Land," productive of the best grains; "Pine barren Land," good only for the forest products derived from it; and finally, the unproductive "Shrubby Oak Land."[8] These names were not particularly original with him, being commonly applied by the Carolinians. Still, Catesby's treatment of them was

[2] "The Source of Sir William Keith's 'New Map of Virginia, 1738,'" *Va. Mag.*, XXXIV (1926), 364-65; *Carolina*, I, "A List of the Encouragers of this Work," unpaged, preceding Preface.

[3] *The Record of the Royal Society of London* (ed. 4, London, 1940), 404.

[4] *Carolina*, II, i-iii.

[5] *Carolina*, II, ii, xxi.

[6] *Carolina*, II, iii-vii. We are indebted to Professor George W. White of the University of Illinois for permission to use a manuscript study of Catesby as a geologist as a basis for much of the material that follows. Many of the insights are Professor White's; however, the present authors assume full responsibility for all judgments.

[7] *Carolina*, II, iii.

[8] *Carolina*, II, iii-v.

careful and precise, as was his later delineation of the soils of the Bahamas. In the latter he recognized the three major soils of the islands — "White Ground," coral sand; "Black Land," Bahama black loam; and "Red Land," Bahama red loam — and treated their capabilities for agriculture quite accurately.[9] In both areas his sense of ecology, of the interrelationship between soils and plants, was sound.

Catesby's account of the change of Carolina landscape from the coastal plain through the piedmont was especially acute, clearly recognizing the characteristics of those areas which shaded almost imperceptibly into the mountains beyond. The section on the mountains themselves was quite good, although based on more scanty data than that of the areas below. It derived from observations made upon Catesby's trip up the James River in 1714, possibly to the edge of the Blue Ridge, together with the tales of Indian traders, and the kind of fuzzy geography concerning anything beyond the coastal plain found in maps such as that of Popple. In consequence, Catesby placed the southern end of the "Appalatchians" too near the "Bay of Mexico." The sections founded on Catesby's experience such as his description of the rocks which he saw in the mountains — mostly mica schist and other metamorphic types — were far better.[10] Indeed, these are among the first accounts of America in which there was detailed specification of rock types.

In the section "Of the Water," Catesby's recognition of the existence and the significance of the fall line and of the differences in the streams above and below their cataracts shows clearly.[11] He saw the role of the rivers in creating and destroying land, recognizing again, as in the case of the seacoast, a changing Creation.[12] He did not share the erroneous but commonly held beliefs of his time about the origins of water in streams. Down to the middle of the eighteenth century, even highly educated men continued to hold that water was carried subterraneously from the sea to the mountains, from whence it flowed in springs and rivers. Catesby clearly and even radically recognized the correct source. This was not original with him, as correct hypotheses had been advanced as long before as the late sixteenth century; but Catesby was abreast of the best thought on the subject.[13] In his description of a flood at Fort Moore in September, 1722 — an inundation he could not have witnessed, as he was an invalid in Charles Town at the time — he noted that it "proceeded only from what Rain fell on the Mountains. . . ."[14]

Catesby here also made a few assays into paleontology. If he saw a world in flux in the case of the rivers and sea, Creation was a more static affair when he dealt with fossils. On these matters Catesby was a diluvialist, strongly influenced by such late seventeenth-century works as Thomas Burnet's *Theory of the Earth* and John Woodward's *Essay Towards a Natural History of the Earth*.[15] These works had ascribed to the biblical Flood a compelling influence in the topography and structure of the earth, together with the origin and distribution of fossils. Catesby wrote:

There is no Part of the Globe where the signs of a Deluge more evidently appears than in many Parts of the Northern Continent of America, which, though I could illustrate in many Instances, let this one suffice. Mr. Woodward [not the author referred to above but the husband of Catesby's niece, Ann Cocke] at his Plantation in Virginia, above an Hundred Miles from the Sea . . . in digging a well above seventy feet deep, to find a Spring, discovered at that depth a Bed of the *Glossopetrae*, one of which was

[9] *Carolina*, II, xxxix-xl. See George Burbank Shattuck, ed., *The Bahama Islands* (New York, 1905), 155-67, for a modern treatment of these soils.

[10] *Carolina*, II, iv-vi.

[11] *Carolina*, II, vi-vii.

[12] *Carolina*, II, iv.

[13] Frank Dawson Adams, *The Birth and Development of the*

Geological Sciences (Baltimore, Md., 1938), 443-60.

[14] *Carolina*, II, vii.

[15] Thomas Burnet, *The Theory of the Earth* . . . (2 vols., London, 1684) and later editions, published as *Telluris theoria sacra* (2 vols., London, 1681-89); John Woodward, *Essay Towards a Natural History of the Earth* (London, 1695).

sent me. All Parts of Virginia abound in Fossil Shells of various Kinds, which in *stratum* lie imbedded a great Depth in the Earth, in the Banks of Rivers and other Places, among which are frequently found the Vertibras and other Bones of Sea Animals.[16]

This diluvial view at least had the advantage of seeing the organic origin of fossils, unlike the idea of Martin Lister, who thought these stones *"lapides sui generis,* and never were part of an animal."[17] Even so, Catesby's diluvialism belonged to his own and past ages and not to the future.

More important than his account of marine fossils was his recognition of the similarity of the bones of the mammoth to the elephant: "At a place in Carolina called Stono, was dug out of the Earth three or four Teeth of a large Animal, which, by the concurring Opinion of all the Negroes, native Africans, that saw them, were the Grinders of an Elephant, and in my opinion could be no other; I having seen some of the like that are brought from Africa."[18]

This was easily — in 1724 or early 1725 at the latest — the earliest technical identification of the mammoth and even of a vertebrate fossil in America. It certainly predated the similar discovery and recognition by Charles Le Moyne, Baron de Longueil, in the Ohio valley in 1739, which has been taken as the beginning of vertebrate paleontology in America.[19] Certainly its publication in 1743 preceded by a year the first published news of Longueil's work in Nicholas Bellin's map of Louisiana.[20] The question of priority lacks real significance though, as it is the sort of futile antiquarianism which infects a certain species of the history of science. The teeth uncovered at Stono remained in Carolina, while those found by Longueil returned to Paris and to the world of science.

Despite Catesby's primary interest in natural history, no account of America would have been complete without some word on the Indians. In "Of the Aborigines of America" and "Of the Indians of Carolina and Florida," Catesby made his major effort as an anthropologist.[21] The Indians, he believed, were of Asian origin. "The Difference from the easternmost part of the Old World to America not being known, there is a probability that the Continent of the northeast Part of Asia, may be very near, if not contiguous to that of America; or according to the Japonese Maps in Sir Hans Sloan[e]'s Museum the Passage may be very easy from a Chain of Islands there laid down."[22]

All Indians, he thought, were similar. "Though the difference between the Inhabitants of the various Parts of the old World is such as would startle one's Faith, to consider them all as Descendants of Adam, in America it is otherwise." They were all from the same stock, having similar features and similar knowledge of the arts. Consequently, Catesby discounted the writings of "Herrera, Solis and other Spanish Authors" as to the "Knowledge and Politeness of the Mexicans even in the more abstruse Arts of Sculpture and Architecture."[23]

---

[16] *Carolina,* II, xii.

[17] Martin Lister, "A Letter of . . . ," *Phil. Trans.,* VI (1671), 2281-84.

[18] *Carolina,* II, xii.

[19] George Gaylord Simpson, "The Beginnings of Vertebrate Paleontology in North America," *Proceedings of the American Philosophical Society,* LXXXVI (1942), 135-37. Possibly the term "technical identification" can be applied to the discovery of the bones of some prehistoric reptile near the falls of the James River almost contemporaneously with Catesby's "elephant." Cotton Mather, in a letter to Dr. James Jurin, June 3, 1723, described it as a "Supposed Snake of a Monstrous size," *R.S. Journal Book,* XIII, 327-30; *R.S. Letter Book,* XV, 383-87. These may be the same

bones described later as "like the back bone of a Whale" in a letter of Thomas Jenner to Sir Hans Sloane, Charlestown, Mass., May 29, 1740, *Sloane* 4056, fol. 242.

[20] Jacques Nicholas Bellin, "Carte de la Louisiane . . . ," in Pierre François Xavier de Charlevoix, *Histoire et description de la Nouvelle France . . .* (6 vols., Paris, 1744), I, opp. p. 1.

[21] *Carolina,* II, vii-xvi.

[22] *Carolina,* II, vii.

[23] Antonio de Herrara y Tordesillas, *Historia general de los castellanos en las ilas i tierre firme del mar oceano* (Madrid, 1601); Catesby probably used the inaccurate translation and abridgment by John Stevens, *The General History of the Vast Continent and Islands of America . . .* (6 vols., London, 1725-26). Antonio Solis y Rivadenyra, *Historia de la*

The major part of Catesby's essay, which dealt with Indians he had seen, was taken with due credit from John Lawson's *History of Carolina,* "As I had the same Opportunities of attesting that Author's Account as he had in writing it. . . ."[24] Such honesty was commonplace in botanical writings of the time but was unusual in the accounts of travelers, where most material on the Indians was found, and where plagiarism was the rule rather than the exception. Catesby's use of Lawson, who often seasoned his relation with an admixture of fancy, was quite judicious. He wrote: "I might have been more prolix, but I chose rather to confine myself to what I learn'd by a personal Knowledge of them; and as Natural History is the Subject of this Book, I conceive it impertinent to relate tedious Narratives of Religious Ceremonies, Burials, Marriages, etc., which are too often the Product of Invention, or Credulity of the Relator."[25] This was a wise decision, but it denied to Catesby's account the lusty appeal which Lawson's "tedious Narrative" of the sexual customs of the Indians might have supplied. By limiting his accounts to those things which he had personally observed, Catesby often sacrificed a good story to scientific accuracy.

If the Indians appeared as noble savages anywhere in Catesby's works, this was not the case when he wrote about their aid to him when he was collecting in the piedmont.[26] He recognized the essential irrationality — from the European point of view — of these savages. The Indians, said Catesby, made war not from interest, as in eighteenth-century Europe, but rather from imagined wrongs or for matters of honor.[27] Nor were they susceptible of taking on the ways of white men, though Catesby saw modification of their culture in the fact that firearms had superseded the bow and arrow and that the iron

hatchet had replaced the stone tomahawk.[28] They remained savages nonetheless:

The Indians are generally allowed to have a good Capacity which seems adapted and even confined to their savage Way of Life. Reading and Writing is the highest Erudition I have known or heard of any of them attain to; though a great Number of them have been, and still continue to be educated at Williamsburg-College in Virginia, by the Benefaction of the great Mr. Boyle, whose pious Design was, that after attaining a true Qualification, they should inculcate amongst their Brethren true Religion and Virtue, yet I have never heard of an Instance conformable to that worthy Intention.[29]

Actually, for all of Catesby's treatment of the customs and habitations of the Indians, as a naturalist and especially as a practical botanist, he was more concerned with their uses of various herbs in medicine and of plants for food.[30] His next section, "Of the Agriculture of Carolina," was much nearer his heart.[31] It was an accurate, if brief, account of the farming practices and principal crops of the Carolina Tidewater in the 1720's. He described the wasteful use of land — of moving to new lands as soon as the fertility of the old was exhausted — and explained it in the same terms as present-day historians of early agriculture. His account was based largely on his own careful observation, as in the case of his excellent description of rail fences. In other cases, he was assisted by knowledgeable American authorities — by his old botanizing companions, Robert Johnson, several times the Governor of South Carolina, who supplied some of the material on the history of rice cultivation; and William Byrd, who informed him on the uses of Indian corn.[32]

Closely connected with agriculture was Catesby's account of the pines of Carolina and "The Manner

---

conquista de Mexico . . . (Madrid, 1684); Catesby probably saw the translation by Thomas Townshend, *The History of the Conquest of Mexico . . .* (London, 1724), or the later edition of 1738.

[24] *Carolina,* II, viii. See John Lawson, *The History of Carolina . . .* (London, 1714), 169-238.

[25] *Carolina,* II, xvi.

[26] *Carolina,* I, viii-ix.

[27] *Carolina,* II, xiii.

[28] *Carolina,* II, xi.

[29] *Carolina,* II, xii.

[30] *Carolina,* II, ix-x, xv.

[31] *Carolina,* II, xvi-xxii.

[32] *Carolina,* II, xvi-xvii.

of Making Pitch and Tar."[33] Strangely, the Carolinian pines were the only common group of trees which he did not etch for *The Natural History*. Possibly one of the reasons for this failure was the difficulty he had experienced, along with Robert Johnson, in finding cones while he was in Carolina.[34] He could have, and probably did, remedy this by having specimens sents to him in England after his return. More likely this omission was out of deference to Peter Collinson, "who, by procuring from the different Parts of America a great Variety of seeds, and specimens of various kinds, has a large Fund for a complete History of this useful Tree."[35] Perhaps Catesby should have drawn the *Pinaceae,* however, as Collinson's promised history never appeared. The related material on the production of pitch and tar was a detailed and careful summary, not only of the process itself, but also of the construction of the kilns in which the tar was extracted.[36] This provided an excellent source for Englishmen of the eighteenth century, who might understandably have been concerned with these important naval stores; it serves the modern economic and technological historian as well — though for different purposes.

The remaining sections of the "Account of Carolina and the Bahama Islands" either have been dealt with earlier or will be considered in the course of this chapter. Several of these, dealing with the fishes of Carolina and "Of the Sea, Encompassing the Bahama Islands, with Its Productions,"[37] laid the scene for what was, next to the birds, the most important division of fauna covered in the book. The first thirty-one plates of the second volume — together with one

of the *Appendix* — constituted the whole of Catesby's attempt to delineate the fish life of American waters.[38] On these plates, he figured a total of forty-six fishes, all except one of which was American, and most of which he found in Bahaman waters.

At least one recent commentator has said that Catesby's fishes were superior to his birds.[39] This is patently untrue. The fishes taken as a whole rank among the poorest of Catesby's plates in the book. An estimate nearer Catesby's own day, and nearer the truth as well, was that of Alexander Garden, Catesby's great successor in South Carolina. In 1760, after Linnaeus had written Garden asking him to check some of Catesby's fishes, Garden replied:

Please to observe the Albula, our Mullet; and you may immediately perceive that he [Catesby] has not only forgotten to count and express the rays of the fins, but that he has, which is hardly credible, left out the pectoral fins entirely, and overlooked one of the ventral ones. So he has done in most other instances. It is sufficiently evident that his sole object was to make showy figures of the productions of Nature, rather than give correct and accurate representations. This is rather to invent than to describe. It is indulging the fancies of his own brain, instead of contemplating and observing the beautiful works of God.[40]

Garden's comment on Catesby's mullet was justifiable.[41] It was probably the worst of the fishes in *The Natural History of Carolina.* Garden was, however, a novice at ichthyology when he wrote the letter and, in this and other cases, he misled Linnaeus.[42] Garden, who contributed so much to the twelfth edition of the *Systema naturae,* always took a derogatory view of Catesby. His pique leaves the impression that he was

---

[33] *Carolina,* II, xxii-xxiv.

[34] See above, p. 27.

[35] *Carolina,* II, xxii.

[36] *Carolina,* II, xxiii-xxiv. Collinson did publish brief accounts of the pines, in *Gentleman's Magazine,* XXV (1755), 503-4, 550-51.

[37] *Carolina,* II, xxxiii-xxxv, xli-xliii.

[38] *Carolina,* II, *Appendix,* 19.

[39] Robert Henry Welker, *Birds and Men* . . . (Cambridge, Mass., 1955), 12.

[40] Garden to Linnaeus, Charles Town, Jan. 2, 1760, in Smith, *Corresp. Linnaeus,* II, 300-306.

[41] *Carolina,* II, 6, fig. 2.

[42] See David Starr Jordan, "An Identification of the Figures of Fishes in Catesby's Natural History . . . ," *Proceedings of the U.S. National Museum,* VII (1884), 190-99. Identifications of Catesby's fishes are taken from the above article and D. S. Jordan, Barton Warren Evermann, and Howard Walton Clark, *Check List of the Fishes and Fishlike Vertebrates of North and Middle America* . . . (*Report of the U.S. Commissioner of Fisheries, 1928,* pt. II, Washington, D.C., 1930). See also the note to Chapter 7 below, pp. 84-85.

jealous of the author of *The Natural History of Carolina.*

Garden was correct, however, in saying that Catesby was careless in portraying fins, particularly pectoral and dorsal fins.[43] In some plates, Catesby had difficulty in translating the bright coloration of these tropical and subtropical species into water color. This is easily understandable, especially as fish change color rapidly after being removed from water. Catesby tried to avoid this by painting them "at different times, having a succession of them procur'd while the former lost their colors. . . ."[44] Yet he did not have this advantage with all of the species that he depicted, as he saw some of them only once or twice. In at least one case, "The great Hog-Fish," Catesby saw only the head, which was all he illustrated.[45] It was, nevertheless, a fair figure. Two other species, "The mangrove Snapper"[46] and "The Cat Fish,"[47] were apparently done from memory; but they were, nonetheless, the bases of Linnaean designations. Much of Catesby's inaccuracy was due, then, to the fact that his original sketches had often to be made very quickly and that his time in the Bahamas was not sufficient to see enough specimens of the species he drew. In other cases, it may have resulted from his original sketches and water colors having lain too long before being transferred to copper plates for *The Natural History.*

Some of Catesby's fishes were, however, relatively good productions. His figures of "The Black-Tail,"[48] "The Squirrel,"[49] "The Yellow Fish,"[50] and "The Lane-Snapper"[51] were all well done, and still others can be placed in the fair category. Of the forty-six fishes which Catesby figured, not more than four can be classed as dubious or unidentifiable.

Again, as in the case of his birds, Catesby's plates and descriptions were used by Linnaeus and later scientists as the bases for binary names. Twenty-six modern scientific names of fishes were based at least in part on Catesby's figures, and three others were included in the synonymies of the original designations of names which have been retained.[52] Some of Catesby's polynomials, again as in the case of the birds, were used in part in Linnaean names. Unlike the birds, however, few of Catesby's Latin names were mere translations of the English ones which he used. For the latter, he almost always used names which were in use in the Bahamas and in Carolina. Many of them, indeed, have remained in use by Bahaman fishermen down to the present.[53] For the Latin he depended principally on the efforts of John Ray and Francis Willughby — this time on *De historia piscium*[54] — for the designation of kind, to which he added his own differentiating adjectives. As might be expected, some also were derived from Dr. Hans Sloane, who had dealt with a number of West Indian species in his work on Jamaica.

What was the sum of Catesby's accomplishment as an ichthyologist? As compared with his ornithological work, it was small. He was not an innovator in any sense. His pictures of fishes were rather stiff profiles, either without any background, or, in several cases, set against land plants which were singularly inappropriate.[55] Moreover, his descriptions were hardly adequate. Catesby's brief acquaintance with the fishes that he included in his book was insufficient to give an adequate description of their environment. He

[43] See *Carolina,* II, 10, fig. 1, 14, fig. 2, 24, 27.

[44] *Carolina,* I, xi.

[45] *Carolina,* II, 15; *Lachnolaimus maximus* (Walbaum).

[46] *Carolina,* II, 9; *Lutianus griseus* (Linnaeus).

[47] *Carolina,* II, 23; *Haustor catus* (Linnaeus).

[48] *Carolina,* II, 7, fig. 2; *Haemulon melanurum* (Linnaeus).

[49] *Carolina,* II, 3, fig. 2; *Holocentrus rufus* (Walbaum).

[50] *Carolina,* II, 10, fig. 2; *Cephalopholis fulvus fulvus* (Linnaeus).

[51] *Carolina,* II, 17, fig. 1; *Lutianus synagris* (Linnaeus).

[52] See the note to Chapter 7 below, pp. 84-85.

[53] Jordan, "Identification," 190; G. Brown Goode, *Catalogue of the Fishes of the Bermudas (U.S. National Museum Bulletin,* No. 5, Washington, D.C., 1876), 15-17.

[54] John Ray and Francis Willughby, *De historia piscium . . .* (Oxford, 1686). See Charles E. Raven, *John Ray, Naturalist* (Cambridge, 1942), 352, for the authorship of this volume.

[55] See *Carolina,* II, 24, 26, 28.

noted those few species which were fresh-water varieties and indicated the few that came from Carolina and Virginia. Other than that he could tell only in a few instances that certain species inhabited the shallow waters. Nevertheless, for all of the weaknesses of *The Natural History of Carolina* as a study of fishes, it contributed to the knowledge of the American fauna by Europeans and enabled Linnaeus and the taxonomists of the later eighteenth century to include materials in their systems from a relatively unexplored area.

Catesby's study of the marine life of the Bahamas did not stop with the fishes of the area but included shellfish also. He considered the subject generally in his "Account" in the section "Of Shells."[56] He dealt with Mollusca only in this introductory section, leaning most heavily on the works of Martin Lister for reference, and leaving Crustacea for the plates and text. In this discussion he noted that "Every Species of Shell-fish inhabit particular Parts of the Sea agreeable to their Natures: This seems to have some Analogy to Plants, whose different Kinds affect a different Soil and Aspect." He continued this discussion by recounting that certain shellfish had an affinity for certain types of islands, for water of various depths, or other environments. After naming a few species that inhabited shallow waters, he concluded that "from these few instances it is reasonable to conclude that all other Shell-fish that lye in deeper waters, abide in a depth adapted to every species."[57] This was undoubtedly one of the early considerations of marine ecology and illustrates that Catesby's under-

standing of organic environment, derived from his botanical studies, had been transferred to other fields of natural history. He realized his inadequacy in marine researches, a fault not altogether his own. He "hoped that at some time or other an opportunity may favour the curious, in enquiring into the knowledge of this beautiful part of the Creation [the Mollusca] which hitherto extends little farther than the shell or covering of the animal."[58]

The plates and text in the main body of *The Natural History of Carolina* were devoted to the Crustacea rather than Mollusca, though these, too, tended to probe "little farther than the shell or covering of the animal" — or, at least, its superficial appearance. The seven species of crabs — all of them Bahaman — which Catesby included were inexact by modern standards, but were reasonably good for his own time. Indeed, one of them, "The Hermit Crab," was copied years later for the *Tableau encyclopédique et méthodique* and thus became the basis of a modern designation.[59] Two other plates by Catesby, "The red motled Rock Crab"[60] and "The red claw Crab,"[61] provided the sources of bionomials which have survived. Of the remainder, two can be easily identified,[62] while the other two can be identified with a fair degree of certainty.[63] The total performance, then, for a branch of natural history which played such a small part in Catesby's book, was remarkably good.

Catesby continued his study of sea animals with the large turtles. His three figures, "The green

[56] *Carolina*, II, xliii-xliv.

[57] *Carolina*, II, xliii.

[58] *Carolina*, II, xliv.

[59] *Carolina*, II, 33; *Cenobita diogenes* (Latreille); Pierre André Latreille, *Tableau encyclopédique et méthodique . . . crustacés, arachnides et insectes* (Paris, 1818), 2, pl. 284, figs. 2, 3.

[60] *Carolina*, II, 36, fig. 1; *Grapsus grapsus* (Linnaeus). See Mary J. Rathbun, *The Grapsoid Crabs of America* (*U.S. National Museum Bulletin*, No. 97, Washington, D.C., 1918), 227.

[61] *Carolina*, II, 37; *Dromia erythropus* (George Edwards). The trivial name is taken from the Linnaean index to the 1771 edition of *The Natural History of Carolina*. See Mary J. Rathbun, *Oxytomatous and Allied Crabs of America* (*U.S. National Museum Bulletin*, No. 166, Washington, D.C., 1937), 31.

[62] *Carolina*, II, 35; *Ocypode albicans* (Bosc). See Rathbun, *Grapsoid*, 367. *Carolina*, II, 36, fig. 2; *Callapa flammea* (Herbst). See Rathbun, *Oxytomatous*, 198.

[63] Catesby's "Land Crab," *Carolina*, II, 32, is probably the common land crab, *Gecarcinus laterales* (Freminville), and his "Sea Hermit Crab," *ibid.*, 34, may be *Dardanus venonosus* (Milne-Edwards).

Turtle,"[64] "The Hawks-bill Turtle,"[65] and "The Loggerhead Turtle,"[66] were all rather crude, but they are easily recognizable as the animals which still retain these common names. The names, however, were of current use in the Bahamas, and Catesby adopted but did not originate them. Unlike the rest of his fauna, no scientific names were based upon them, though Linnaeus, because of an error by Catesby in giving "The Hawks-bill" the Latin designation *Testudo caretta,* mistakenly placed it among his synonyms for the loggerhead turtle.[67]

Catesby's discussion of these amphibious reptiles was significant in that he dealt with their economic importance for the Bahamas, and particularly — as he did also with the fishes — in their use as a food. He noted that large numbers of green turtles were taken to the Carolinas, where their meat was esteemed a rarity. Further, he gave a detailed account of the methods used by the Bahamans in capturing these gigantic reptiles.[68]

Although the sea turtles must have aroused the interest of the "curious," the twenty plates which followed — the eighth part of *The Natural History of Carolina* — probably held their attention to an even greater degree. Catesby devoted this entire section to snakes, or, as he included the legless lizard, "The Glass Snake,"[69] to what he considered to be snakes. No other part of the natural history of British America had so much fascination for those who demonstrated an interest in that subject either in England or in the colonies themselves. Snakes, and particularly rattlesnakes, were the subject of as much folklore, and of as much sheer nonsense, as all the rest of the fauna. Mark Catesby, along with some of his English colleagues — particularly Sir Hans Sloane — did his best to dispel the misapprehensions of the ignorant and idly curious, misapprehensions which, alas, are still a part of the mythology surrounding serpents.[70]

One of these myths, that the juices of certain plants (snakeroots) had antiveninous qualities, in snake bite, especially rattlesnake bite, was generally believed in America and was advocated by many who fancied themselves followers of the science of nature, including William Byrd.[71] Catesby was too careful an observer to condone anything so patently untrue and even dangerous. "Having by travelling much with Indians had frequent Opportunities of seeing the direful Effects of the Bites of these Snakes," he wrote, "it always seemed and was apparent to me, that the good Effects usually attributed to these their Remedies, is owing more to the Force of the Bite of a small Snake in a muscular Part. . . . The Person thus bit, I have known to survive without any Assistance for many Hours, but where a Rattle-Snake with full Force penetrates his deadly Fangs, and pricks a Vein or Artery, inevitably Death ensues. . . ." Catesby realized that the best of the Indian remedies had nothing to do with roots or potions, but rather involved cutting the bite open and sucking out the poison.[72]

Other items of herpetological apocrypha incurred the scorn or, at least, obvious disbelief of this acute observer. There were many advocates of the theory that rattlesnakes charmed their prey. Catesby's patron, Sir Hans Sloane, disproved this in experiments in England, but American correspondents of the Royal Society continued to send their accounts of this sub-

[64] *Carolina,* II, 38; *Chelonia mydas* (Linnaeus). The modern names of Reptilia and Amphibia are those given in Karl Patterson Schmidt, *A Check List of North American Amphibians and Reptiles* (ed. 6, Chicago, 1953).

[65] *Carolina,* II, 39; *Testudo imbricata* (Linnaeus).

[66] *Carolina,* II, 40; *Caretta caretta* (Linnaeus).

[67] Carl Linnaeus, *Systema naturae . . .* (ed. 10, 2 vols., Stockholm, 1758-59), I, 197.

[68] *Carolina,* II, 38, 39.

[69] *Carolina,* II, 59.

[70] See Karl Patterson Schmidt, *The Truth About Snake Stories* (*Field Museum Zoology Leaflet* 10, Chicago, 1929); and Lawrence M. Klauber, *Rattlesnakes . . .* (2 vols., Berkeley, Calif., 1956), II, 1213-60.

[71] See Louis B. Wright and Marion Tinling, eds., *The Secret Diary of William Byrd of Westover, 1709-1712* (Richmond, 1941), 587.

[72] *Carolina,* II, 41.

ject across the Atlantic.[73] Catesby was unusually non-committal in this matter. He indicated that it was generally believed in America and that those who had told him about it agreed "in the manner of the Process. . . ." He indicated clearly his own disbelief, however, by noting that he had never seen it occur.[74]

Catesby dealt abruptly with a few other spurious items as well. He denied that the tail of "The Water Viper," the water moccasin,[75] was as deadly as its head, and that "The Coach-whip Snake"[76] could "by a jerk of their Tail separate a Man in two Parts. . . ." On the other hand — and this was inevitable — Catesby did repeat some doubtful items. He told the story, which is still repeated, that "The Black Snake," the black racer,[77] swallowed rattlesnakes, and that the survivors of rattlesnake bites experienced annual recurrences of the pain.[78] The latter had probably been told him as a fact, but it could hardly have been more than psychosomatic.

It is rather difficult to appraise the quality of Catesby's drawings of snakes. Some of the species which he drew are subject to almost infinite variations, so that identification from his plates is difficult, especially with little qualifying information in the text. Had he supplied more material on the scales, for example, his illustrations would have been more dependable. Unfortunately, such items were rather stylized in his plates. Even so, the quality of snake illustration, particularly where it concerned Ameri-

can varieties, did not improve much within the sixty or seventy years after Catesby's material saw print (c. 1736). The third volume of George Shaw's *General Zoology,* printed in 1802, contained a number of plates copied in detail from those of Catesby, and copied without credit, though *The Natural History of Carolina* was cited often in the text.[79]

Linnaeus apparently mistrusted Catesby's snakes — they lacked sufficient detail for his purposes — and so he included *The Natural History of Carolina* only twice in his synonymies in the tenth edition of the *Systema naturae* in 1758.[80] By the time the first volume of the twelfth edition was published, eight years later, Linnaeus had developed a reasonably trustworthy correspondent in South Carolina, Alexander Garden. Accordingly, most of the snakes which Linnaeus classified from the area which Catesby had visited were based on specimens which Garden sent to the great taxonomist at Uppsala. As type specimens in the modern sense were unknown, however, Catesby's plates were included with many of these as the only secondary citation in order to give a visual reference. Four of Catesby's snakes were used by Linnaeus in designations which have been retained, while three others were subsequently used by later and less suspicious naturalists as the basis for names of American snakes which likewise remain in use.[81]

Catesby continued his consideration of reptiles in *The Natural History of Carolina,* after a two-page

---

[73] Sir Hans Sloane, "Conjectures on the Charming or Fascinating Power Attributed to the Rattle-Snake . . . ," *Phil. Trans.,* XXXVIII (1734), 321-31. See Joseph Breintnall to Peter Collinson, Philadelphia, Nov. 3, 1735, *R.S. Journal Book,* XVII, 44-46; printed in *Phil. Trans.,* XLI (1740), 359-60.

[74] *Carolina,* II, 41.

[75] *Carolina,* II, 43; *Ancistrodon piscivorus piscivorus* (Lacépède).

[76] *Carolina,* II, 54; *Masticophis flagellum flagellum* (Shaw).

[77] *Carolina,* II, 48; *Coluber constrictor constrictor* (Linnaeus).

[78] *Carolina,* II, 41.

[79] George Shaw, *General Zoology* (14 vols., London, 1800-1826), III, pt. 2, *passim.*

[80] *Syst. nat.* (ed. 10), I, 222, 226.

[81] Linnaeus used the following snakes to illustrate specimens sent by Garden: "The Small Rattle-Snake" (ground rattler, *Sistrurus miliarius miliarius*), the ribbon snake (*Thamnophis sauritus sauritus*), and "The Chain Snake" (king snake, *Lampropeltis getulus getulus*). Similarly he used the glass snake (*Ophisaurus ventralis*) which Catesby had included with his snakes but which was actually a legless lizard. Linnaeus utilized others in this way for other species for which he had made prior designations. The designation for the water moccasin (*Ancistrodon piscivorus piscivorus* [Lacépède]) and copper-belly snake (*Natrix erythrogaster erythrogaster* [Forster]) were based partly on Catesby, while that of the coachwhip snake (*Masticophis flagellum flagellum* [Shaw]) was based entirely on the account and figure in *The Natural History.* See *Carolina,* II, 42, 43, 46, 50, 52, 54, 59.

interruption, with six lizard-like animals. The first figure was that of a newly hatched alligator, not a particularly good one, but better than some of the dragon-like representations of this species which were drawn by eighteenth-century artists.[82] Catesby had at least seen a number of alligators in the swamplands of Carolina and Georgia, though his description contained more material of a hearsay nature than was his wont. He had had sufficient contact with the animal to note that the "hind part of the belly and tail are eat by Indians," but that the flesh had "so perfumed a taste and smell" that he could "never relish it with pleasure."[83] Many of the plates of this group which followed were of a high order artistically, though they were scientifically vague. The Bahaman "Guana"[84] and "The Green Lizard of Carolina"[85] were posed skillfully against botanical backgrounds, in a manner reminiscent of some of Catesby's better bird plates. The latter and its near relative, "The Green Lizard of Jamaica,"[86] were drawn delicately, even beautifully, but lacked detail. None of this early group of Catesby's lizards provided the bases for Linnaean names, though his two final efforts, which had pronounced markings, did. "The Blue-Tail Lizard" (the blue-tailed skink)[87] was the sole source for Linnaeus' designation, and "The Lyon Lizard" was included by Linnaeus in the same manner as Catesby's snakes, as a reference for a specimen sent by Garden.[88]

Catesby's Amphibia were much better from the point of view of accuracy than were his lizards, though none of them had much aesthetic appeal. All five of them — four in the body of the second volume, and one in the *Appendix* — can be identified without difficulty. Unlike the preceding group of plates, these few were used heavily by post-Linnaean authors for establishing modern scientific names. The most imposing plate, and, indeed, the largest of Catesby's Amphibia, was named in his honor by George Shaw, the English zoological compiler. Catesby's bullfrog became the *Rana catesbeiana* in the third volume of Shaw's *General Zoology*[89] — which was only just for an author who had leaned so heavily upon *The Natural History of Carolina*. Though Shaw cited Catesby often, only one other of his binary names of Amphibia based on Catesby's work has been retained — that of the spotted salamander,[90] which Catesby had figured as being carried ominously in the mouth of a great blue heron.[91] The poorest picture of this group, that of the southern toad, was used by the Abbé Bonnaterre for his designation of that species.[92] Catesby thought it resembled a toad but called it "The Land Frog" because it hopped. Of Catesby's true frogs, however, one, "The Water Frog," was included correctly in Daniel Schreber's designation of the leopard frog,[93] and the other, "The Green Tree Frog," though its identity is clear, was ignored in Johann Gottlob Schneider's *Calamita cinereous*.[94] This oversight was probably the result of

[82] *Carolina*, II, 63; *Alligator mississipiensis* (Daudin). See William Bartram, *Travels in Georgia and Florida, 1773-74* (Francis Harper, ed., *Transactions of the American Philosophical Society*, XXXIII, pt. 2, Philadelphia, 1934), pl. XIV.

[83] *Carolina*, II, 63.

[84] *Carolina*, II, 64; probably *Cyclura baeolopha* (Cope).

[85] *Carolina*, II, 65; *Anolis carolinensis* (Voight).

[86] *Carolina*, II, 66; probably *Anolis grahami grahami* (Gray), though it has been identified with *Anolis grahami iodurus* (Gosse). See William Gardner Lynn and Chapman Grant, *The Herpetology of Jamaica* (Bulletin of the Institute of Jamaica Science Series, No. 1, [Kingston], 1940), 87.

[87] *Carolina*, II, 67; *Eumeces fasciatus* (Linnaeus); *Syst. nat.* (ed. 10), I, 209.

[88] *Carolina*, II, 68; *Cnemidophorus sexlineatus* (Linnaeus);

Carl Linnaeus, *Systema naturae* (ed. 12, 3 vols., Stockholm, 1766-68), I, 364.

[89] Shaw, III, pt. 1, 185, pl. 4.

[90] Shaw, III, pt. 1, 304; *Ambystoma maculatum*.

[91] *Carolina*, II, *Appendix*, 10; great blue heron, *Ardea herodias herodias* (Linnaeus).

[92] *Carolina*, II, 69; *Bufo terrestris* (Bonnaterre); Joseph Pierre Bonnaterre, *Tableau encyclopédique et méthodique . . . erpetologie* (Paris, 1789), 8.

[93] *Carolina*, II, 70; *Rana pipiens* (Schreber); *Die Naturforscher*, XVIII (1782), 185, pl. 4.

[94] *Carolina*, II, 71; *Hyla cinerea* (Schneider); Johann Gottlob Schneider, *Historiae amphibiorum . . .* (2 vols., Jena, 1799-1801), I, 174.

the fact that Schneider's source, Thomas Pennant's *Arctic Zoology,* considered Catesby's a separate species.[95]

The remaining zoological plates of *The Natural History of Carolina* were given over to insects, marine zoophytes, and mammals. The insects, though their number was fairly large and some of them — particularly the butterflies — had real beauty, were largely drawn as mere appendages to Catesby's botanical plates. Moreover, they had relatively little long-range influence. Linnaeus did cite Catesby occasionally in the *Systema,* but he referred far more often to the works of Browne and Sloane on Jamaica, and to James Petiver's published accounts of insects sent to him by collectors on the North American mainland.[96]

Catesby's zoophytes, mainly *Gorgonacea,* were relatively inconsequential. Indeed, Catesby, in common with most of his contemporaries, considered them to be plants. Not until 1755, when John Ellis published his *Natural History of the Corallines,* in which he expanded Jean Andre Peyssonnel's discovery of the animal nature of corals and corallines, did many consider them otherwise.[97] Although Catesby's work was cited by Linnaeus,[98] and some of the items he collected in America fell into the hands of John Ellis,[99] his work tended to be prescientific and unused.

The mammals included in *The Natural History* were far more important than any of these other minor groups. Catesby dealt with the majority of them in "Of Beasts" in his "Account of Carolina. . . ."[100] There he made a tripartite division of American mammals including those which belonged to different genera from European animals, those which belonged to the same genera but to different species, and, finally, those which belonged to the same species. This was perhaps the clearest statement of taxonomic principals found anywhere in the book; but it may also have been one of the reasons that Catesby figured so few mammals. For those which were supposed to be identical with European species, there appeared to be no point in including them in a book designed to illustrate American natural history for European readers. The failure to discriminate between widely scattered species was not Catesby's alone, for Linnaeus, too, was frequently guilty of it. Another factor which may have led Catesby to consider several of the mammals only in the introduction was that he had no intention to attempt a definitive treatment of all varieties of fauna other than the birds.[101] As a consequence, some of the animals in the "Account" were not natives of the regions which Catesby visited, and others he either had not seen or had made inadequate sketches of them while he was in the field. The buffalo belong to the latter category, although Catesby eventually included a rather poor representation of the *Bison americanus* as the last plate of the *Appendix.*[102] It is possible, even likely, perhaps, that originally he had not planned to include any mammals in the book. He had seen buffalo; indeed, he had hunted them in the Carolina piedmont,[103] and his description of their feeding habits indicated that he had watched them at such length that his original sketches, had he made them, should have been good

[95] (2 vols. + supp., London, 1784-87), II, 330.

[96] See *Syst. nat.* (ed. 10), I, *passim;* James Petiver, *Musei Petiverani . . .* (London, 1695-1703); *Gazophylacii naturae et artis . . .* (London, 1702-6); *Catalogus classicus et topicus . . .* (London, 1709-11).

[97] John Ellis, *An Essay Towards a Natural History of the Corallines . . .* (London, 1755). Peyssonnel's views were set forth in a manuscript presented to the Royal Society, "Traite du corail contenent les novelle découvertes qu'on a fait sur le corail. . . ." It was abstracted by William Watson and read to the Society in May, 1752. *R.S. Journal Book,* XXII, 99-100; printed in *Phil. Trans.,* XLVII (1751-52), 445-69.

[98] *Syst. nat.* (ed. 10), I, 80, 81.

[99] Daniel Solander and John Ellis, *The Natural History of Many Curious and Uncommon Zoophytes . . .* (London, 1786), 14-15, 28-29.

[100] *Carolina,* II, xxiv-xxxi.

[101] *Carolina,* I, ix.

[102] *Carolina,* II, *Appendix,* 20.

[103] Catesby to William Sherard, Charles City, May 10, 1723, *Sherard Letters,* II, No. 171.

enough to have been included in the body of the work.

Aside from identifying American mammals too closely with European ones, Catesby's discussion of them showed his usual discrimination. He denied, for example, the folk tale that opossums were born at the breast of the mother, citing Tyson's anatomical discussions in the *Philosophical Transactions* to prove his point.[104] On other occasions his descriptions were vivid even though his prose was stilted. In writing of "The Pol-Cat" (the Alleghenian spotted skunk) he noted that the first thing the animal did at the approach of danger was to raise its fur, but, he continued, "This menacing Behaviour, however insufficient to deter its Enemy, is seconded by a Repulse far more prevailing, for from some secret Duct, it emits such fetid Effluviums, that the Atmosphere for a large Space round shall be so infected with them, that Men and other Animals are quit of it."[105] Catesby's consideration of mammals also displayed his usual concern for utility as well as accuracy. He suggested, for example, that domestic cattle be crossed with the bison in order to produce a breed better suited to the climate of the American South.[106] This suggestion was not as implausible as it might seem, as these species can be hybridized. The suggestion certainly indicated an active and inquiring mind and made Catesby a precursor of modern experimenters.

Catesby's drawings of mammals usually failed to endow them with lifelike qualities. His two plates of "The Flying Squirrel" were, at least, well posed, and the second of these gives a strong sense of mo-

tion.[107] The others, however, tended to be stiff, lacking dynamic features. "The Pol-Cat" was apparently drawn from a stuffed pelt brought to Catesby from the mountains by Indian traders, which perhaps accounts for its lifeless pose.[108] "The Java Hare," however, was drawn from life, and was no better.[109]

Two of Catesby's mammals, "The Pol-Cat"[110] and "The Black Squirrel,"[111] furnished the only sources for Linnaean names, themselves variants of Catesby's Latin designations. In addition, the buffalo was included in Linnaeus' synonymy for *Bos bison*,[112] and "The Ground Squirrel" was used in the synonymy, with Catesby's Latin name, *Sciurus striatus*, adopted by Linnaeus without change.[113]

Thus, in some cases, Catesby's mammals, too, retained their importance, in spite of the Linnaean revolution in natural history. That they did so, together with a large part of his other fauna and some of his flora, was a tribute to Mark Catesby and to his remarkable book. With all of its faults, *The Natural History of Carolina* was a magnificent accomplishment. When we remember that Catesby was largely self-taught both in science and in art, and that *The Natural History of Carolina* was the product of his labor (and practically his alone) from the observations and sketches in the field through the writing of the text, the preparation of engravings, and even the water colors on the plates, the accomplishment appears all the more remarkable. Little wonder, then, that Mark Catesby and his book won a secure and enviable place in the natural science of the eighteenth century, a place which the chapters that follow will attempt to assess further.

[104] Edward Tyson, "The Anatomy of an Oppossum," *Phil. Trans.*, XX (1698) 105-64.

[105] *Carolina*, II, 62.

[106] *Carolina*, II, xxvii.

[107] *Carolina*, II, 76, 77; *Glaucomys volans* (Linnaeus). This is a case where Linnaeus, following Catesby, misidentified this species with a European one. *Syst. nat.* (ed. 10), I, 63, 64. Modern names of mammals are taken from Gerrit S. Miller, Jr., and Remington Kellogg, *List of North American Mammals* (*U.S. National Museum Bulletin*, No. 205, Washington, D.C., 1955).

[108] *R.S. Journal Book*, XV, 422.

[109] *Carolina*, II, *Appendix*, 18. We have not identified this animal. "The Gray Fox," *Urocyon cinereoargenteus cinereoargenteus* (Schreber), is another rather sad figure. *Ibid.*, 78.

[110] *Carolina*, II, 62; *Spilogale putorius* (Linnaeus); *Syst. nat.* (ed. 10), I, 44.

[111] *Carolina*, II, 73; *Sciurus niger niger* (Linnaeus); *Syst. nat.* (ed. 10), I, 64.

[112] *Carolina*, II, *Appendix*, 20; *Bison bison bison* (Linnaeus); *Syst. nat.* (ed. 10), I, 72.

[113] *Carolina*, II, 75; *Tamias striatus striatus* (Linnaeus); *Syst. nat.* (ed. 10), I, 64.

Note: *Catesby's Fishes*

The following identifications are based primarily on David Starr Jordan, "An Identification of the Figures of Fishes in Catesby's Natural History . . . ," *Proceedings of the U.S. National Museum*, VII (1884), 190-99, and D. S. Jordan, Barton Warren Evermann, and Howard Walton Clark, *Check List of the Fishes and Fishlike Vertebrates of North and Middle America . . .* (*Report of the U.S. Commissioner of Fisheries, 1928*, pt. II, Washington, D.C., 1930). The number at the left indicates the page and plate in *Carolina*, II.

1, fig. 1. *Umbla minor, marina maxillis longioribus*, "Barracuda," is *Sphyraena barracuda* (Walbaum). After Catesby.

1, fig. 2. *Vulpis bahamensis*, is *Albula vulpes* (Linnaeus). Based on Catesby.

2, fig. 1. *Perca marina gibbosa cinerea*, "The Margate Fish," is *Haemulon album* Cuvier and Valenciennes. Not Catesby.

2, fig. 2. *Saurus ex cinereo nigricans*, "The Sea Sparrow-Hawk," is *Synodus foetens* (Linnaeus). Catesby in synonymy.

3, fig. 1. *Perca marina, pinna dorsi divisa*, "The Croker," is *Micropogon undulatus* (Linnaeus). Catesby in synonymy.

3, fig. 2. *Perca marina rubra*, "The Squirrel," is *Holocentrus rufus* (Walbaum). After Catesby.

4, fig. 1. *Perca marina rhomboidalis fasciata*, "The Pork Fish," is *Anisotremus virginicus* (Linnaeus). Not Catesby.

4, fig. 2. *Perca marina pinnis branchialibus carens*, "The Schoolmaster," is *Lutianus apodus* (Walbaum). After Catesby.

5. *Perca marina venenosa punctata*, "The Rock-Fish," is *Trisotropis venenosus* (Linnaeus). After Catesby.

6, fig. 1. *Perca marina capite striato*, "The Grunt," is *Haemulon plumieri* (Lacépède). Not Catesby.

6, fig. 2. *Albula bahamensis*, "The Mullet," is *Querimana curema* (Cuvier and Valenciennes). Not Catesby.

7, fig. 1. *Perca marina puncticulata*, "The Negro Fish," is *Cephalopholis fulvus punctatus* (Linnaeus). Based on Catesby.

7, fig. 2. *Perca marina cauda nigra*, "The Black-Tail," is *Haemulon melanurum* (Linnaeus). Based on Catesby.

8, fig. 1. *Hirundo*, "The Flying Fish," is *Dactylopterus volitans* (Linnaeus), though this identification is open to doubt. Not Catesby.

8, fig. 2. *Perca marina sectatrix*, "The Rudder Fish," is *Kyphosus sectatrix* (Linnaeus). After Catesby.

8, fig. 3. *Perca fluviatilis gibbosa ventre luteo*, "The Fresh-Water Pearch," is *Eupomotis gibbosus* (Linnaeus). After Catesby.

9. *Turdus pinnis, branchialibus carens*, "The mangrove Snapper," is *Lutianus griseus* (Linnaeus). After Catesby.

10, fig. 1. *Turdus rhomboidalis*, "The Tang," is *Acanthurus caeruleus* Bloch and Schneider. Partly after Catesby.

10, fig. 2. *Turdus cauda convexa*, "The Yellow Fish," is *Cephalopholis fulvus fulvus* (Linnaeus). Based on Catesby.

11, fig. 1. *Turdus flavus*, "The Hog-Fish," is *Bodianus rufus* (Linnaeus). After Catesby.

11, fig. 2. *Turdus cinereus peltatus*, "The Shad," is *Gerres cinereus* (Walbaum). After Catesby.

12, fig. 1. *Turdus oculo radiato*, "The Pudding-Wife," is *Iridio radiata* (Linnaeus). Based on Catesby.

12, fig. 2. *Alburnus americanus*, "The Carolina Whiting," is *Menticirrhus americanus* (Linnaeus). Based on Catesby.

13. *Mormyrus ex cinereo nigricans*, "The Bone-Fish," is possibly *Ulaema lefroyi* (Goode). Not Catesby.

14, fig. 1. *Cugupuguacu brasil*, "The Hind," is *Promicrops itaiara* (Lichtenstein). Not Catesby.

14, fig. 2. *Saltatrix*, "Skipjack," is *Pomatomus saltatrix* (Linnaeus). Based on Catesby.

15. *Suillus*, "The great Hog-Fish," is *Lachnolaimus maximus* (Walbaum). After Catesby.

16. *Aurata bahamensis*, "The Porgy," is *Calamus calamus* Cuvier and Valenciennes. Not Catesby.

17, fig. 1. *Salpa purpurascens variegata*, "The Lane-Snapper," is *Lutianus synagris* (Linnaeus). After Catesby.

17, fig. 2. *Petimbuabo brasil*, "The Tobaccopipe-Fish," is *Fistularia tabacaria* (Linnaeus). Catesby in synonymy.

18. *Novacula caerulea*, "The Blue Fish," is *Scarus caeruleus* (Bloch). After Catesby.

19. *Unicornis, piscis bahamensis*, "The Bahama Unicorn Fish," is *Osbeckia scripta* (Osbeck). Not Catesby.

20. *Muraena maculata, nigra et viridis*, "The Muray," is *Gymnothorax funebris* Ranzani. Not Catesby.

21. *Muraena maculata nigra*, "The black Murey," is *Gymnothorax moringa* (Cuvier). After Catesby.

22. *Turdus oculo radiato*, "The Old Wife," is *Balistes vetula* Linnaeus. Not Catesby.

23. *Bagre secundae speciei marggr. affinis*, "The Cat Fish," is *Haustor catus* (Linnaeus). Based on Catesby.

24. *Harengus minor, bahamensis*, "The Pilchard," is probably *Harengula sardina* Poey. Not Catesby.

25. *Anthea quartus rondeletii,* "The Mutton Fish," is *Lutianus analis* (Cuvier and Valenciennes). Not Catesby.

26. *Remora,* "The Sucking-Fish," is *Remora remora* (Linnaeus). Catesby in synonymy.

27. *Solea lunata et punctata,* "The Sole," is *Platophrys lunatus* (Linnaeus). Based on Catesby.

28. *Orbis laevis variegatus,* "The Globe Fish," is *Cheilichthys testudineus* (Linnaeus). Not Catesby.

29. *Psittacus piscis viridis, bahamensis,* "The Parrot Fish," is *Sparisoma viride* (Bonnaterre). After Catesby.

30. *Acus maxima, squammosa, viridis,* "The green Gar-Fish," is *Lepisosteus osseus* (Linnaeus). Based on Catesby.

31. *An Acarauna major pinnis cornutis; an Paru brasiliensibus,* "The Angel Fish," is *Angelichthys ciliaris* (Linnaeus). Not Catesby.

Appendix, 19, fig. 1. *Cataphractus americanus.* Unidentifiable.

Appendix, 19, fig. 2. *Vipera marina,* "The Viper-Mouth." Unidentifiable.

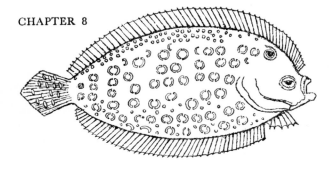

CHAPTER 8

Mark Catesby and the Natural History Circle

Science is itself cosmopolitan, and during Mark Catesby's lifetime the naturalists, more than the devotees of the other branches of natural philosophy, formed an international brotherhood. This followed from the status of the sciences involved, as both botany and zoology were in a period of collection and classification which involved gathering data from all over the world. Common problems and common interests fostered ties which bound together the naturalists of all nations. These connections were further strengthened by the necessity to correspond and to send the actual specimens involved. Only a few journals were devoted to the natural sciences, and these, together with the transactions of the academies, offered relatively small opportunity to spread the news of discoveries; consequently, an active and well-organized system of international correspondence was not only desirable but also a necessity.

If the fraternity of naturalists was cosmopolitan, it was also democratic. In it, tradesmen mingled easily with gentlemen, apothecaries shared intelligence with

noble lords, and simple carpenters contributed as much as highly placed baronets. A man of the "middling sort," such as Catesby's friend and fellow delineator of birds, George Edwards, might proudly proclaim that, though his work had brought him into contact with the mighty, he had always maintained his proper station in life. Even though he did not lose his respect for his betters, the conservative Edwards had associated with such powerful figures as the Duke of Richmond and Sir Hans Sloane.[1] Catesby himself, though born the son of a gentleman, had, nevertheless, so impoverished himself through his devotion to natural history that he was essentially déclassé. Yet he, too, mixed with the great in the Royal Society or in the informally organized, but nevertheless real, world-wide society of naturalists.

Possibly this arose in part from the fact that Mark Catesby lived during a period of transition in the sciences comprising natural history. Botany, for example, was a relatively uncomplicated art which a man could master — at the collector's level, at least — with no formal training beyond the knowledge of a little Latin. Even John Bartram, unschooled as he

[1] George Edwards, *Gleanings of Natural History* (3 pts., London, 1758-64), pt. II, ii-iv.

was, could learn enough of this language to make out a simple description.[2] This, plus the fact that botany — indeed all of natural history — involved outdoor activity, made it a favorite avocation of country gentlemen as well. The situation changed, though, or was in the process of changing, by the end of Catesby's life, as Peter Collinson complained to Linnaeus in 1754:

I have had the pleasure of reading your *Species Plantarum,* a very useful and laborious work. But, my dear friend, we that admire you are much concerned that you should perplex the delightful science of Botany with changing names that have been well received, and adding new names quite unknown to us. Thus Botany, which was a pleasant study and attainable, by most men, is now become, by alterations and new names, the study of a man's life, and none now but real professors can pretend to attain it.[3]

The day of the gifted amateur, of the self-taught botanist, was ending, and the professionalization of botany was beginning. This professionalization — in part the result of the Linnaean revolution — would soon make men like Bartram and even Catesby obsolete. Had Mark Catesby been born a half-century later, his accomplishments might well have been impossible. As it was, his talents earned him a secure position within the natural history circle.

Catesby had one important advantage in this matter: he was English. England maintained an especially favored position in studies of nature despite the fact that, after the death of John Ray, leadership in systematic natural history passed to the Continent. She maintained renowned botanical gardens, and, more than that, her colonies and commerce gave her easy access to the natural produce of the entire world. These matters alone, however, would not have given England her pre-eminence in collecting exotic speci-

mens and disseminating knowledge of them had it not been for the initiative shown by the Royal Society of London and of a group of scientific entrepreneurs closely associated with the Society. During Catesby's lifetime, this group included James Petiver, Sir Hans Sloane, William Sherard, and Peter Collinson. All of these men carried on a tremendous correspondence in the interests of natural history. Petiver had some eighty correspondents in the New World alone,[4] and, while his great period of activity was largely at an end before Catesby's really started, he did help to publicize Catesby's efforts in Virginia.[5]

Catesby's connections with all of these scientific promoters were close and especially significant for him. William Sherard was, of course, the first and, for Catesby, perhaps the most important of the group. After his own introduction to Catesby through Samuel Dale, it was he who really made possible the trip to Carolina and thus enabled Catesby's talents to flower. He did more than this, however, as, in the course of raising subscriptions for the journey to America, it was necessary to bring Catesby's name to the attention of the Royal Society and the collectors and botanists around London. While Catesby was in Carolina, Sherard helped to spread knowledge of his activities throughout the scientific world. He published an account of some of Catesby's collections in the *Philosophical Transactions,* so that interested botanists could learn of the activities of the collector in America.[6] More than that, Sherard shared his receipts from Catesby with many of his circle of "Curious Correspondents," a circle which ranged from America through all of Europe, as far as Aleppo in the Levant.[7] Of course he sent items to English friends who had not subscribed to Catesby's

[2] See James Logan to John Bartram, Stenton, June 19, 1736, in Darlington, *Memorials,* 307-8; Earnest Earnest, *John and William Bartram . . .* (Philadelphia, 1941), 7-9.

[3] Collinson to Linnaeus, London, April 20, 1754, in Smith, *Corresp. Linnaeus,* I, 31.

[4] Raymond P. Stearns, "James Petiver, Promoter of Natural Science," *Proceedings of the American Antiquarian Society,* n.s., LXII (1952), 243-365.

[5] James Petiver, "Botanicum hortense, IV," *Phil. Trans.,* XXIX (1715), 357-59, 362.

[6] William Sherard, "A Further Account of the Same Tree [the "Poyson Wood"]," *Phil. Trans.,* XXXI (1721), 147.

[7] "The Names of Dr. Wm. Sherard's Curious Correspondents," *Sherard Letters,* IV, No. 465a, addressed to John Ellis, *c.* 1725, was incomplete but listed some thirty-nine widely scattered correspondents.

expedition, such as Dr. Richard Richardson, the physician, botanist, and antiquary of North Bierly, Yorkshire.[8] However, these activities did not stop at the English Channel but extended to many of the leading Continental naturalists. While Catesby was still in Carolina, Sherard sent some of his collections to the great Hermann Boerhaave in Leyden, to Caspar Commelin in Amsterdam, and to Johann Philip Breynius and Jakob Theodor Klein in Danzig.[9] Thus, through the kind offices of William Sherard, Catesby's reputation spread afar before the publication of *The Natural History of Carolina* and even before his return to England from America.

Sir Hans Sloane's activity as a promoter of natural science spanned a period of at least sixty years up to his death in 1753.[10] He was easily the most influential of Catesby's patrons and friends. As a Court Physician, his popularity was sufficient to merit his being made a Baronet — the first physician to be so honored — and Physician General to the Army. In his professional capacity he also served many years as President of the College of Physicians, from which post he was able to aid Catesby's fellow ornithological illustrator, George Edwards, who served for many years as librarian to the college while acting informally as secretary to Sloane.[11] Aside from his profession, though, he was a natural scientist in his own right, the author of *The Natural History of Jamaica* as well as of many contributions to the *Philosophical Transactions*. As a patron of science in general he served the Royal Society well as Secretary, Vice-President, and finally as President from 1727 to 1741. An almost unparalleled collector of all sorts of curiosities, Sloane's need for correspondents was great. It

was, of course, this need which made him, next to Sherard, the major subscriber to Catesby's expedition to Carolina. After Catesby's return from Carolina, Sloane continued his assistance, though in a different manner. Sloane's elevation to the presidency of the Royal Society occurred in the year after Catesby returned, and from this privileged position Sloane was able to assist the struggling artist and author to strengthen his ties with the natural history circle and with science in general. As has been indicated previously, Sloane and his protégés played a large part in Catesby's early contacts with the Royal Society and in his election as F.R.S.[12] The added prestige and widened acquaintanceship which this gave Catesby made possible a greater number of subscribers for his *Natural History*.

Even later, Sloane was able, through his connections on the Continent, to increase the circulation and influence of *The Natural History of Carolina* and to keep its author in contact with the work of European naturalists. Sloane maintained a rather extensive correspondence with Johann Amman, the young Swiss physician who had worked with him after having studied under Boerhaave at Leyden. In 1733 Amman moved to St. Petersburg, where he became professor of botany,[13] and began an account of the Russian flora, a part of which appeared as the *Stirpium rariorum* in 1739; but this was cut short by Amman's death in 1741, apparently the victim of the harsh climate about which he had complained to Sloane.[14] Catesby had known Amman in London, and, indeed, Amman later corresponded with Catesby,[15] although most of their transactions were carried on through Sloane. Possibly it was Sloane who first suggested that Amman subscribe to *The*

[8] *MS Radcliffe Trust*, C. IV, fols. 84, 86; C. V, fol. 42.

[9] *MS Radcliffe Trust*, C. V, fols. 87, 98; *Sherard Letters*, I, 59, 95; II, 159.

[10] Gavin Rylands de Beer, *Sir Hans Sloane and the British Museum* (London, 1953), 83-107.

[11] George Edwards, *A Natural History of Uncommon Birds* (4 pts., London, 1743-51), pt. III, 121-24.

[12] The summary of Sloane's career is from de Beer, *Sir Hans*

Sloane, passim.

[13] Sloane to Richard Richardson, Aug. 7, 1733, in Nichols, *Illust. Lit. Hist.*, I, 287.

[14] Johann Amman, *Stirpium rariorum in Imperio Rutheno . . .* (St. Petersburg, 1739); Amman to Sloane, St. Petersburg, Jan. 24, 1741, *Sloane* 4056, fol. 355.

[15] *R.S. Journal Book*, XVI, 201-2.

Natural History of Carolina,[16] and certainly it was through the intermediary efforts of Sir Hans that Amman received successive parts of the work.[17] In addition, Sloane relayed to Catesby the questions of Amman about American plants in the garden or in the hortus siccus of the Academy at St. Petersburg. Thus, in 1740, he promised Amman, apparently at the latter's request, that he would ask Catesby whether he had noticed the smell of camphor in the root of the tulip tree.[18]

Sloane was also instrumental in sending *The Natural History of Carolina* to Johann Philip Breynius of Danzig. Breynius, a member of a famous Danzig family of botanists, was a highly regarded Fellow of the Royal Society to whose *Transactions* he often contributed.[19] As in the case of Amman, Sloane sent the successive parts of Catesby's work to Breynius as they appeared along with the *Philosophical Transactions* and other leading English publications in natural history.[20] Breynius, who belonged to a very active group of naturalists in the Baltic City (which included Jakob Theodor Klein), thought very highly of Catesby's book, calling it "that very fine and precious Work. . . ."[21]

Through Sloane's efforts also, Catesby's work reached Paris, the center of European culture. Sir Hans sent *The Natural History* as a gift to Claude Joseph Geoffroy, a member of the *Académie* and the author of books on botany, pharmacy, and chemistry.[22] The products of Catesby's American correspondence reached Paris through Sloane also, for the benefit of the *Jardin du Roi*. In 1737 the great physician sent some sixty packets of seeds which Catesby had received from Virginia to Antoine de Jussieu, who had succeeded the renowned Tournefort as head of the garden.[23]

In addition to maintaining Catesby's contacts in Europe and increasing the circulation and influence of *The Natural History of Carolina*, Sloane probably continued to aid Catesby financially by employing him to draw curiosities for his museum. Certainly he aided George Edwards in this manner.[24] In any event, there were among the items in Sloane's hoard, which was purchased to form the basis of the British Museum, a number of drawings by Catesby. Most of these later found their way into *The Natural History of Carolina*, but were probably drawn by Catesby at Sloane's request from items that the renowned physician kept in his cabinets.[25]

Next to William Sherard and Sir Hans Sloane, Peter Collinson contributed greatly to Catesby's career as a scientist. This busy merchant, reared in the gentle ways of the Society of Friends, was more than a friend to American natural science. With something over a hundred correspondents in America and Europe, he provided a clearinghouse of almost unbelievable proportions in the materials of natural history — unbelievable in that he was not a man of leisure, but a busy mercer and haberdasher.[26] Collin-

[16] Amman to Sloane, St. Petersburg, June 12, 1734, *Sloane* 4053, fol. 231.

[17] Same to same, Aug. 16, 1736, *Sloane* 4054, fol. 297; same to same, Nov. 7, 1739, *ibid.*, 4056, fols. 132-33.

[18] Sloane to Amman, London, June 30, 1740, *Sloane* 4069, fol. 48.

[19] *Phil. Trans.*, XXIV (1705), 2045-55; XXVII (1712), 447-59; XXXIII (1725), 353-60; XXXIV (1726), 154-56; XXXVII (1732), 444-47; XL (1737), 124-28; XLI (1741), 557; *The Record of the Royal Society of London* (ed. 4, London, 1940), 389.

[20] See Breynius to Sloane, Danzig, Nov. 18, 1733, *Sloane* 4053, fol. 84, and *ibid.*, fol. 321; 4055, fols. 232-33; 4056, fols. 96, 137-38; 4068, fol. 321.

[21] Same to same, Danzig, Nov. 21, 1739, *Sloane* 4056, fols. 137-38.

[22] Geoffroy to Sloane, Paris, April 8, 1736, *Sloane* 4054, fol. 28; Sloane to Geoffroy, Feb. 10, 1736/37, *ibid.*, 4068, fol. 307.

[23] Sloane to Jussieu, April 16, 1737, *Sloane* 4068, fol. 308.

[24] Edwards, *Gleanings of Natural History*, pt. II, iii-iv.

[25] See "Drawings of Fishes," *Add. MS* 5267 (British Museum), fols. 83, 93, 99, *et passim;* "Drawings of Insects, Petrofac., Corals, Etc.," *ibid.*, 5271, fols. 174, 315, 319-21, *et passim;* "Drawings of Plants by Massey, Catesby, Etc.," *ibid.*, 5283, fols. 46, 59, *et passim*.

[26] Collinson lacks an adequate biography. Norman G. Brett-James, *Life of Peter Collinson* . . . (London, [1926]), is, at best, a collection of antiquary's notes. Earl G. Swem, ed.,

son's aid to the Library Company of Philadelphia and his patronage of Benjamin Franklin are well known; but his aid to American botanists played a far more important part in his life. This was particularly true in the case of John Bartram, who was, in the words of Collinson's friend, Dr. John Fothergill, the creature of Collinson.[27] By securing regular customers for the plants which Bartram collected, Collinson enabled the Pennsylvania naturalist to live by his botanical work.[28]

This combination of Collinson and Bartram provided the source of more plates for *The Natural History of Carolina* than any other except, of course, Catesby's own exertions in America. At least ten of the items figured in the second volume were specimens which were grown in Collinson's garden at Peckham in Surrey.[29] At first, Catesby and Bartram dealt principally through Collinson. The Pennsylvania collector was first made aware of Catesby's work when, in 1737, Collinson admonished him to wait upon Thomas Penn — another of Catesby's subscribers — in his "best habits," so he might see *The Natural History of Carolina*.[30] During the next few years, Catesby depended on Collinson to transmit his requests, particularly for a specimen of the papaw, to Pennsylvania.[31] Finally, on May 20, 1740, Catesby initiated a correspondence with Bartram in asking that he send him specimens, "though not without an intention of retaliation." He proposed to send a section of his *Natural History* yearly in return for Bartram's efforts on his behalf.[32] Possibly Catesby

feared that this first letter had not reached its intended receiver, as he enclosed a copy of it with another which he sent in February, 1740/41.[33]

Thus began a fruitful exchange which lasted at least until 1747 and possibly until Catesby's death two years later.[34] Bartram was pleased with their arrangement, which, though it did not enrich him, added Catesby's "excellent performance" to his meager botanical library. He regretted only that their correspondence had not begun ten year earlier.[35] Catesby also profited from their correspondence in getting from Bartram minute descriptions of the flowers of plants which he could not bring to blossom in England. His letters to Bartram asked for information about a good many American plants and animals which he had not seen. He also wrote Bartram of his experiences in growing American plants in England and gave him instructions about packing birds and other zoological specimens for shipment.[36] As might be expected, their correspondence often miscarried. On April 23, 1746, Bartram inquired of Collinson: "How doth our friend Catesby do? He wont speak a word to me nowadays. He hath had several opportunities, within these two years, of writing to me, and I have sent some curiosities to him every year."[37] The explanation from Catesby was already on its way, however. Both Bartram's plants and the letters and books which Catesby had sent during those two years had been lost at sea.[38] This was, after all, a time of war, which

"Brothers of the Spade . . . ," *Proceedings of the American Antiquarian Society*, LVIII (1948), 17-190, provides an excellent short biography (19-26) and fine bibliographical notes (109-22) on Collinson. See *ibid.*, 154-56, for a list of Collinson's correspondents.

[27] John Fothergill, *Some Account of the Late Peter Collinson* (London, 1770), 11.
[28] Brett-James, *Collinson*, 53.
[29] *Carolina*, II, 56, 71, 72, 73, 98; *Appendix*, 1, 4, 5, 6, 17.
[30] Collinson to Bartram, London, Sept. 8, 1737, in Darlington, *Memorials*, 100-101.
[31] Same to same, Jan. 26, 1738/39, in Darlington, *Memorials*, 123-24; same to same, April 12, 1739, *ibid.*, 128-31; same

to same, Sept. 2, 1739, *ibid.*, 133-35.
[32] Darlington, *Memorials*, 319-20.
[33] Darlington, *Memorials*, 320.
[34] Bartram informed Cadwallader Colden on Oct. 6, 1747, that he had recently received a letter from Catesby. *Colden Papers, 1743-1747* (*Collections of the New York Historical Society, 1919*, New York, 1920), 270-72.
[35] Bartram to Catesby, [1741?], in Darlington, *Memorials*, 321.
[36] Catesby to Bartram, [1741 or 1742], in Darlington, *Memorials*, 321-22.
[37] Darlington, *Memorials*, 177.
[38] Catesby to Bartram, April 15, 1746, in Darlington, *Memorials*, 323-24.

added to the difficulties of transatlantic communication. Thus, while the ties between the naturalists of the New World and Old were close, they were also subject to many hazards.

Actually, as Catesby was too busy with his *Natural History* to transmit all of his wants personally to Bartram, many of his requests continued to go through Collinson, who somehow found the time.[39] Collinson remained at the center of the relationship between the two men, just as he was the crucial tie between Catesby and many other naturalists on both continents.

Catesby's main interests lay in North America and his own correspondence with the naturalists of that continent was much heavier than with those of Europe. He was favored here by his connections in Virginia. During the first few years after his return from Carolina and the Bahamas, Catesby was apparently too involved in the preparation of his *Natural History* to find time to cultivate all his ties with the New World. By about 1730, though, the situation had changed. He had finished at least the first section of his book and could offer it to his old botanizing companions in exchange for specimens. This he did with John Custis of Williamsburg, the gardener and amateur botanist with whom he had worked during his stay in Virginia.[40] Custis answered in June, 1730, thanking Catesby for his "pretty present" — probably the first part of *The Natural History of Carolina*. "I will put them in frames and glasses," he wrote, "and keep them in memory of you; and shall always esteem them as a very valuable part of my furniture. . . ."[41] This correspondence

may have continued beyond this first exchange, though in all probability Catesby depended upon Peter Collinson to convey his later requests to Custis. Five years after these first letters, Collinson asked Custis to procure some seed from a "sorell tree" which Catesby had seen between Williamsburg and York, and later the two men exchanged a series of letters in a fruitless effort to find a peach-colored dogwood which Catesby had planted in Custis' garden.[42] Catesby drew the blossom, but not from life. The efforts of his friends produced nothing but the suggestion that it was "a common dogwood in decay. . . ." The plants which Catesby had set out in Custis' garden years before had never bloomed, and when Custis sent them — bloomless as they were — they were lost at sea.[43] While Custis profited from Catesby's work, the results of their correspondence upon *The Natural History of Carolina* were small at best.

John Clayton, whose importance in Virginia botany was far greater than that of Custis, played a correspondingly greater part in Catesby's work. Clayton was one of the better botanists produced in the colonies. He began primarily as a collector, sending plants to Johann Friedrich Gronovius in Leyden, who, with the aid of Linnaeus, arranged them in the *Flora Virginica*, published in two parts in 1739 and 1743.[44] Clayton soon passed beyond the collector's stage, however, and became a systematic botanist as well. The second edition of the *Flora Virginica*, published in 1762, was principally the result of his own additions to the earlier production, enlarged also by the efforts of Collinson, John Ellis, and other English

[39] Collinson to Bartram, London, Feb. 25, 1741/42, in Darlington, *Memorials*, 139-42; same to same, London, March 3, 1741/42, *ibid.*, 150-53; same to same, April 25, 1742, *ibid.*, 153-54; same to same, London, Jan. 16, 1743/44, *ibid.*, 166-67.

[40] Catesby's letter is not extant.

[41] Custis to Catesby, June, 1730, in Swem, ed., "Brothers of the Spade," 39.

[42] Collinson to Custis, London, Dec. 15, 1735, in Swem, ed.,

"Brothers of the Spade," 45-48; Custis to Collinson, [July 29, 1736], *ibid.*, 47-50. The "sorell tree" is *Oxydendrum arboreum* (Linnaeus).

[43] Collinson to Custis, London, Jan. 25, 1736/37, in Swem, ed., "Brothers of the Spade," 57-58; same to same, London, Feb. 20, 1737/38, *ibid.*, 66-68; Custis to Collinson, [1738], *ibid.*, 70-72; Collinson to Custis, London, Jan. 25, 1738/39, *ibid.*, 70-71; *Carolina*, I, 27.

[44] Gronovius to Richard Richardson, Sept. 2, 1738, in Smith, *Corresp. Linnaeus*, II, 179.

botanists.[45] Though the Clayton-Catesby correspondence has not survived — except in fragments which were included in *The Natural History of Carolina* — it was apparently carried on advantageously for a number of years. Catesby received the *Magnolia flore albo* from Clayton in 1736 and, seven years later, a specimen of *Hamamelis*. In all, three plants and one bird — all in the *Appendix* to *The Natural History of Carolina* — owed their places to Clayton's exertions in behalf of his English friend.[46] Catesby was, however, able to reciprocate. Clayton received a copy of *The Natural History of Carolina* inscribed to him by the author.[47] On at least one occasion, in December, 1744, Catesby also aided in the transmission of Clayton's specimens to Gronovius, although in all probability this traffic ordinarily passed through the hands of Peter Collinson.[48]

Catesby also renewed his association with William Byrd during this time. Their friendship, which had flourished in their walks around Byrd's plantation and their travels together during the early part of Catesby's stay in Virginia, had languished when Byrd traveled to London in support of his struggle against Governor Spotswood and Catesby's brother-in-law, William Cocke. Byrd did not return to Virginia until Catesby himself was ready to sail for England. Probably they renewed their relationship around 1730 when Catesby sought subscribers for *The Natural History,* as Byrd was listed among the "encouragers" of that work.[49] Certainly they must have corresponded prior to 1735 or 1736 when Byrd wrote to an agent in England, "I wish you would be so kind as to call upon my Friend, Mr. Cat[e]sby, now

and then to know if he has any Letter or commands for me. He is Such a Philosopher that he needs a monitor to put him in mind of his Friend."[50] The complaint was probably justified, as Catesby's "philosophy" did take up most of his time and prevent him from writing to America as often and at as great length as did Peter Collinson. Nonetheless, the exchange was resumed shortly afterward. Its immediate occasion was that Catesby had seen the rough journal which Byrd had kept as Commissioner to settle the boundary between Virginia and North Carolina in 1728, and which served as the basis for his long-unpublished *History of the Dividing Line.*[51] Byrd sent the manuscript to Peter Collinson in 1736 with instructions to show it to no one save Sir Charles Wager;[52] but in spite of his instructions, Collinson allowed Catesby to see it. Sometime early in 1737 Catesby wrote Byrd about the journal and apparently about other matters closer to his work on the second volume of *The Natural History of Carolina.* Byrd answered, "I am obliged to you for the Compliments you are pleased to make to my poor performances. 'Tis a Sign you never saw them that you judge so favourable." He warned Catesby, however, not to expect more, as he was engaged in founding a city at the falls of the James River — the future Richmond — and in planting a colony of "Switzers" upon the Roanoke.[53] His protestations, however, did not quite correspond to his ambitions. While his *History* was never published during his lifetime, Byrd had high hopes for it. A short time later (June 5, 1737) he wrote to Collinson: "I intend this next Winter to cover this dry Skeleton, and

[45] Collinson to Linnaeus, Dec. 25, 1757, in Smith, *Corresp. Linnaeus,* I, 42; Ellis to Linnaeus, April 25, 1758, *ibid.,* 93.

[46] Cucumber tree, *Magnolia acuminata* (Linnaeus); *Carolina,* II, *Appendix,* 15; Witch hazel, *Hamamelis virginiana* (Linnaeus), *ibid.,* 2, 12, 15, 16.

[47] Clayton's descendants had this copy as late as 1906. Swem, ed., "Brothers of the Spade," 176.

[48] Catesby to Gronovius, London, Dec. 20, 1744, *Personal Miscellany* (MS in the Library of Congress), II, 36-G1.

[49] *Carolina,* I, unpaged, preceding Preface.

[50] Byrd to Capt. Porford, [1735 or 1736], in "Letters of William Byrd 2nd," *Va. Mag.,* IX (1901), 128.

[51] See William K. Boyd, ed., *William Byrd's Histories of the Dividing Line Betwixt Virginia and North Carolina* (Raleigh, 1929), for both *The History of the Dividing Line* and *The Secret History of the Dividing Line.*

[52] Byrd to Collinson, Virginia, July 18, 1736, in "Letters of the Byrd Family," *Va. Mag.,* XXXVI (1928), 353-55.

[53] "Part of a Letter," Byrd to Catesby, Virginia, June 27, 1737, *R.S. Letter Book,* XXIV, 115-18.

make it appear more to advantage; and, as I shall occasionally mention several Plants and Animals, I shou'd be obliged to my Friend Mr. Catesby if he'll be so good as to add the figures of them."[54] Unfortunately this combination of Byrd's prose with Catesby's art was never realized. Had it been, it might have made a considerable addition to early American letters.

Possibly Catesby gave too much credence to Byrd's opinions. He disagreed with Byrd as to whether good wine might be produced in Virginia, but Byrd's strong beliefs in the power of rattlesnakes to fascinate their prey was probably one of the main reasons Catesby would not completely deny it. In addition, though Catesby forwarded to Byrd Sir Hans Sloane's correct opinion that the American ginseng was not the same as that of China, he accepted Byrd's contrary belief.[55] The error was not a serious one, however, as the two plants belonged to the same genus, and the American variety later became a staple of the China trade.

Even beyond these excellent contacts in America through Byrd, Custis, Clayton, and Bartram, Mark Catesby had the further advantage of his family connections in Virginia. His sister Elizabeth, who, after the death of her first husband, William Cocke, in 1720, became the wife of John Holloway, supplied him with a number of items which he required for his *Natural History*, as well as seeds and plants for his gardening activities.[56] The flying squirrel, which Catesby figured twice for the second volume of his work, probably came from her hands, as did such other curiosities as the deer horn which Catesby passed on to his old friend Samuel Dale, the apothecary.[57] There is no evidence that Elizabeth Hollo-

way was especially interested in natural history, but she was helpful to her younger brother by supplying him with fresh specimens of flora and fauna from Virginia. She was also a subscriber to his work — probably a paying one, in view of her relative affluence and Mark's poverty.[58]

The children of Elizabeth Cocke-Holloway also supplied their uncle with specimens and information. This was particularly true of the eldest daughter, Elizabeth, whose second husband, Thomas Jones, had been Catesby's gardening companion during his early days in Virginia and was also in close contact with John Custis. Catesby probably saw his niece while she was in England shortly after his return there; and, after her return to Virginia, he continued to correspond with her. As in the case of most of his American correspondents, the exchange of items was on the basis of *quid pro quo*. Catesby asked for such items as "popler and Cypress seeds with some White Walnuts," and, later, a ground squirrel, "if it lies in your way conveniently to send me one." In return he sent the parts of his *Natural History* as they appeared, and seeds of English plants for the Jones's garden.[59] Whether the other children of William and Elizabeth Cocke did as well by their uncle as Elizabeth Cocke Jones is impossible to say, for most of her papers have survived, while those of the others have disappeared. Apparently, though, Catesby did receive word from some of them, especially Ann Cocke, the wife of William Woodward, either directly or through his sister or Mrs. Jones.[60]

Even among his English friends, some of Catesby's most important ties were essentially colonial. Peter Collinson, with his manifold ties to British North

[54] Byrd to Collinson, Virginia, July 5, 1737, *R.S. Letter Book*, XXIV, 217-19.

[55] *R.S. Letter Book*, XXIV, 115-18; Byrd to Sloane, Virginia, May 31, 1737, *Sloane* 4055, fols. 112-13; same to same, Aug. 20, 1737, *ibid.*, fol. 367; *Carolina*, II, *Appendix*, 16. The Chinese ginseng is *Panax schinseng*, while Catesby's is *Panax quinquefolium*.

[56] Jones, *Capt. Roger Jones*, 117.

[57] Samuel Dale to Hans Sloane, Braintree, March 26, 1732, *Sloane* 4025, fol. 98b; see also *R.S. Letter Book*, XX, 90-96; and *Phil. Trans.*, XXXIX (1736), 384-89; *Carolina*, II, 76-77.

[58] *Carolina*, I, unpaged, preceding Preface.

[59] Catesby to Elizabeth Jones, Hoxton, March 1, 1729/30, in Jones, *Capt. Roger Jones*, 218-19; same to same, Dec. 30, 1731, *ibid.*, 219-20.

[60] *Carolina*, II, vii.

America, belonged to this category even though he never visited the New World. Aside from Collinson, the English naturalist with whom Catesby was most profitably connected in his later years was John Mitchell, who returned to England in 1746 after years in Virginia.[61] As his return was only a little more than three years before Catesby's death, their relationship was necessarily brief. It has been suggested that the two men had known one another in Virginia and even traveled together to England in 1719. But this appears unlikely, as it is based upon conjectures that Mitchell was born in Virginia rather than in Scotland or England and upon the nearness of Catesby's return to Mitchell's probable matriculation at Edinburgh in 1720.[62] However improbable such early contact between them may have been, they must have known of each other and possibly even corresponded while Mitchell was practicing as a physician in Urbanna, Virginia. Certainly Mitchell knew of *The Natural History of Carolina* while he was still in America, as he used it in his botanical writings.[63] In addition, Mitchell was acquainted with several of Catesby's other American correspondents — Custis, Byrd, Clayton, and Bartram — and he, in turn, corresponded with Collinson and Dillenius in England.[64]

As might be expected of men with so many interests in common, Catesby and Mitchell collaborated closely during those few years in which they had the opportunity. Catesby was probably the principal beneficiary, as Mitchell had the benefit both of recent residence in America and, more remotely, formal studies at Leyden, where he had acquired scientific training which gave him an advantage over most of the botanists of his time in the British colonies of America. Mitchell's arrival in England was too late to have been of any assistance in the production of *The Natural History of Carolina*. However, Catesby added new botanical materials gained from Mitchell to the *Appendix* of his great work and to the *Hortus Britanno-Americanus*.[65] Catesby also used Mitchell's observations on the habits of Virginia birds in his essay "Of Birds of Passage."[66] Catesby's returns for these favors were varied in nature. After his return to England, Mitchell largely turned his attention to other activities, principally to his great *Map of the British and French Dominions in North America*[67] and to three books on America which were directed primarily toward political ends.[68] Despite this change, which he probably intended to be temporary, Mitchell did not forsake natural history completely. He kept up a correspondence with Linnaeus, and to this Catesby made contributions. For example, he called Mitchell's attention to Linnaeus' description of the plant which he and Linnaeus had called the *Stewartia* but which Mitchell had included in his "Nova genera" as the *Malachodendron*.[69] Further,

[61] Note by Peter Collinson to letter of J. F. Gronovius to John Bartram, Leyden, June 2, 1746, in Darlington, *Memorials*, 354-57.

[62] Herbert Thatcher, "John Mitchell, M.D., F.R.S., of Virginia," *Va. Mag.*, XXXIX (1931), 211. This is a rather confused study even though it does make some important contributions toward untangling the details of Mitchell's life. Mark Catesby appears in it as "Charles" Catesby.

[63] See Mitchell to Dr. Charles Alston, Urbanna, Oct. 4, 1738, *Va. Mag.*, XL (1932), 50-57, and his "Nova genera plantarum," reprinted, *ibid.*, 272-74.

[64] Custis to Collinson, 1741, in Swem, ed., "Brothers of the Spade," 91-92; Collinson to Custis, London, Feb. 6, 1742/43, *ibid.*, 98-102; same to same, London, Feb. 20, 1742/43, *ibid.*, 102-3; Bartram to Mitchell, June 3, 1744, in Darlington, *Memorials*, 363-64; J. J. Dillenius, *Historia muscorum* (London, 1741), viii.

[65] *Carolina*, II, *Appendix*, 13; *Hortus Britanno-Americanus* (London, 1763).

[66] *Phil. Trans.*, XLIV, pt. 2 (1747), 444.

[67] (London, 1755).

[68] John Mitchell, *A New and Complete History of the British Empire in North America* (London, 1756); *The Contest in America Between Britain and France* (London, 1757); *The Present State of Great Britain and North America* (London, 1767). See Lyman Carrier, "Dr. John Mitchell, Naturalist, Cartographer, and Historian," *American Historical Association Annual Report for 1918* (2 vols., Washington, D.C., 1921), I, 201-19.

[69] See Mitchell to Linnaeus, London, April 6, 1747, in Smith, *Corresp. Linnaeus*, II, 443. Linnaeus eventually used both names, calling it *Stewartia* [*Stuartia*] *malachodendron*. *Species plantarum* (2 vols., Stockholm, 1753), II, 698.

he took Mitchell as his guest to meetings of the Royal Society and subsequently sponsored his candidacy as a Fellow of the Society.[70] Obviously both men profited from their association.

In England, in addition to those whose interests were essentially North American, Catesby was a member of the group of naturalists which was centered in the Royal Society, but which was also closely associated both with the antiquaries and literati of the time as well as such ordinary mortals as gardeners and nurserymen. Catesby's ties were strongest with the botanists. As a collector, he had had his beginnings with this group and, in his continuing work on *The Natural History of Carolina* and in his horticultural activities, he had maintained primary interests in common with them. His acquaintances included the leading English botanists of his day, such as John Martyn and Philip Miller, both of whom respected Catesby's abilities to the extent that they had helped to introduce him to the Royal Society.[71] Miller particularly benefited from Catesby's work as a collector. As chief of the Apothecaries' Garden at Chelsea, and, in his *Gardener's Dictionary* — probably the most popular English botanical work of the eighteenth century — Miller often noted plants which Catesby had introduced to England and borrowed freely from Catesby's descriptions of plants in *The Natural History of Carolina*.[72]

Catesby was also connected closely with Johann Jacob Dillenius, who, with his Continental training, was undoubtedly the greatest academic botanist in England. Their cooperation had begun in the 1720's while Dillenius acted as William Sherard's assistant, and it continued beyond Sherard's death. Both of Dillenius' major works owed a great deal to the activities of Mark Catesby. His *Hortus Elthamensis* included many plants which Catesby had sent from America,[73] and his magnum opus, the *Historia muscorum*, utilized specimens which Catesby had collected as well as materials from *The Natural History of Carolina*.[74]

Apart from these botanists, however, the individual who gained the most from Catesby's unselfish aid and from his example was George Edwards. Edwards built upon the advances which Catesby had made in ornithological illustration and, with a technique which was superior to Catesby's, succeeded him as the leading English ornithological artist. Catesby shared his specimens with Edwards — even some of those which he included in his own work.[75] But Catesby's help was not limited to specimens. As Edwards himself wrote:

I was discouraged, upon first thinking of this Work [*A Natural History of Uncommon Birds*], at the great Expence of graving, printing, and the other things, which I knew would be a certain Cost attended with a very uncertain Profit, till my good Friend Mr. Catesby put me on etching my Plates myself, as he had done in his Works; and not only so, but invited me to see him work at Etching, and gave me all the necessary Hints and Instructions to proceed, which Favour I think myself obliged publickly to acknowledge.[76]

Thus Catesby did for Edwards what Joseph Goupy had done for him at the inception of *The Natural History of Carolina*. In spite of the fact that their works were competitive, the two men acted in a spirit of friendly cooperation — a spirit which did not always accompany the scientific endeavors of their contemporaries.[77] This cooperation between Catesby and Edwards displayed itself in a number of ways. Catesby was a sponsor for Edwards' abortive

---

[70] *R.S. Journal Book*, XX, 171, 527.

[71] *R.S. Journal Book*, XIV, 336, 521; *Certificates* (MSS in the Library of the Royal Society of London), I, 41.

[72] See various editions, particularly ed. 3, corrected (3 vols., London, 1740-43, Vol. III, 1740), *passim;* or ed. 8 (London, 1768), *passim*.

[73] (London, 1732), 2.

[74] (London, 1741), vii. In addition to Catesby's assistance, Dillenius acknowledged the help of John Bartram, John Clayton, Peter Collinson, and John Mitchell.

[75] *Natural History of Uncommon Birds*, pt. I, 27-31; pt. II, 63; pt. III, 109; *Carolina*, II, *Appendix*, 16.

[76] *Natural History of Uncommon Birds*, pt. I, xii-xiii.

[77] William Sherard and Sir Hans Sloane were often at bitter odds, even while they both subscribed to Catesby's support.

first candidacy for membership in the Royal Society.[78] Catesby generously cited species which Edwards had drawn but which he had not.[79] Edwards, on the other hand, deferred to his older friend during Catesby's lifetime. When figuring species already drawn by Catesby, he did so only apologetically. He wrote: "I should not have presumed to re-publish any thing that was directly the same with what has been published by Mr. Catesby because I know myself not capable to add any Amendments to what he has done."[80] This deference did not extend long after Catesby's death, however, as Edwards almost immediately began to illustrate items already shown in *The Natural History of Carolina,* mostly without apology. He copied some of them directly, and contented himself with merely "improving" on others.[81]

As has already been indicated, most of Catesby's contacts with the natural history circle were in England and America. He lacked both the leisure and the inclination to correspond at great length on subjects with which he was little concerned; and for most of his life he was concerned almost exclusively with the flora and fauna of North America and the West Indies. He was far more inclined to leave his contacts with other parts of the world to those who, like Sloane and Collinson, already had extensive correspondence, or who, like John Mitchell, worked very hard to build a European reputation for themselves. Catesby did exchange ideas with a few men on the Continent, but these consumed a relatively small part of his time.

Like his earlier experience in America, at least a part of Catesby's contact with Europe was through his own family, principally at the hands of John Catesby, his eldest brother. It was perhaps a sign of the decline in the family fortune that John served in the Army as a lieutenant when he was well past sixty. In 1725, while Mark was still in America, John had been garrisoned at Berwick-on-Tweed, although earlier he had been across the Channel at Calais, probably in a private capacity.[82] In 1726, the year in which Mark returned to England, John was commissioned in Colonel Henry Grove's Regiment of Foot (the Tenth Foot), and went with them to Gibraltar in 1730, where he remained at least until 1736.[83] Mark received a number of specimens from his military brother, although, as they were not American, they were useful only for comparison with American species in *The Natural History of Carolina.*[84] Nevertheless, those items which Mark Catesby could not use were not lost to the world of science, as he passed them on to George Edwards, whose *Uncommon Birds* were not limited geographically as Catesby's had been.[85]

The only Continental naturalist with whom Catesby corresponded at any length was Johann Friedrich Gronovius. This is not surprising, as the latter's *Flora Virginica* gave Catesby and the Leyden naturalist a large area in common. Unfortunately, only fragments of their correspondence have survived. Apparently their exchange of letters was flourishing by 1735, when Gronovius sent Catesby a letter and the first edition of the *Systema naturae* of his friend and co-worker, Linnaeus.[86] Probably it had its beginnings, as was so often the case, in the efforts of Peter Collinson to promote the scientific contacts of his friends.

[78] *R.S. Certificates,* I, 286.

[79] *Carolina,* II, xxx.

[80] *Natural History of Uncommon Birds,* pt. I, 24; pt. II, 78, 80, 101.

[81] *Natural History of Uncommon Birds,* pt. III, 130, 132, 135, 141, 144, 151; pt. IV, 181, 191; *Gleanings of Natural History,* pt. I, 62, 63, 67, 70, 92, 94, 98; pt. II, 132, 135, 143, 161, 173; pt. III, 300, 319.

[82] John Catesby to Elizabeth Pratt, [Berwick], 1725, *The Papers of the Jones Family . . .* (MSS in the Library of Congress), I, No. 218.

[83] Charles Dalton, *George the First's Army, 1714-1727* (2 vols., London, 1912), II, 289-90; Richard Cannon, *Historical Record of the Tenth Foot* (London, 1847), 34-35.

[84] *Carolina,* II, *Appendix,* 11.

[85] *Natural History of Uncommon Birds,* pt. I, 27-31; pt. III, 109.

[86] *R.S. Journal Book,* XVI, 219.

The one letter from Catesby to Gronovius which has survived provides a good contrast between him and Collinson. Catesby's part of it was a simple statement written December 20, 1744, which "advertised" Gronovius of a box of seeds from John Clayton. Below this short communication, however, was a three-and-a-half-page "post script" added on Christmas Day by Collinson. This included such diverse things as an inquiry as to whether Gronovius liked the "Jam of Cranberries" which Collinson had sent him, questions concerning labels for plants, comments on a letter of Gronovius to John Bartram, recommendations for a plant from Tonkin which Collinson thought cured rabies and other disorders, a promise to forward a memorandum to Catesby, and, finally, word on the springlike weather of that December.[87] Catesby was always too matter-of-fact in his communications and too pressed for time to indulge in matters which were not to the point. Even so, his other letters to Gronovius must have been more informative than this one, as Gronovius valued both his correspondence and his friendship. After Catesby's death, Gronovius noted with a tinge of regret that now he had only Collinson left among his correspondents in London.[88] This, plus the fact that it was Gronovius who named the genus *Catesbaea* for Catesby, indicated the degree of esteem which Gronovius had for the author of *The Natural History of Carolina*.

Except for Gronovius and Johann Amman, apparently the only other Continental naturalist with whom Catesby corresponded was Linnaeus. And to him he appears to have written only once. In 1745 he sent Linnaeus a note to accompany a shipment of American plants which he had selected for the great Swedish naturalist as a gift from Dr. Isaak Lawson, their mutual friend and Linnaeus' former patron,

along with a list of plants from which Linnaeus might choose further specimens.[89] That this was the extent of their correspondence is understandable. Catesby, with his emphasis on American plants and his lack of interest in systems, had too little in common with Linnaeus to deal with him more extensively. Catesby did inquire later as to whether his shipment had reached Sweden, but this was through the good offices of John Mitchell.[90] Both Mitchell and Collinson also kept their great Swedish correspondent informed of Catesby's progress on *The Natural History of Carolina*.[91] Catesby's modesty and single-minded devotion to his own work probably prevented him from doing this himself; but surely he need have felt no modesty where Linnaeus was concerned. Linnaeus, though he had doubted Catesby's accuracy earlier in the matter of nomenclature,[92] nevertheless paid Catesby and his *Natural History* the supreme compliment — that of use.

Catesby, then, played an important supporting role in this international fraternity of naturalists. His activities were not on the grand scale of Peter Collinson, but then Collinson was almost exclusively a promoter, a broker in the ideas and things of natural history, while Catesby contributed through his book in a more original manner. Just how closely Catesby was connected with the natural history circle is nowhere better illustrated than in a letter which John Bartram wrote to Cadwallader Colden in 1745: "I find by my correspondents in Europe that they have been informed of our Phylosophical Society and have great expectation of fine accounts therefrom tho I durst not so much as mention it to my correspondents for fear it should turn out poorly, but I find the[e] mentioned [it] to Collinson, hee to Catesby, & hee to Gronovius, which was to him from Cla[y]ton."[93]

[87] *Personal Miscellany*, II, 36-G1.

[88] Gronovius to John Bartram, Leyden, July 2, 1750, in Darlington, *Memorials*, 358.

[89] London, March 26, 1745, in Smith, *Corresp. Linnaeus*, II, 440-41.

[90] Mitchell to Linnaeus, London, Sept. 20, 1748, in Smith, *Corresp. Linnaeus*, 448.

[91] Collinson to Linnaeus, April 16, 1747, in Smith, *Corresp. Linnaeus*, I, 18; Mitchell to Linnaeus, London, April 16, 1747, *ibid.*, II, 443.

[92] See Dillenius to Linnaeus, Oxford, Nov. 28, 1737, in Smith, *Corresp. Linnaeus*, 103-7.

[93] Oct. 4, 1745, in *Colden Papers, 1743-1747*, 158-60; for the history of this predecessor of the American Philosophical

That news of the abortive American Philosophical Society should have reached a scholar in the Netherlands twice, once through a chain of correspondents which involved Colden, the testy philosopher and perennial Lieutenant Governor of New York, Collinson, and again by Catesby, indicates the truly international character of the circle and the fact that

Society see Brooke Hindle, *The Pursuit of Science in Revolutionary America, 1735-1789* (Chapel Hill, N.C., 1956), 59-79.

Catesby was an important part of it. It is true that this arose, in large part, from his connection with Peter Collinson; but this connection might never have been made had Collinson failed to recognize Catesby's talents. And, in final analysis, Catesby's honored place in the natural history circle stemmed from his own extraordinary ability as displayed in *The Natural History of Carolina, Florida, and the Bahama Islands.*

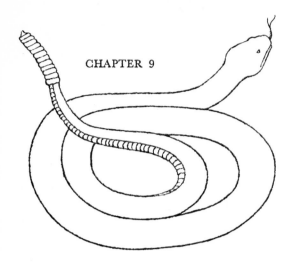

CHAPTER 9

The History of
The Natural History of Carolina

The Natural History of Carolina was the principal source of Catesby's reputation during his own lifetime and throughout the eighteenth century. As a collector, as an importer of specimens and seeds, and as a gardener, his activities were essentially ephemeral. To be sure, his accomplishments in these fields were large, and the number of American species in the Old World was increased thereby; but this was a time in which England led the world in these activities. If Catesby had not set his hands to them, they would have been accomplished by others, though perhaps not so soon. *The Natural History,* though, was a permanent and unique accomplishment, which, despite its relatively limited area, was a widely used and highly respected work in Catesby's own time and long afterward.

As might be expected, *The Natural History of Carolina* continued to exert wide influence in England after Catesby's death. Many of the naturalists whom he had known — men like Peter Collinson, George

Edwards, and Philip Miller — bridged the gap between Catesby's generation and the group which was active in the late eighteenth and early nineteenth century so that the element of friendship played some part in perpetuating the popularity of his work.[1] Certainly these friendships helped to account for the tenacity with which many English naturalists held to *The Natural History of Carolina.* In 1753, for example, when Linnaeus changed the generic name of Catesby's *Meadia* to *Dodecatheon,*[2] British botanists howled in protest. Their outrage arose partly from the apparent slight to Dr. Richard Mead, for whom Catesby had named the plant; but it was also at Linnaeus' substitution of a name which they described variously as obsolete and barbarian for one invented by their dead compatriot.[3]

Mere friendship, however, was not enough to account for the popularity of Catesby's work in England. Booksellers, impelled by the hard commercial realities of their trade, found it to be a saleable item.

---

[1] Collinson died in 1768, Miller in 1771, and Edwards in 1773.

[2] *Dodecatheon meadia* Linnaeus; *Species plantarum* (2 vols., Stockholm, 1753), I, 144; *Carolina,* II, *Appendix,* 1.

[3] John Ellis to Linnaeus, in Smith, *Corresp. Linnaeus,* I, 85-

88; Earl of Bute to Peter Collinson, *c.* 1755, *ibid.,* 35; Peter Ascanius to Linnaeus, London, April 7, 1755, in *Bref och Skrifvelser af och til Carl von Linne* (Theodor Magnus Fries and Johann Markus Hulth, eds., 2 vols., Uppsala, 1907-22), II, pt. 1, 101-2.

A further indication of continuing interest in Catesby was seen in the *Gentleman's Magazine* which, during the four years which followed Catesby's death late in 1749, printed a number of Catesby's plates and exerpts from his descriptive text. Items of natural history were popular in eighteenth-century England, and the fact that Edward Cave, who published the *Gentleman's Magazine,* found Catesby's birds and plants worth printing demonstrated a popular interest in these things which, in the form in which they were first published, were beyond the financial capacities of most men.[4]

Moreover, *The Natural History of Carolina* went through two more English editions after the death of its author. The first of these editions, "Revis'd" by George Edwards, appeared in London in 1754.[5] The prints, being made from Catesby's plates, were unchanged from those in the original, although the numbers which had appeared incorrectly in the earlier volumes were set right.[6] The colors of these pictures were, if anything, brighter and less natural than in the edition done under Catesby's own supervision and, indeed, largely by his own hands. Edwards, who ostensibly supervised the coloring of these pictures, attempted to correct a few errors in the originals and to make some conform more closely to the text.[7] By and large, however, most of the changes were not improvements, and many — probably the work of careless copyists — were distinctly harmful to the accuracy of the work.

The text of this edition underwent no fundamental changes from that of the first. What changes were made were minor: removing the list of subscribers, which of course no longer applied, and modifying slightly the capitalization, punctuation, and spelling. Catesby was always more erratic in these matters than was considered good form even in mid-eighteenth-century England. Other than these differences, the only ones were changes in the pagination of the Preface and, very slightly, in the "Account of Carolina. . . . ,"[8] and the pages of text in the *Appendix* were numbered with the second volume rather than having a separate numeration, as in the original.

The second posthumous edition of *The Natural History of Carolina* was issued in 1771, forty years after the date of the original title page of Catesby's first volume, thus testifying to the continuing popularity of the work.[9] Four decades is not impossibly long, but these years were marked by the general adoption of the Linnaean system in England whereby many pre-Linnaean works were rendered obsolete.[10] Catesby's plates, however, were as good as before, although his names had come to appear rather quaint and antique.

This edition contained one concession to the new age which distinguished it from either of the preceding printings. Each of the volumes contained a catalog of the flora and fauna with Linnaean names assigned to Catesby's species.[11] The catalogs have been credited to George Edwards, whose name again

[4] *Gentleman's Magazine,* XXI (1751), 10, 11; XXII (1752), 276, 300, 364, 412, 474, 572; XXIII (1753), 29, 128, 180, 268, 324, 512, 609.

[5] [Title unchanged from ed. 1]. . . . *By the Late Mark Catesby, F.R.S. Revis'd by Mr. Edwards, of the Royal College of Physicians, London* ([ed. 2], 2 vols., London, 1754).

[6] The first twenty pages of text of the second volume of the first edition were originally numbered for consecutive pagination with the first volume and were corrected by hand; pls. 62 and 80 had their numbers interchanged.

[7] *Carolina,* I, 17; II, *Appendix,* 20.

[8] *Carolina,* ed. 1, has Preface, I, v-xii; "Account," II, i-xliv; *Carolina,* ed. 2, has Preface, I, i-vii; "Account," II, i-xliv (with differences from page to page from ed. 1).

[9] *The Natural History of Carolina . . . Containing the*

Figures of Birds, Beasts, Fishes, Serpents, Insects, and Plants: Particularly, Those Not Hitherto Described, or Incorrectly Figured by Former Authors, with Their Descriptions in English and French. To Which Is Prefixed, a New and Correct Map of the Countries; with Observations on Their Natural State, Inhabitants, and Productions. By the Late Mark Catesby, F.R.S. Revised by Mr. Edwards, of the Royal College of Physicians, London. To the Whole Is Now Added a Linnaean Index of the Animals and Plants ([ed. 3], 2 vols., London, 1771). The plates of this edition were printed on paper watermarked as late as 1815. See the copy in the South Caroliniana Library, University of South Carolina, Columbia.

[10] *Pulteney,* II, 348-52.

[11] Ordinarily bound following the title page of each volume.

appeared as the reviser, although it does not seem likely that he had much to do with it. His name had apparently been purchased with the plates by the new publisher, Benjamin White. The compiler — he must remain an anonymous scientific hack hired by White to give the volumes currency — accomplished nothing original in this addition. He merely borrowed Linnaeus' references to Catesby either from the *Species plantarum* or the *Systema naturae.* Where Linnaeus had not cited one of Catesby's figures, the compiler turned to Johann Reinhold Forster's *Catalogue of the Animals of North America,*[12] and where not even Forster supplied the deficiency, the author made no attempt to propose a name of his own.

Other than this, the changes in this edition from that of 1754 were few. The general index and that of the *Appendix,* which had been separate in both earlier printings, were combined,[13] and the title page appeared in one color rather than in two as before. This was a more modest production. The pagination throughout this edition remained the same as that of 1754. As a whole, the pictures were inferior to those in either of the earlier English editions. The plates again were Catesby's, but the colors were brighter and less accurate than in either of the previous editions, and they lacked the corrections in plumage which Edwards had made in 1754.

The Natural History of Carolina was thus continuously available to British naturalists in much the same form as Catesby's original over an extended period of time. Although most of the purchasers of these elegant folios were gentlemen with little more than a superficial interest in natural history, their more serious contemporaries used the work in compiling their own studies of nature.

This was particularly true of zoologists, who continued to find *The Natural History of Carolina* an important source for the American fauna down to the end of the eighteenth century and even into the early nineteenth. The major English compilers of this period still depended heavily on Catesby's work. Thomas Pennant in his *Arctic Zoology*[14] used the *Natural History* for a number of American species, and George Shaw, whose *General Zoology*[15] was the major English attempt at a general history of animals during this period, leaned heavily — almost exclusively — on Catesby for his American Reptilia and Amphibia. By means of Shaw, too, some of Catesby's names of American Reptilia and Amphibia entered the scheme of modern nomenclature permanently, as Shaw used binary names.[16] Still another late eighteenth-century naturalist who utilized Catesby for some American animals was Johann Reinhold Forster, to whom we have already referred and who did much of his work in England despite his German origins. From Forster's pen came at least two permanent additions to zoological nomenclature based either entirely or in part on figures in *The Natural History of Carolina.*[17] John Latham, the foremost English ornithologist of the eighteenth century, was less dependent on Catesby than his major interest might suggest, as he could follow the many intervening compilers. He relegated Catesby's name to an inferior place in his synonymy. Even so, he often cited information on the habits of American birds which had come originally from Catesby's *Natural History.*[18]

English botanists — and this was true of botanists in general — came to depend less upon Catesby's work as the eighteenth century wore on. In spite of the admiration expressed by Richard Pulteney for *The Natural History of Carolina,* there was simply so much other material available on the American flora — much of it containing better descriptions than Catesby's — that the latter's volumes became useful for little more than pictorial reference. To a large

[12] (London, 1771).
[13] At the end of Vol. II.
[14] (2 vols. + supp., London, 1784-87). Pennant's own copy of Catesby's *Carolina* is in the Pierpont Morgan Library.
[15] (14 vols., London, 1800-1826). See esp. Vol. III.

[16] *Masticophis flagellum* and *Rana catesbeiana.*
[17] *Natrix erythrogaster* and *Chordeiles minor.*
[18] See esp. *A General Synopsis of Birds* (3 vols. + supp., London, 1781-85).

extent, this had been true even in Catesby's lifetime, and it became even more the case after the publication of Linnaean works, particularly Thomas Walter's *Flora Caroliniana*,[19] which covered much the same area that Catesby had dealt with and with far greater thoroughness.

In tracing the impact of Catesby's *Natural History* on the European Continent, it is well to remember that there, to a much greater extent than in England and even America, the book had to make its own way on the basis of merit, as friendship played no part except possibly with Gronovius and Amman. Still, it was used widely by European scholars long after its publication — a reflection, no doubt, both on the merit of Catesby's work and on the fact that Europeans (with the exception of the French and, to a lesser extent, the Dutch) lacked the opportunities enjoyed by the British for receiving collections from North America and the West Indies.

Aside from Sir Hans Sloane's efforts to distribute *The Natural History* among his European correspondents, the importance of the book was quickly recognized by Continental naturalists. Its publication was noticed in some of the leading scholarly publications, such as the *Journal des sçavans* of Paris and the North German *Hamburgische Berichte*.[20] The German journals found it especially praiseworthy. The *Nova acta eruditorum* of Leipzig reviewed the first volume with unreserved compliments for both the work and its author.[21] The *Commercium litterarium* of Nuremberg took even greater notice of *The Natural History*, printing news from Gronovius in Leyden of the pub-

lication of both volumes, noting Cromwell Mortimer's accounts of the book as they appeared in the *Philosophical Transactions*, and finally presenting reviews of both volumes, full of praise and including detailed lists of Catesby's subjects.[22]

With such a favorable German press, it was not surprising that the artists of Nuremberg soon set themselves to pirating editions of *The Natural History of Carolina*. The first of these began to appear even before Catesby's death. This was the *Sammlung verschiedener ausländischer und seltener Vögel*, which was published in seven parts between 1749 and 1770.[23] Essentially it was a combination of Catesby's first volume with George Edward's *Natural History of Uncommon Birds* and *Gleanings of Natural History*. The first four parts (Vols. I and II) ordinarily alternated copies of Edwards' and Catesby's birds by the Nuremberg artist, engraver, and art dealer, Johann Michael Seligmann, while the last three parts contained those of Edwards alone.[24] Facing each of the plates, as in the originals, were their descriptions, translated into German by the Nuremberg physician, Georg Leonhard Huth, who also translated items from the *Philosophical Transactions* for the *Commercium litterarium* and was responsible for rendering Philip Miller's *Gardener's Dictionary* into German.[25] Included in Huth's work, as a preface to the fourth part published in 1755, was Catesby's Preface to the first volume and his "Account of Carolina and the Bahama Islands," along with the maps usually bound with the "Account" in the English editions.[26] Seligmann's plates were generally

[19] (London, 1788).

[20] *Journal des sçavans* (1730), pt. 2 [Amsterdam ed.], 379-80; *Hamburgische Berichte von gelehrten Sachen* (1736), 388, facsimile in *Linnaeus im Auslande* (Felix Byrk, ed., Stockholm, 1919), 132.

[21] *Nova acta eruditorum*, I, (1731 [1734]), 193-95.

[22] *Commercium litterarium ad rei mediciae et naturalis*, II (1733), 185, 390; III (1734), 278-80, 284-88, 293-96, 345-47; IX (1739), 7; XI (1741), 261-63; XV (1744), 81-82.

[23] *Sammlung verschiedener ausländischer und seltener Vögel, worinnen ein jeder dererselben nicht nur auf das genaueste beschrieben, sondern auch in einer richtigen und sauber illuminirten Abbildung vorgestellet wird von Johann Michael Seligmann* [Vols. I and II bear an additional engraved title page, *Catesby und Edwards Sammlung seltener Vögel*] (3 vols., 7 pts., Nuremberg, 1749-70). Pt. VII (1770), alters the title to *Sammlung verschiedener ausländischer und seltener Vögel und andere Seltenheiten der Natur. . . .*

[24] *Allgemeine deutsche Biographie* (Rochus von Lilliencron et al., eds., 56 vols., Leipzig, 1875-1912), XXXIII.

[25] Georg Andreas Will, *Nürnbergisches Gelehrten-lexicon . . .* (3 vols., Nuremberg, 1755-57), II, 210-13.

[26] This also appeared separately as *Die Beschreibung von Carolina, Florida, und der Bahamischen Inseln . . .* (Nuremberg, 1755).

good (but smaller) copies of Catesby's originals, their coloring again — as in most of the editions which were not Catesby's own — tending to be far too bright.

This project was apparently a profitable one for Seligmann and, after his death in 1768, for his heirs. Not content with exploiting the German market, Seligmann's heirs issued a somewhat smaller French edition, *Recueil de divers oiseaux étrangers et peu communs,* in eight volumes between 1768 and 1776.[27] In this printing the copies of Catesby's plates were included in the first three volumes and his Preface, "Account," and map were bound with the third.[28] Still another and expanded version retaining Seligmann's plates was published in Amsterdam in nine parts between 1772 and 1781 as *Verzameling van uitlandsche en zeldzaame vogelen, benevens eenige vremde dieren en plantgewassen.*[29] Catesby's contributions, as in the German version, were in the first four parts. The Dutch translation, by Martyn Houttyn,[30] a physician and botanist, was taken from Huth's German rather than the original English of Catesby and Edwards. Nevertheless, this edition compared very favorably with those printed by the Seligmanns.

These lengthy and generally excellent — if unauthorized — copies of Catesby's plates were not the only ones which came from the engravers of Nuremberg. In 1750 two other Nuremberg artists, Nicholaus Friedrich Eisenberger and Georg Lichtensteger,[31]

began a copy of the second volume of *The Natural History of Carolina* which appeared during the next few years as *Piscium, serpentum, insectorum, aliorumque nonnullorum animalum.* . . .[32] This edition contained the text in parallel Latin and German columns, again translated by Huth. This appears to have been the poorest of all the editions of Catesby, artistically and scientifically. Many of the figures tended to be stiffer, shadings were generally accomplished by crosshatching — unlike Catesby's own figures — and the colors were consistently brighter — sometimes almost glaring — than in any of the other editions. Even so, this version must have been a commercial success, as it too was reissued in an expanded form in 1777.[33]

Thus, through these pirated European editions, Catesby's work reached a much larger public than it could have from those produced in England from his original engravings. That they were issued and even reissued was a tribute to their author, even though neither he nor his family profited from them. These books, with their pictures, helped to make Europeans aware of the natural produce of America in a way that more scientific but nonpictorial works could not. They were a part of Europe's continuing discovery of America.

Alongside the great Linnaeus, whose contributions have sometimes obscured the work of the other eighteenth-century naturalists, the systematists of

[27] *Recueil de divers oiseaux étrangers et peu communs qui se trouvent dans les ouvrages de messieurs Edwards et Catesby representés en taille douce et exactment coloriés par Jean Michel Seligmann* [Vols. I-III bear an additional engraved title page, *Recueil des oiseaux étrangers de Catesby et Edwards. Catesby und Edwards Sammlung seltener Vögel*] (8 vols., Nuremberg, 1768-76).

[28] Again issued separately as *Histoire naturelle de la Caroline, la Floride, et les Isles Bahama* . . . (Nuremberg, 1770).

[29] *Verzameling van uitlandsche en zeldzaame vogelen, benevens eenige vremde dieren en plantgewassen* . . . (5 vols., 9 pts., Amsterdam, 1772-81).

[30] *Biographisch woordenboek der Nederlanden* (A. J. Van der Aa *et al.,* eds., 21 vols., Haarlem, 1852-78), VIII, 1334-35.

[31] Will, *Nürnbergisches Gelehrten-lexicon,* I, 338-39; II,

438-40; *Allgemeines Lexikon der bildenden Künstler* (Ulrich Thieme *et al.,* eds., 37 vols., Leipzig, 1907-50), X, 432; XXXIII, 192.

[32] *Piscium, serpentum, insectorum, aliorumque nonnullorum animalum nec non plantarum quarundam imagines, quas Marcus Catesby in posteriore parte splendidi illius operis Carolinae Floridae et Bahamensium Insularum tradidit historiam nautralem eiusque appendice descripsit.* . . . *Die Abbildungen verschiedener Fische, Schlangen, Insecten, einiger andern Thiere, und Pflanzen* . . . (Nuremberg, 1750-[?]). This work, which has pls. 1-100 of Catesby's second volume, was probably also designed to include the *Supplementa* below.

[33] *Piscium, serpentum* . . . (Nuremberg, 1777); *Supplementa* (Nuremberg, 1777). The latter has pls. 2, 4, 6, 7, 9, 11, 15, 17, 19 of Catesby's *Appendix* done by Georg Wolfgang Knorr.

Europe used Catesby's plates and descriptions as secondary and, often, as primary sources for many American species. This was particularly true of the ornithologists, who drew extensively on the first volume of *The Natural History of Carolina.* Jakob Theodor Klein, the German naturalist, whose ornithological works followed shortly after the publication of Catesby's book, used it almost exclusively for the North American birds included in his *Historiae avium prodromus . . .*[34] and *Stemmata avium. . . .*[35] The great French ornithologists of the later eighteenth century, Mathurin Jacques Brisson and Georges Louis Leclerc, Comte de Buffon, also depended greatly upon Catesby's *Natural History.* Brisson especially (Buffon could depend in large part upon the earlier effort of his fellow countryman) took many species directly from Catesby's pages.[36] Brisson thought well of Catesby's work: the descriptions he wrote were too short but exact, and the figures of birds were well done.[37] Brisson, who criticized his sources carefully, usually noted *avec une figure exacte* after his references to Catesby's plates, with occasionally an *assez exacte,* and only rarely a *pas assez exacte.* With more sources to draw upon, Buffon, in his *Histoire naturelle des oiseaux,* usually used Catesby only as a pictorial reference; but he also quoted directly from *The Natural History of Carolina* and "Of Birds of Passage," though he chided others, particularly Jakob Theodor Klein, for quoting some of Catesby's descriptions without criticism.[38]

A catalog of late eighteenth- and early nineteenth-century European authors who used *The Natural History of Carolina* even after the general adoption

of Linnaean names would be rather tedious. These two volumes remained a major source for the American flora and fauna — particularly the latter — long after they were published. Catesby's fish are a case in point, though any of the fauna other than the birds would do. Of the twenty-six modern names of species based in whole or part upon items in *The Natural History of Carolina,* nine were named by post-Linnaean scientists. Five of them came from Johann Julius Walbaum's edition of Peter Artedi's *Bibliotheca et philosophia ichthyologica* in 1792,[39] others came from Marc Elieser Bloch's *Ausländischen Fische* in 1786,[40] one from Bloch and Johann Gottlob Schneider's *Systema ichthyologiae* in 1801,[41] and one from Joseph Pierre Bonnaterre's *Tableau encyclopédique* in 1788.[42] As late as 1829 one designation based on Catesby was made by Georges Cuvier in the second edition of his *Regne animal.*[43] And these numbers are not inclusive, for these same authors also used Catesby for species for which prior designations existed or as secondary reference for other designations.

European naturalists who followed Catesby to the New World also found Catesby's work to be a necessary guide — something to confirm or refute. Peter Kalm, Linnaeus' pupil who visited America for the Swedish Academy of Science between 1748 and 1751, depended greatly upon it. For example, he checked Catesby's rather strange theory that the species diminish in size and number in the more northerly latitudes with John Bartram, and concurred in the negative answer which he received from the Pennsylvania botanist.[44] Kalm frequently commended

[34] (Lübeck, 1750).

[35] (Leipzig, 1759).

[36] Mathurin Jacques Brisson, *Ornithologie . . .* (6 vols., Paris, 1760).

[37] Brisson, *Ornithologie,* I, xiii.

[38] Comte de Buffon, *Histoire naturelle des oiseaux* (18 vols., Paris, 1770-85), I, 312-13; IV, 248; V, 134.

[39] *Petri Artedi renovati . . . i.e. Bibliotheca et philosophia ichthyologica* (3 vols., 5 pts., Greifswald, [1788-92]). The identifications are in pt. 3, *. . . Sueci genera piscium . . .* (1792), 94, 228, 261, 351, 353.

[40] Marc Elieser Bloch, *Naturgeschichte der ausländischen Fische* (3 vols., Berlin, 1785-95), 120, pl. 176.

[41] M. E. Bloch and Johann Gottlob Schneider, *Systema ichthyologiae . . .* (Berlin, 1801), 214.

[42] Joseph Pierre Bonnaterre, *Tableau encyclopédique et méthodique . . . ichthyologie* (Paris, 1788), 96.

[43] Georges Cuvier, *Regne animal . . .* (ed. 2, 5 vols., Paris, 1829-30), II, 352.

[44] Adolph B. Benson, ed. and tr., *The America of 1750: Peter Kalm's Travels in North America* (2 vols., New York, 1937), I, 15.

Catesby's plates as he saw their live subjects, though occasionally these differed sufficiently for him to correct Catesby's colors.[45]

Johann David Schoepf, the German naturalist who visited the middle and southern states, the Floridas, and the Bahamas in 1783 and 1784, after serving as a military surgeon during the Revolution, also referred many of the species he saw to Catesby. Even at this date, Schoepf, who ordinarily used Linnaean names, occasionally had to refer to Catesby's Latin descriptions.[46] After following Catesby's trail to the Bahamas, Schoepf did criticize him for not specifying where he found some plants, as it caused others to assign some Bahaman plants to the environment of South Carolina.[47] Even so, where he had previously suspected Catesby of falsifying the colors of fishes, his own observations confirmed that Catesby had been true to nature.[48]

Catesby's plates also furnished the subjects for zoological illustrators well into the nineteenth century. A German edition of Buffon's *Histoire naturelle* which appeared between 1772 and 1809 contained many illustrations copied from Catesby as well as from George Edwards.[49] As late as 1818, Pierre André Latreille's *Tableau encyclopédique et méthodique* contained an exact copy of Catesby's hermit crab, an illustration which supported the modern designation of that species.[50]

After the early decades of the nineteenth century, scientists did not stop using and citing *The Natural History of Carolina*; but it appeared much less frequently in their synonymies. It remained a necessary tool for the taxonomist in fixing or revising the species based upon it by Linnaeus and later authors; but the primary importance of the work diminished as it was succeeded by newer and better studies. The really amazing fact about *The Natural History* is that it was used for so many years after Linnaeus had combed it so thoroughly.

Even in America, where there were fewer students of natural history but greater familiarity with the things which Catesby had drawn, *The Natural History* was used and admired well beyond the time of Catesby's own circle of friends and correspondents, only two of whom, the elder Bartram and John Clayton, survived until the time of the American Revolution.[51] A later group of American naturalists continued, though, to use and to depend upon *The Natural History of Carolina*. Of these men who followed Catesby in seeking the American flora and fauna, only Alexander Garden, the Scottish physician of Charles Town, whose correspondence with Linnaeus helped name so many American species, was seriously and consistently critical of Catesby's work. "Oh my good friend," he wrote John Ellis, "how many blunders and gross misrepresentations have I seen in Catesby! — gross beyond conception!"[52] As has already been suggested, there was more than a little jealousy involved in Garden's disdain for *The Natural History of Carolina*, although his criticism was sometimes justified. Certainly he would have liked to write his own — presumably superior — natural history, possibly with plates by someone of the caliber of Georg Dionysius Ehret.[53] Even so, Catesby's plates and Catesby's names gave Garden and his correspondents in England and Europe common points of reference. Without them, their correspondence would have been far more difficult.

Certainly most American naturalists — even those

[45] Benson, ed., *America of 1750*, 112, 116, 144, 149, 246-48.

[46] Johann David Schoepf, *Travels in the Confederation* (Alfred J. Morrison, ed. and tr., 2 vols., Philadelphia, 1911), II, 176-79, *et passim*.

[47] Schoepf, *Travels*, 274-75.

[48] Schoepf, *Travels*, 276.

[49] *Herrn von Buffon's Naturgeschichte der Vögel* . . . (Wilhelm Martini and Bernhard Christian Otto, eds., 35 vols., Berlin, 1772-1809).

[50] Pierre André Latreille, *Tableau encyclopédique et méthodique . . . crustacés, arachnides et insectes* (Paris, 1818), pl. 284; *Cenobita diogenes*.

[51] Bartram died in 1777 and Clayton in 1773.

[52] *C.* Jan., 1761, in Smith, *Corresp. Linnaeus*, I, 501-6.

[53] He suggested, at least, that one of his descriptions be attached to one of Ehret's plates. Garden to Ellis, Charles Town, March 22, 1756, in Smith, *Corresp. Linnaeus*, 378.

who belonged to a later period than Garden — were much more laudatory in their appraisals of *The Natural History of Carolina*. It graced their libraries; and they valued it as an important part of the literature of natural science. Henry Mühlenberg,[54] the botanist member of the famous family of Pennsylvania German clerics, considered Catesby's work in this light. While he did not cite *The Natural History of Carolina* in his own writings — it had been superseded by other studies which utilized Linnaean nomenclature — he treasured it nonetheless. Writing to William Bartram in 1792, he hoped to lure the naturalist son of John Bartram to his home to see his copies of Edwards, Catesby, and "several other valuable works. . . ."[55]

William Bartram had no need of going to Lancaster to see Mühlenberg's copy of *The Natural History of Carolina* as he had the copy which his father had received from Catesby in return for his collections. The younger Bartram was heavily dependent on it, too, for the identification of specimens which he found on his travels. This was shown especially in the report which he sent to John Fothergill of his explorations of 1773 and 1774, which were the bases of his famous *Travels in East and West Florida*.[56] The report and, to a lesser degree, the published book derived their nomenclature from Catesby, Linnaeus, and Gronovius, with Catesby's names used in some cases where they had been superseded by designations in the other sources. The section in his *Travels* in which he dealt with birds indicated a careful study of *The Natural History of Carolina*. Though Bartram was himself a very competent ornithological artist — actually far superior to Catesby — he con-

sidered the American birds of both Edwards and Catesby to be "well-figured."[57] Where he criticized Catesby, he found extenuating circumstances. For example, where Catesby underestimated the songs of the catbird and fox-colored thrush, it was due, according to Bartram, to the fact that Catesby heard these birds in their winter retreats where they rarely sang.

Alexander Wilson, whom Bartram encouraged to undertake a serious study of birds, also referred frequently to Catesby in his *American Ornithology*. In the six decades which separated the publication of the last of Catesby's birds and the first of Wilson's, there were no studies of the North American avifauna based upon the firsthand observations of their authors comparable with either work. Wilson, the greatest of Audubon's precursors, quoted directly and often from his own most notable predecessor.[58] This was a very high compliment, for Wilson had the opportunity — unlike the European compilers — of confirming from his own observations what Catesby had written.

Thomas Jefferson, that many-sided man whose *Notes on the State of Virginia* included some of the finest writings on natural history of any eighteenth-century American, also esteemed Catesby's work.[59] In 1783 he wrote to Francis Eppes from Philadelphia: "Since I came here there has been sold the Westover copy of Catesby's History of Carolina. It was held near a twelvemonth at twelve guineas, and sold at last for ten. This seems to fix what should be given for Mr. Boling's copy, if you can induce him to let me have it, which I am very anxious for."[60] Jeffer-

[54] See Henry [Gotthilf Heinrich Ernst] Mühlenberg, "Index-florae Lancastriensis," *Transactions of the American Philosophical Society*, III (1793), 57-184; "Supplementum . . . ," *ibid.*, IV (1799), 235-42; *Catalogus plantarum Americae Septentrionalis* . . . (Lancaster, Pa., 1813), in which he used only works which employed the Linnaean system.

[55] Lancaster, Sept. 13, 1792, in Darlington, *Memorials*, 466-67.

[56] William Bartram, *Travels in Georgia and Florida, 1773-74* (Francis Harper, ed., *Transactions of the American Philo-*

sophical Society, XXXIII, pt. 2, Philadelphia, 1934), 31, 153, 165-66, *et passim*.

[57] William Bartram, *Travels Through North and South Carolina, Georgia, East and West Florida* (Philadelphia, 1791), 284. See also *ibid.*, 299-301.

[58] Alexander Wilson, *American Ornithology* . . . (9 vols. [Vols. VIII-IX by George Ord], Philadelphia, 1808-14), *passim*.

[59] Thomas Jefferson, *Notes on the State of Virginia* (William Peden, ed., Chapel Hill, N.C., 1955).

[60] Julian P. Boyd, ed., *Papers of Thomas Jefferson* (Princeton, N.J., 1950——   ), VI, 220.

son apparently eventually acquired two copies of *The Natural History,* one of which he gave to the College of William and Mary.[61]

Jefferson's thoughts on *The Natural History of Carolina* were set forth in his *Notes on Virginia.* There he wrote: "Between ninety and an hundred of our birds have been described by Catesby. His drawings are better as to form and attitude, than coloring, which is generally too high."[62] This was a valid criticism from a man who had among his many accomplishments a careful eye for the products of nature. The criticism mixed with his praise may have derived from his having used one of the later editions of Catesby's work, which were much more highly colored than the original. Jefferson was not content with mere comment, however, but based his list of Virginian birds in the *Notes* upon Catesby.[63]

It is not surprising that Jefferson and other Americans writing on their flora and fauna should have depended upon Mark Catesby's elegant book, as it was, without a doubt, the greatest total accomplishment of any work dealing with the natural history of British North America published before the American Revolution. Others perhaps exceeded Catesby in certain of his accomplishments, but none did more in the large.

Among the botanists who dealt with the colonies, there were many who equaled or excelled Catesby in competence. John Bartram was a far more important collector, but published no really important work in botany, despite the pleas of Peter Collinson that he give an account of the American forest trees.[64] John Mitchell, whose "Nova genera plantarum" gave so much promise of further activities,[65] unfortunately

never found time to do his proposed natural and medical history of North America.[66] Alexander Garden was, like Mitchell, a better-trained naturalist than most who worked in the colonies, but, like Bartram, he remained primarily a collector. His activities — both in botany and zoology — resulted in the designation of many new species, but these were published by others, principally by Linnaeus.[67] Of those botanists who actually published their results, the combination of John Clayton and Johann Friedrich Gronovius undoubtedly produced the most outstanding work in their *Flora Virginica.*[68] Still, though it was far more complete than Catesby's book and used the Linnaean method of classification, the *Flora Virginica* dealt only with botany and lacked the illustrations which gave *The Natural History of Carolina* its value.

In the area of zoology, Catesby's work had no real competitor. Most of the compilers of England and Europe included American animals — some of them derived from Catesby — and many of them contained fine illustrations, but almost none of them was devoted exclusively to North America. Johann Reinhold Forster's *Catalogue of the Animals of North America* might be taken as an exception, but it was not illustrated and consisted of little more than a brief check list.

Actually, *The Natural History of Carolina* was the only colonial attempt to give the whole natural history of any of the North American colonies. Catesby's immediate predecessor in the Carolinas, John Lawson, approached it, but his *History of Carolina* was far less critical and lacked illustrations.[69] John Brickell attempted to accomplish something of the sort in his

[61] Millicent Sowerby, *Catalogue of the Library of Thomas Jefferson* (4 vols., Washington, D.C., 1952-55), I, 468, says without certainty that Jefferson had a 1771 edition. He also acquired a 1754 edition in France in 1789. The latter must have been the one given to the College of William and Mary. *William and Mary Quarterly,* ser. 1, XXI (1912-13), 137.

[62] Jefferson, *Notes,* 65.

[63] Jefferson, *Notes,* 66-69.

[64] Collinson to Bartram, Feb. 13, 1753, in Darlington, *Me-morials,* 189-90.

[65] *Acta physico-medica academiae caesareae,* VIII (1748), 187-224.

[66] Mitchell to Linnaeus, London, April 16, 1747, in Smith, *Corresp. Linnaeus,* II, 442-44.

[67] See Margaret Denny, "Linnaeus and His Disciple in Carolina: Alexander Garden," *Isis,* XXXVIII (1938), 161-74.

[68] Esp. ed. 2 (Leyden, 1762).

[69] (London, 1714).

Natural History of North Carolina; but this book is hardly worthy of consideration, as so much of it was derived from Lawson's earlier effort.[70] Only in the West Indies were there real competitors. The works of Sir Hans Sloane[71] and Patrick Browne[72] on Jamaica, and Griffith Hughes[73] on Barbados compared favorably with Catesby's volumes. Their descriptions were often far better than his, and, like Catesby, included pictures of many of the things they described. Even

so, their illustrations were fewer and depended upon the hands of others to draw them. The excellence of *The Natural History of Carolina* was due, more than anything, to the devoted personal care its author had lavished upon it. It was, after all, the product of a large part of Catesby's life, and an enduring monument to his singular devotion to natural history and science.

[70] (Dublin, 1737).

[71] Hans Sloane, *A Voyage to the Ilands Madera . . . and Jamaica with the Natural History of the Herbs and Trees . . . Etc.* (2 vols., London, 1707-25).

[72] Patrick Browne, *The Civil and Natural History of Jamaica* (London, 1756).

[73] Griffith Hughes, *The Natural History of Barbados* (London, 1750).

A Check List
of Mark Catesby's Published Works

I. ENGLISH EDITIONS OF *THE NATURAL HISTORY OF CAROLINA*

A. *The Natural History of Carolina, Florida, and the Bahama Islands; Containing the Figures of Birds, Beasts, Fishes, Serpents, Insects, and Plants: Particularly, the Forest-Trees, Shrubs, and Other Plants, Not Hitherto Described, or Very Incorrectly Figured by Authors. Together with Their Descriptions in English and French. To Which, Are Added Observations on the Air, Soil, and Waters; with Remarks upon Agriculture, Grain, Pulse, Roots, Etc. To the Whole Is Prefixed a New and Correct Map of the Countries Treated of. By Mark Catesby, F.R.S.*

Histoire naturelle de la Caroline, la Floride, et les Isles Bahama: contenant les desseins des oiseaux, animaux, poissons, serpents, insectes, et plantes. Et en particulier, des arbres des forets, arbrisseaux, et autres plantes, qui n'ont point été decrits, jusques à present par les auteurs, ou peu exactement dessinés. Avec leur descriptions en françois et en anglois. A quoi on a adjouté des observations sur l'air, le sol, et les eaux, avec remarques sur l'agriculture, les grains, les légumes, les racines, etc. Le tout est precedé d'une carte nouvelle et exacte des païs dont s'agist. Par Marc Catesby, de la Société Royale [ed. 1]. 2 vols. London, 1731-43 [1729-47].

B. *The Natural History of Carolina. . . . By the Late Mark Catesby, F.R.S. Revis'd by Mr. Edwards, of the Royal College of Physicians, London. Histoire naturelle*

de la Caroline. . . . Par feu monsieur Marc Catesby, de la Société Royale, et revû par monsieur Edwards, du College Royale des Médecins de Londres [ed. 2]. 2 vols. London, 1754.

C. *The Natural History of Carolina, Florida, and the Bahama Islands: Containing the Figures of Birds, Beasts, Fishes, Serpents, Insects, and Plants: Particularly, Those Not Hitherto Described, or Incorrectly Figured by Former Authors, with Their Descriptions in English and French. To Which Is Prefixed, a New and Correct Map of the Countries; with Observations on Their Natural State, Inhabitants, and Productions. By the Late Mark Catesby, F.R.S. Revised by Mr. Edwards, of the Royal College of Physicians, London. To the Whole Is Now Added a Linnaean Index of the Animals and Plants.*

Histoire naturelle de la Caroline, de la Floride, et des Isles de Bahama: contenant les desseins des oiseaux, des quadrapedes, des poissons, des serpens, des insectes, et des plantes, qui se trouvent dans ces pays-là; et en particulier, de ceux qui n'ont point été decrits jusqu'à present par les auteurs, ou peu exactement dessinés. Avec leurs descriptions en françois et anglois. On trouve au commencement une carte de ces pays, avec des remarques sur leur état naturel, leurs habitans, et leurs productions. Par feu monsieur Marc Catesby, de la Société Royale, reveue par monsieur Edwards, du College Royal des Medicins de Londres. On y a ajouté une table selon le systeme de Linnaeus [ed. 3]. 2 vols. London, 1771.

II. EUROPEAN EDITIONS OF *THE NATURAL HISTORY OF CAROLINA*

A. With George Edwards. *Sammlung verschiedener ausländischer und seltener Vögel, worinnen ein jeder dererselben nicht nur auf das genaueste beschrieben, sondern auch in einer richtigen und sauber illuminirten Abbildung vorgestellet wird von Johann Michael Seligmann.* [Engraved title to Vols. I and II] *Catesby und Edwards Sammlung seltener Vögel.* 3 vols., 7 pts. Nuremberg, 1749-70. Vols. I and II contain copies of Catesby's plates taken from Vol. I of IA above. The translation, as is the case with all of the German editions, is by Georg Leonhard Huth.

B. *Piscium, serpentum, insectorum, aliorumque nonnullorum animalum nec non plantarum quarundam imagines, quas Marcus Catesby in posteriore parte splendidi illius operis quo Carolinae Floridae et Bahamensium Insularum tradidit historiam naturalem eiusque appendice descripsit additis vero imaginibus piscium, tam nostratium quam aliarum regionum auxerunt vivisque coloribus pictas editerunt Nicolaus Fredericus Eisenberger et Georgius Lichtensteger.*

Die Abbildungen verschiedener Fische, Schlangen, Insecten, einiger andern Thiere, und Pflanzen, welche Herr Marcus Catesby in zwieten Theil, und im Anhang seines vortreflichen Werks der natürlichen Historie von Carolina, Florida und den Bahamischen Inseln beschrieben. Mit den Abbildungen der unsrigen und anderer Länder Fische vermehret, und in ihren natürlichen Farben vorgestellet herausgeben von Nicolaus Friedrich Eisenberger und Georg Lichtensteger. Nuremberg, 1750-[?]. A pirated version of Vol. II of IA above.

C. *Die Beschriebung von Carolina, Florida, und den Bahamischen Inseln, worinnen von der Luft, dem Boden, dem Wasser, von dem Einwohnern, den vierfüszigen Thieren, den Fischen, Pflanzen etc. dieser Länder umständliche und zuverläszige Nachright mitgetheilet wird. Zu erst nebst einer neuen und genauen Charte dieser Länder in englischer und französischer Sprach herausgeben von Marcus Catesby, der Königlich Londischen Gesellschaft der Wissenschaften Mitgleid, nunmehr aber in das Deutsche übersezet von D. Georg Leonhard Huth. Verlegt, und herausgeben von D. Leonhard Huth. Verleght, und herausgeben von Johann Michael Seligmann.* Nuremberg, 1755. Part of IIA above, issued separately.

D. With George Edwards. *Recueil de divers oiseaux étrangers et peu communs qui se trouvent dans les ouvrages de messieurs Edwards et Catesby representés en taille douce et exactment coloriés par Jean Michel Seligmann.* [Engraved title to Vols. I-III] *Recueil des oiseaux étrangers de Catesby et Edwards. Catesby und Edwards Sammlung seltener Vögel.* 8 vols. Nuremberg, 1768-76. This is a smaller version of IIA above. Catesby's contributions are in Vols. I-III.

E. *Histoire naturelle de la Caroline, la Floride, et les Isles Bahama contenant les desseins des oiseaux, animaux etc. et en particulier des arbres, des forets, arbrisseaux et autres plantes avec une carte nouvelle des pais, dont il s'agist par Marc Catesby de la Société Royale.* Nuremberg, 1770. Part of IID above, issued separately.

F. With George Edwards. *Verzameling van uitlandsche en zeldzaame vogelen, benevens eenige vremde dieren en plantgewassen: in 't Englesch naauwkeurig beschreeven en naar 't leven met kleuren afgebeeld, door G. Edwards en M. Catesby: vervolgens, ten apzigt van de plaaten merkelyk vebeterd, in 't Hoogduitsch uitgegeven door J. M. Seligmann: thans in 't Nederduitsch vertaald en met anhaalingen van andere autheuren verrykt, door M. Houtuyn, Medic. Doctor.* 5 vols., 9 pts. Amsterdam, 1772-81. This is a Dutch translation of IIA above, by Martyn Houttyn. Catesby's contributions are in Vols. I and II.

G. *Piscium, serpentum . . . eiusque appendice descripsit, vivis coloribus pictas edere coeperunt N. F. Eisenberger et G. Lichtensteger et ad finem peduxerunt beati Georgii Wolfgangi Knorii heredes [Supplementa]. Die Abbildungen verschiedener Fische . . . in ihren natürlichen Farben vorgestellt von N. Fr. Eisenberger, G. Lichtensteger und G. W. Knorr. . . .* Nuremberg, 1777. This is IIB above, expanded by items from the *Appendix* to Vol. II of IA, which are included as the *Supplementa*.

III. OTHER WORKS

A. Gray, Christopher. *A Catalogue of American Trees and Shrubs That Will Endure the Climate of England.* [London, 1737]. The plate of this single-sheet catalog is by Catesby.

B. "Of Birds of Passage by Mr. Mark Catesby F.R.S." *Philosophical Transactions,* XLIV, pt. 2 (1747), 435-44.

C. "Extract from a Paper on the Same Subject [Birds of Passage], Written by Mark Catesby, F.R.S. in Phil. Trans. No. 483." *Gentleman's Magazine,* XVIII (1748), 447-48. Extract of IIIB above.

D. *Hortus Britanno-Americanus: Or, a Curious Collection of Trees and Shrubs, the Produce of the British Colonies* in North America; Adapted to the Soil and Climate of England. With Observations on Their Constitution, Growth, and Culture, and Directions How They Are to Be Collected, Packed up, and Secured During Their Passage. Embellished with Copper Plates Neatly Engraved. London, 1763.

E. Hortus Europae Americanus: Or a Collection of 85 Curious Trees and Shrubs, the Produce of North America Adapted to the Climates and Soils of Great Britain, Ireland, and Most Parts of Europe, Etc. Together with Their Blossoms, Fruits and Seeds; Observations on Their Culture, Growth, Constitution and Virtues. With Directions How to Collect, Pack up, and Secure Them in Their Passage. Adorn'd with 63 Figures on 17 Copper-Plates, Large Imperial Quarto. By Mark Catesby, F.R.S. London, 1767. Same as IIID above, except for the title page.

A Selected Bibliography

The biographer of Mark Catesby is necessarily hampered by the fact that Catesby's own papers do not seem to have survived. Fortunately, his connections with the great and near-great figures of British and American science insured the preservation of a large number of letters and other manuscript materials. The single most important source of these is in *Dr. [William] Sherard's Philosophical Letters,* 5 vols., in the Library of the Royal Society of London. The records of the Royal Society itself have yielded many references to Catesby and his associates. Those which proved particularly useful were the *Certificates,* I, 1731-50; *Classified Papers, 1660-1740,* XXII (2), *Accounts of Books; Council Minutes,* II-IV; *Journal Books,* XIV-XXIII; and *Letter Books,* XXIV-XXV.

The Sloane collections in the British Museum, both those in the *Sloane MSS,* per se, and in the *Additional MSS,* are second in importance only to the Royal Society holdings. *Add. MSS* 4437, 5267, 5271, 5283, and *Sloane* 4438 contain unpublished writings and drawings by Catesby. *Sloane* 3321, 3339, 4025, 4046-47, 4053-56, 4058-69, and 4434 include letters by Mark Catesby and his scientific contemporaries which have been of great use in this study.

Some of the Oxford libraries contain significant items relating to Catesby. The *Richardson Correspondence, MS Radcliffe Trust,* C. I-XII, in the Bodleian, is particularly good. *The Sherardian Pinax,* MS 32, c. 3, in the Library of the Oxford Botanical Garden, does much to explain the motives of William Sherard in sponsoring Catesby's journey to Carolina.

Some of the letters in the Richardson Correspondence have been published in Dawson Turner, ed., *Extracts from the Literary and Scientific Correspondence of Richard Richardson . . . ,* Yarmouth, 1835, and in John Nichols, ed., *Illustrations of the Literary History of the Eighteenth Century,* 8 vols., London, 1817-58. These books, along with Nichols' *Literary Anecdotes of the Eighteenth Century . . . ,* 9 vols., London, 1812-15, and Sir James Edward Smith, ed., *Selections of the Correspondence of Linnaeus,* 2 vols., London, 1821, are absolutely necessary for anyone who would study the British natural history circle of Catesby's time.

The American side of Catesby's life is rich in sources, many of which have been published. *The Papers of the Jones Family of Northumberland County, Virginia, 1649-1889,* 35 vols., in the Library of Congress, shed much light on his connections with his relatives in Virginia. Some of these items have been printed in Lewis Hampton Jones, *Captain Roger Jones of London and Virginia . . . ,* Albany, N.Y., 1891 [1911], and in "Jones Papers," *Virginia Magazine of History and Biography,* XXVI (1918), 70-80, 162-81, 283-89. The large body of works by and on William Byrd II contains much that is useful. Louis B. Wright and Marion Tinling, eds., *The Secret Diary of William Byrd of Westover, 1709-1712,* Richmond, 1941, is particularly good in giving a detailed account of a brief period in Catesby's life. Earl G. Swem, ed., "Brothers of the Spade; Correspondence of Peter Collinson, of London, and of John Custis, of Williamsburg, Virginia, 1734-1746," *Proceedings of the American Antiquarian Society,* LVIII (1948), 17-190, was of great importance for this study in showing Catesby's relations with Collinson and Custis and particularly for the high quality of its editorial notes. The excellent edition of Hugh Jones, *The Present State of Virginia,* Richard L. Morton, ed., Chapel Hill, N.C., 1956, has provided much of the near-contemporary Virginia background for this study, something which is sadly lacking for the Carolina scene.

For Catesby's connections with more northerly American naturalists, William Darlington, ed., *Memorials of John Bartram and Humphrey Marshall . . . ,* Philadelphia, 1849, provided much of the basic material. This volume, inadequate as it is in terms of modern editorial practices, must remain a basic source for the history of eighteenth-century American natural history. Fortunately, it is supplemented — though very little where Catesby is concerned — by *The Letters and Papers of Cadwallader Colden, Collections of the New York Historical Society,* 9 vols., New York, 1918-37.

In the way of secondary materials, Brooke Hindle, *The Pursuit of Science in Revolutionary America, 1735-1789,* Chapel Hill, N.C., 1956, provides the best survey of American science, in general, for the period. There is no adequate modern treatment of the British natural history group with which Catesby was associated. Richard Pulteney, *The Historical and Biographical Sketches of the Progress of Botany in England . . . ,* 2 vols., London, 1790, is still far the best book on the subject.

As for Catesby himself, he has been treated most extensively by Elsa G. Allen, *History of American Ornithology Before Audubon, Transactions of the American Philosophical Society,* XLI, Philadelphia, 1951, and "New Light on Mark Catesby," *The Auk,* LIV (1937), 349-63. William G. Miller, "Mark Catesby, an Eighteenth Century Naturalist," *Tyler's Quarterly Historical and Genealogical Magazine,* XXIX (1948), 167-80, has dealt with Catesby generally, without access to some of the materials used by Mrs. Allen. C. Bernard Peterson, "The Elusive Mr. Catesby," *Frontiers,* X (1946), 71-73, is a popular treatment based largely on Mrs. Allen's work. Witmer Stone, "Mark Catesby and the Nomenclature of North American Birds," *The Auk,* XLVI (1929), 447-54, and "Some Early American Ornithologists: Mark Catesby," *Bird Lore,* VII (1905), 126-29, has provided some useful material on Catesby's importance as an ornithologist. W. L. McAtee has also written a number of valuable articles in this area. See his "The North American Birds of Mark Catesby and Eleazer Albin," *Journal of the Society for the Bibliography of Natural History,* III, pt. 4 (1957), 177-94; "Catesby's Tropic Bird," *The Auk,* LXII (1945), 137-40; "Confusion of Eastern Caprimulgidae," *ibid.,* LXV (1948), 128-29; "Unorthodox Thoughts on Migration," *ibid.,* LVII (1940), 135-36; and "Torpidity in Birds," *American Midland Naturalist,* XXXVII (1947), 191-206.

Other areas of Catesby's scientific interests have been covered less thoroughly than the ornithological ones. David Starr Jordan, "An Identification of the Figures of Fishes in Catesby's Natural History . . . ," *Proceedings of the U.S. National Museum,* VII (1884), 190-99, remains the best in its province, although it is in part obsolete because of subsequent nomenclatural changes. Professor George W. White of the University of Illinois has written, but not published, a paper on Catesby as a geologist which he kindly let the present authors use.

Appendix: Thomas More and His Expedition to New England

Approximately at the same time that Mark Catesby went to Carolina to collect specimens and data in natural history for William Sherard and his fellow patrons, a parallel scheme was proposed by Sherard and a like body of subscribers to send one Thomas More on a similar mission to New England, New York, and Pennsylvania. Compared with Catesby's fruitful years in the southern and island colonies, very few profits to science accrued from More's expedition, the scanty returns clearly having been the consequence of More's carelessness and cantankerous bent of mind — or, at best, his carelessness together with his indignation at New Englanders and *their* cantankerous ways.

This particular Thomas More is, moreover, a very elusive person. He appears to have left behind him too few bits of historical evidence for a satisfactory biographical sketch. We have no convincing evidence with regard to the place and date of his birth, his parentage, the nature and extent of his education, his means of livelihood, his marriage and family (if any), and the time, place, and manner of his death. Thomas More flits in and out of the scientific circles of England from the 1670's until the 1720's, leaving literary traces indicative of the life of a collector with wide travels and experience and a boastful attitude about his own accomplishments. His correspondents and patrons refer to him with amused tolerance, evidently disposed to wink at his occasional outbursts of extravagant pretentiousness.

Thomas More may have been the "Mr. More lately stolen from us to Oxford," as lamented by a correspondent of Thomas Smith, recently elected Fellow of Magdalen College, Oxford, in 1667.[1] Certainly, by the 1690's, he was closely associated with Jacob Bobart, Edward Lhuyd, and the Oxford circle of naturalists of that day — though his position is uncertain and may have been that of a menial.[2] A dozen years later, Thomas Tanner wrote to Dr. Hans Sloane from Norwich: "The bearer Mr. More has for the great part of this summer applyed himself with unwearied diligence on the Sea Coast of Norfolk and Suffolk in search of Shells, Marine Plants, and other Natural Curiosities. . . . I believe he's very honest and willing to take pains, so that he may be usefull to you or some other of the [Royal] Society, if you should have occasion to send any person into any part of the world on any searches of this nature."[3] Two years afterward More turned up in the west country, where he combined collecting with peddling subscriptions for Edward Lhuyd's catalog of the figured fossils in the Ashmolean Museum (*Lithophlacii Britannici ichnographia*, 1699). He wrote to Lhuyd from Truro, in Cornwall: "I make now bold to

[1] W. Lloyd to Thomas Smith, n.p., Feb. 22, 1678/79, In *MS Smith* 52 (Bodleian Library), fol. 37.

[2] J. Bobart to [Hans Sloane], Oxford, April 24, 1693, *Sloane* 4036, fol. 148.

[3] Tanner to Sloane, Norwich, Oct. 19, 1792, *Sloane* 4039, fol. 35.

tell you that as to my Collections I have succeeded very well; but as to my Subscriptions even to a Miracle; the Isles of Wight, Purbeck, Portland, the sea coasts of Hantshire, Dorset, Devonshire, and all Cornwall having given me their hands excepting only such of Cornwall as were up at Parliamt. or necessaryly gone from home."[4] Evidently More made good impressions upon several of Lhuyd's friends and correspondents in the west. William Musgrave wrote from Exeter to tell Lhuyd of More's visit.[5] Indeed, Musgrave was so impressed with More that he wrote two letters to Hans Sloane, the first to "recommend to you such a virtuoso as you have rarely met with, a Philosophical Pilgrim, who is now examining the western Coasts (as He has many others) . . ."; the second to serve as a letter of introduction of More to the Royal Society in order that he might visit the Society and become acquainted with its Fellows: "I find he is a very fit person to be employed in gathering materials for a History of Nature . . . and may be employed at an easy rate."[6]

On the following July 12 (1704), the "Philosophical Pilgrim" visited the Royal Society of London. The minutes of the Society's meeting for that date record both that he was present and that "Mr. More shewed some of his Tables for Reducing Nature under several heads. Some of the members present encouraged this Design."[7] Evidently More was going beyond mere collection to have a fling at system. Jacob Bobart, who succeeded his father as Superintendent of the Oxford Botanical Garden,[8] wrote later in the year to James Petiver a note referring sarcastically to "the Bearer, Mr. More, the great Philosopher, who promises to give us an account of the whole creation from an Angell to an Attome."[9] This tone of humorous sarcasm recurs frequently in the references to More by members of the English circle of naturalists. Still, they appear to have appreciated his energy and enthusiasm as a collector, and Petiver, Sloane, and members of the

Oxford group employed his services from time to time.[10]

More's collecting appears to have been mostly in the British Isles, although he may have accompanied some of his benefactors on trips farther afield. His later letters refer to collecting seeds in Europe, and on one occasion he spoke of having been in Egypt.[11] The former, however, may have been done by correspondence, and of the alleged trip to Egypt no further evidence has come to light whereby we can determine when or in what capacity or circumstances he may have gone. He wrote to Dr. Sloane in March, 1707, to seek aid for "My Stubborne boy," who was evidently in the British Army en route from Ireland to Flanders.[12] This is the only reference to the "Stubborne boy," and we cannot be confident that he was More's son; if so, it is the only evidence that the "Philosophical Pilgrim" had a family of his own. In some manner, too, as appears later in More's letters from New England, he met one or more of the Indian chiefs who visited the Court of Queen Anne in 1709 and 1710.[13] Possibly it was in April, 1710, at the time of the chiefs' visit to the Royal Observatory at Greenwich, when many Fellows of the Royal Society and their friends were present.[14] But it may have been earlier and on more than one occasion, for More spoke familiarly of his Indian friends and makes it clear that he had been invited to visit the chiefs in America if ever the opportunity arose.

The opportunity did not arise until more than a decade later, after William Sherard had returned to England from his consulate in Aleppo, had resumed his work on the *Pinax,* and had matured the plans for Catesby's voyage to Carolina. Sometime before the end of 1721 Sherard had met the "Pilgrim Philosopher," and he wrote to Richard Richardson on December 7 of that year:

The Pilgrim Botanist, Mr. More, whom we heard of in Wales, is desirous of going to New England and the rest of our Colonies in North America. He is an excellent collector of all parts of Natural History, and desires no more than a

[4] March 22, 1704, *Ashmole MS* 1816 (Bodleian Library), fol. 383.

[5] Musgrave to Lhuyd, April 10, 1704, *Ashmole MS* 1816, fol. 448.

[6] *Sloane* 4060, fols. 56, 60. The letters have no place or date, but the second is written from Oxford.

[7] *R.S. Journal Book,* X, 82.

[8] For the Bobarts, father and son, see *Pulteney,* I, 164-66, 312-13.

[9] Oxford, Nov. 10, 1704, *Sloane* 3321, fol. 157.

[10] See, for example, More to Petiver, Dec. 5, 1711, *Sloane* 4065, fols. 8 ff.

[11] See especially More to Lord Carteret, May 16, 1723, *C.S.P., Col., 1722-1723,* XXXIII, 254-58; and More to William Sherard, Boston, Oct. 27, 1722, *Sherard Letters,* IV, 561.

[12] *Sloane* 4040, fol. 231.

[13] For accounts of this unusual event, see William T. Morgan, "The Five Nations and Queen Anne," *Mississippi Valley Historical Review,* XIII (1926), 169 ff.; Samuel G. Drake, *The Aboriginal Races of North America* (Philadelphia, 1859), 509-12; Abell Boyer, *History of the Reign of Queen Anne* (11 vols., London, 1703-13), X, 189-91.

[14] Dr. Sloane acquired as a present an Indian arrow which he later presented to the Royal Society. *R.S. Journal Book,* XI, 193.

poor subsistence; a mere Philosopher, who designs printing tables of all parts of Natural History, he is now busy in copying them out on parchment (his paper scheme being worn out and torn); they look like so many taylor's measures joined at top and rolled up. It is a pity he is not younger, and I am sorry I did not know him sooner; he would have done more service than all that have been sent abroad.[15]

Presumably, More's "paper scheme," now so worn and tattered, was his tables of an "account of the whole creation from an Angell to an Attome," which he had displayed to the Royal Society in 1704.

During the early months of 1722, largely under Sherard's entrepreneurship, subscriptions were raised to send More to the northern English colonies on the mainland of North America. On January 27, 1721/22, Sherard wrote to Richardson both that Catesby was on the point of departure for Carolina and that "I have not seen Mr. More of a long time, and believe he is not in town; if he applies to me, I shall get him subscriptions, and then I will put you and our friend the Doctor [Sloane] down for a small sum. Sir Hans is ready to promote such designs, wallowing in money; but he will not procure a subscription amongst his friends, as he easily might. I cannot think he has been unsuccessful, having had a large share of all that has come into England, and I never yet had a single Plant."[16] Evidently, with such encouragement, More did apply for aid. On May 12, 1722, Sherard again wrote to Richardson: "I have advanced money to send Pilgrim Moore to New England & all is ready; I have put you down for one [subscription] at 20s. per annum. He is to go to New York, New Jersey, and Pensilvania,"[17] The number and amount of the subscriptions raised for More's support appears in a memorandum found among Sherard's letters. It bears no date, but it probably was written during the late spring of 1722. It reads as follows:

Whereas Thomas More Naturalist has Undertaken a Voyage to New England, Maryland, New York, Jersey and others of our Plantations in America, There to seek for and discover all sorts of Land and Sea Plants, Seeds, Fruits, Barks, Metalls, Stones, Sparrs, Ores, Marchasites, Earths, Serpents, Insects, Fishes, Beasts, Birds, and all such other Naturall Bodys frequenting those Countrys as yet unknown to Us Towards the Subsistance of the said Thomas More in such his performance, Wee whose Names are under written do each of Us severally for our selves Subscribe the Sums following yearly

£.	s.	d.	
1	— 1	— 0	Rich. Richardson
1	— 0	— 0	W. Sherard
1	— 0	— 0	Hans Sloane
1	— 0	— 0	Charles Dubois
1	— 0	— 0	John Bellers
1	— 1	— 0	R. Mead
1	— 1	— 0	Herman Boerhaave[18]

The list of More's patrons was not so numerous, so impressive, or so lucrative as Catesby's had been, although it contained four of the same subscribers, namely, Sherard, Sloane, Dr. Richard Mead, and Charles Dubois. The other three were Dr. Richard Richardson, a well-to-do physician and naturalist of North Bierly, Yorkshire, and a close correspondent of Sloane and the Royal Society of London, to whose *Philosophical Transactions* he frequently contributed articles on medical subjects and natural history; Mr. John Bellers, F.R.S., a Quaker philanthropist who wrote many books advocating educational and social reforms; and Dr. Hermann Boerhaave, the great Dutch physician and Leyden professor of medicine, botany, and chemistry. It appears likely that More had additional financial aid from Sherard or others. Probably the cost of his Atlantic passage was borne by his benefactors, but the "Pilgrim Botanist" may have had to draw upon his own apparently slender resources for part of his expenses; and there is no record that anyone made such a generous subscription (twenty pounds per year) as Governor Nicholson of Carolina made available to Mark Catesby.

More went well supplied with seeds for New England, where he arrived in the early autumn of 1722, too late, Sherard feared, "to perform any great matters this year."[19] The Reverend Joseph Green wrote from Boston to a friend at Long Meadow on October 1, that

There is a certain Gent. (by name More) come over to N. Engld. to survey & descry the nature & use of our Plants seeds & all our vegetables, & to send them over to the King & Royal Society by whom he is sent over, who indeed seems to be a man of great ingenuity, who has been over the greatest part of ye world on that very Errand, & tells me that he finds very many things here that are very choice & that will bring a vast advantage to the Country, what he finds here that is not to be found there, he sends over to them, he has brought over several hundred sorts of seed never known in this Country, & intends to try our Soil with them, if he could gett a suitable Spott of Ground of some

---

[15] *MS Radcliffe Trust,* C. IV, fol. 57; printed in Nichols, *Illust. Lit. Hist.,* I, 377.

[16] Nichols, *Illust. Lit. Hist.,* I, 378.

[17] *MS Radcliffe Trust,* C. IV, fols. 67-68; Nichols, *Illust.*

Lit. Hist., I, 379.

[18] *Sherard Letters,* III, 385.

[19] Sherard to Richardson, Oct. 13, 1722, in Nichols, *Illust. Lit. Hist.,* I, 382.

hundred acres. I suppose you'l see him in your parts for he intends to go all over the Country; for ye King has ordered the Government to assist him with what shall be tho't necessary for his viaticum thro' the country. . . .[20]

The "Pilgrim Botanist" went armed with a letter from Dr. James Jurin, Secretary of the Royal Society, to the Honorable Mr. Paul Dudley, son and grandson of Bay Colony governors and himself a public personage of note who recently (1718) had been appointed Judge of the Superior Court of the Massachusetts Bay Colony. Dudley was also an accomplished naturalist who contributed frequently to the Royal Society, which, in 1721, had elected him Fellow.[21] Of further importance to More's interests and activities was the fact that, as Dudley had also been appointed Colonial Agent to visit the Indians at Albany in order to seek, with New York Governor Burnet's approval, the aid of the Six Nations against the "Frenchefied" Indians who attacked New England,[22] he could assist More in the latter's desire to visit the Indian "Kings" whom he had met in London in 1710. More's introduction to Paul Dudley served well to enlist Bay Colony officialdom in behalf of his mission, although because of the rift between Dudley and Cotton Mather it evidently did nothing to recommend him to the Mather-Boylston circle in Boston, which, as it was also actively in correspondence with the Royal Society of London, was another powerful element in Massachusetts which might have furthered More's work. But, without the Mather faction, as Dudley wrote to Dr. Jurin (November 3, 1722), "The diligent and engenious Mr. More has lost no time in his searches after the productions of Nature in the Country since his arrival. . . ."[23]

This was well attested by the long letter which More had already addressed to William Sherard a week before (October 27). This letter, designed to accompany a box of specimens gathered in New England, is one of the few long letters by More still surviving, and it sheds considerable light upon the author.[24] It demonstrates, for example, that Thomas More was not abreast of the works of John Winthrop the Younger, John Jocelyn, and others with reference to the flora and fauna of New England, else he

would hardly have sent such commonplace specimens to his patrons, most of whom were already familiar with everything he sent. Again, while the reader is charmed with More's quaint personification of specimens, his descriptions fall far short of scientific requirements even for his own day. His excuse for not "methodizing" his collection and "laying them curiously" is plausible, but one is left to wonder whether the Pilgrim Botanist was capable of much more than the mere collection and recitation of folklore about the specimens that he gathered. His exasperated criticisms of New Englanders' wasteful, extensive ways in agriculture, while a token of More's tidy, Anglian husbandry, suggested possible unpleasant relations with the common folk from whom More would be required to seek favors. And, while More appears to have made an industrious — if not always an intelligent — beginning, his penchant for politics and obvious desire for personal advancement scarcely bespoke a soul dedicated to the new science.

It was early in 1723 before Sherard received More's first letter and his box of specimens, both of which came to his hands almost simultaneously with a shipment by Catesby from Carolina. On February 23 Sherard complained to Dr. Richardson:

Mr. More has been very diligent for the short time he was in the country before the ship came away, but most of what he gathered were common, and spoiled in coming over by his fault; for he put in the same box with dried plants, Fruits, and seeds, Limes, Gourds, and such like trash, and to fill it up, put sea-weeds atop. I took him for a great philosopher, and shall give him orders how to pack for the future. I do not question his diligence, and hope next summer he will make amends. Mr. Catesby has been ill, and kept his room above three months in the proper season for collecting Fruits and Seeds; however, he sent a good number of specimens well dried, and seems much concerned he has been able to make no better returns.[25]

Consul Sherard sent his new "orders" to More on March 20, but it was many months before he heard from the latter and a year before More's next shipment reached him. Paul Dudley, in the meantime, sent at least two

[20] Joseph Green to Stephen Williams, Oct. 1, 1722, quoted in Kenneth B. Murdock, "Cotton Mather and the Rectorship of Yale College," Publications of the Colonial Society of Massachusetts, XXVI (1926), 392.
[21] Dudley to Jurin, Roxbury, Nov. 3, 1722, Guard Books (MSS in the Library of the Royal Society of London), D-1, 77. For Dudley see Dean Dudley, The Dudley Genealogies and Family Records (Boston, 1848), 73-74; History of the Dudley Family (2 vols. + 2 supps., Wakefield, Mass., 1886-

1901), I, 521-24; D.A.B.
[22] C. H. McIlwain, ed., An Abridgement of the Indian Affairs . . . 1678 to the Year 1751 by Peter Wraxall (Cambridge, 1915), lxv-lxviii, 143 ff.
[23] R.S. Guard Book, D-1, 77; R.S. Letter Book, XVI, 340-42.
[24] The letter is printed in full in Note 1 at the end of this Appendix.
[25] MS Radcliffe Trust, C. V, fol. 4; Nichols, Illust. Lit. Hist., I, 383-84.

communications to Dr. Jurin of the Royal Society, including a shipment of specimens of New England flora and a long paper entitled "Observations on Some Plants in New-England — with Remarkable Instances of the Nature & Power of Vegetation," a paper which subsequently (February 4, 1724/25) was read before the Society.[26] In July Dudley reported that "our friend Mr. More is gone to the neighbouring colonys with all the recommendations we could possibly give him from hence." In August Sherard reported that he had heard from More, who was sending "specimens & seeds which I expect in 2 months."[27] But the Pilgrim Botanist had gone "to visit his old acquaintances the Indian Kings that were in England,"[28] and it was December before he was ready to ship his second collection of specimens to his patrons in England. In the letter accompanying it, dated from Boston, December 12, 1723, More made it clear that his opinion of New Englanders had worsened considerably: "I have travel'd thro Six Countrys of New England this year and Doctor Dillenius was all wrong when he represented this as a hospitable Country, for here they bite like sharks and in some things outdoe the very Hollanders themselves."[29] His criticisms of New Englanders and his efforts to prevent them from cutting masting timbers reserved for the Crown won him, as he said, "many sowre looks." Indeed, in this regard, the Pilgrim Botanist seemed on the point of raising in New England an odor which might far exceed that of the skunk which he described at such great length and whose "stinck," as he affirmed, carried from Roxbury to Boston. His specimens reached Sherard by the end of February, 1724, after lying at the Customs House for a month without Sherard's knowledge.[30] But, as the Consul reported later, they were "good for little,"[31] and, evidently, the subscribers to More's enterprise in New England received very little for their patronage.

Months earlier, as his first letter to Sherard from New England had indicated, More had become interested in schemes to reform the economy and the government of New England. As he saw more of it, he was dismayed at the state of the economy (which, obviously, he did not fully comprehend); he became enraged at New England's illegal trade in timbers reserved for the Crown and the Royal Navy; and he deeply resented the New England attitude toward royal authority and the treatment accorded the Governor of the colony. All of these were matters which had been in hot dispute in the Bay Colony for many years,[32] and a wiser man, or, at least, a newcomer devoted to natural philosophy with the dedication of the true virtuoso, would have avoided becoming involved. Perhaps the Pilgrim Botanist's support was enlisted by the Dudley faction or by Governor Samuel Shute himself. Whatever the motivating impulse, Thomas More addressed a long letter to Lord Carteret, Secretary of State, on May 16, 1723. The letter was filled with bitter complaints against New England, including such statements as: "I am come into a country pleasant, delightful, healthful, fruitful in itself, nothing wanted but order, oeconomy, Government, and husbandry. . . . All [are] merchants yet have no trading nor one staple commodity in the whole country. . . . [The] true state of this country has never been yet known to H.M. or his Ministers. . . . [The] Ship of this Government has sprung so many leaks, your Lordp., as a Master Carpenter ought to stop 'em, and I as your mate have made good pluggs for you to drive in, etc. . . ."[33]

After this rather presumptuous beginning, More offered fourteen "pluggs" for the reform of the civil government and the economy of New England. The program was reminiscent of that of the late Governor, Joseph Dudley, and it clearly reflected the troubles which had led Governor Shute to return to England early in 1723.[34] To the public disorders, however, More added private peeves against the people and the General Court of Massachusetts, who had exhibited no great interest in the seeds he had brought from Europe and who offered him no ground to sow them — "unless," as he said, "I bought it." In order that he might take part in putting things right in New England, More begged that he might have a grant of land, a patent for a tin mine he said he had found,

[26] Dudley to Jurin, Oct. 3, 1724, *R.S. Letter Book,* XVIII, 143; *R.S. Guard Book,* D-1, 80; Dudley's other letter, dated July 6, 1723, is in *R.S. Guard Book,* D-1, 78; *R.S. Letter Book,* XVI, 445-46.

[27] *MS Radcliffe Trust,* C. V, fol. 18; Nichols, *Illust. Lit. Hist.,* I, 388.

[28] Sherard to Richardson, Jan. 18, 1723/24, *MS Radcliffe Trust,* C. V, fol. 35; Nichols, *Illust. Lit. Hist.,* I, 391-92.

[29] *Sherard Letters,* IV, 560. This letter, which is incomplete, is printed in Note 2 at the end of this Appendix.

[30] Sherard to Richardson, Feb. 29, 1723/24, *MS Radcliffe Trust,* C. V, fol. 42; Nichols, *Illust. Lit. Hist.,* I, 392.

[31] Same to same, April 25, 1724, *MS Radcliffe Trust,* C. V, fol. 48; Nichols, *Illust. Lit. Hist.,* I, 392-93.

[32] See J. G. Palfrey, *A Compendious History of New England* (4 vols., Boston, 1884), III, 360 ff.

[33] *C.S.P., Col., 1722-1723,* XXXIII, 530.

[34] See Palfrey, *New England,* III, 226 ff., 398.

and a position as His Majesty's "Forest Ranger." The last was obviously a bid for the office of Surveyor General of the Woods, an office which had been dormant since John Bridger's dismissal a short time before.[35]

More's letter was submitted through the good offices of William Sherard, who endorsed it, and the Pilgrim Botanist himself returned to England in the late winter of 1723-24 to press his claims in person. Sherard noted on April 25 that "He [More] is come over & will return next month. I hope to get a place of one of the King's rangers for preserving timber in that country, which will give him a power & opportunity of making his subscribers amends."[36] But More was still in England at the end of June, although he proposed to return to New England "speedily," and, as Sherard said, he promised "to follow my instructions for the future better than he has hitherto."[37] Nothing further appeared with regard to his candidacy for the office of Surveyor General of the Woods, and, apparently, the Pilgrim Botanist received neither the office nor the land patents he had sought.

Indeed, it is not certain that More reached New England in the summer of 1724. Paul Dudley, in a letter to Dr. Jurin in October, sent "a few observations on the plants of New England as a gleaning after Mr. More's greater harvest which I hope he has long since spread before the Society";[38] but it is impossible to say whether Dudley referred to More's earlier shipments or to collections he may have made in the summer of 1724. There is no indication in Sherard's letters nor in the *Journal Books* of the Royal Society that any "harvest," great or small, was reaped in New England by Thomas More in that year.

Years later, in 1735, in reply to an inquiry by Dr. Cromwell Mortimer, Secretary of the Royal Society, Dr. Zabdiel Boylston wrote (April 25, 1735):

Yours of September 14, 1734, I received some months past. I have agreeable to your desire made diligent Inquiry after Mr. Thomas Moor, not only by word of mouth but also by Advertisements in our Prints; but hitherto cannot hear any thing of him: but am inclined to think it may be the same Gentleman that was here some ten or eleven years past, making such a Collection as you mention of Plants &c (tho' I never heard that he was curious in the Species of Dogs) and it was supposed here as he related for the use of the Royal Society. He went from hence in a Ship bound for London in the year 1724; since when we have heard nothing of him.[39]

The Pilgrim Botanist passed out of the English botanical circles as anonymously as he had entered them.

Thomas More's patrons gained very little for their trouble and expense, especially when the results were compared with the fruits of Mark Catesby's labors. Still, the Pilgrim Botanist's exertions were not wholly without profit in England. In 1730 Philip Miller, the London gardener and nurseryman, published a catalog listing a fir tree and "The New England Ash" which he said had been grown from seeds supplied by Thomas More.[40] Of the fir, called after Plunkenet the "Small-Con'd Virginia Firr (Abies, minor, pectinatis foliis, *Virginiana,* conis parvis subrotundis)," Miller wrote that it "was formerly growing in the Garden of the Bishop of *London,* at *Fulham,* with many other curious Exotic trees and Plants, which have been since destroy'd. This Firr was again retrieved in *England* from Seeds sent from *New-England* by Mr. Moore, Anno 1724. . . ." The ash, known as the New England, or American, ash (*Fraxinus americana*), was also "rais'd from Seeds sent from *New England* by Mr. Moore, Anno 1723." Miller added that it was "very hardy, but hath not produced Flowers in *England* as yet." These two trees, one a reintroduction to England, appear to have been the only lasting fruits of Thomas More's expeditions.

[35] Palfrey, *New England,* 366-81.

[36] Sherard to Richardson, *MS Radcliffe Trust,* C. V, fol. 48; Nichols, *Illust. Lit. Hist.,* I, 392-93.

[37] Sherard to Nicholson, June 30, 1724, *MS Radcliffe Trust,* C. V, fol. 57; Nichols, *Illust. Lit. Hist.,* I, 393.

[38] Dudley to Jurin, Oct. 3, 1724, *R.S. Guard Book,* D-1, 80; *R.S. Letter Book,* XVIII, 143.

[39] *R.S. Letter Book,* XXI, 467-69.

[40] *Catalogus plantarum . . .* (London, 1730), 2, 33. See also J. C. Loudon, *Arboretum et fruticetum Britannicum . . .* (ed. 2, 8 vols., London, 1854), I, 81, which lists the *Fraxinus americana* (American ash) as having been introduced to England by Thomas More between 1721 and 1730.

Notes

Note 1: *Thomas More's First Letter to William Sherard from New England, accompanying a box of Specimens herein catalogued with observations on the People and Colony of Massachusetts Bay. Dated at Boston, 27 October, 1722* [from *Sherard Letters,* IV, No. 561].

Honour'd Sir,

Full ten weeks I was upon my passage hither, the winds being very much contrary. Upon my arrival, so soon as I could I delivered my Credentials to the Governour and Grandees of the Country who all highly approved of my design & made me very welcom; most of them invited me to their Country seats, but I excused myself telling them the season was farr spent, winter hastning, and my work great and time short, but in my travels up and down would pay my respects to them, when I had sent a Cargo of things to London for my friends to be working upon until I got them more. We parted well satisfied & I betook my self to the woods, & by the help of an Indian fell to work, where I found the most part of all trees & herbs quite parcht dryed & burnt up. Such a hot and dry Summer has not been seen here in the memory of man, the Farmers telling me such of them as used to make 30 hogsheads of Cyder will this year hardly make two. The specimens I send you are but faint & languid, Except it be such who take deep rooting in the ground where the particles of earth having an Innate moisture and by reason of their lying in close stratums packt together they Sweat amongst themselves so emitting a moisture for the fibres & tenors of the roots to feed on, whereas those that grow Shallow are void of this help and depend altogether upon the Rain and Dews, which failing they are altogether lost. This I have observed in Egypt & several other Countrys where it rains little or none at all. Take what I have learnt and been informed concerning some of them.

1. Candleberry, a Shrub growing about 3 yards high of smal beauty and appearance but one of the most necessary & profitable Plants in the world as giving that fine Emerald Green wax for candles & other uses, and so much admired every where. When the berrys come to be turgid & fall ere they come to be hard, Boyle them in common Water, The Wax arriseing like a Scum, out of a Ladle or Spoon poure into a Mold of Metall, before provided with some Forms or Wick of Cotton, Flax, Rush, &c where it indures the form of the Mold & hardens like a peece of wood. The Berrys I send you are too hard for that work and only fit for seed enough to serve Great Britain & litle Britain also. By his Aromatick smell and taste as also by the form and Site of the leaves he seems to belong to the Bayes & not the Myrtles as I have been told. The Plant you shewed me in your Chamber by that name is none of he.

2. Silk Plant hollow as a Reed full of Milky Juice which Issues abundantly out of him which the Indians eat of[f] warts withal; he grows on a Stem thick as a small walking stick full of Podds containing a beautiful fine white silk. Of those scattered Panicles you see, many

whereof growing out of one root. I have made some Pencils for painting, yet a better use may be made of him for makeing fine hats and that either mixed with Beaver wool or alone; if mixed with wool, Cotton, or Flax I suppose he would Spin, but the best Inventers in the world for such gewgaws are *those dark Angels in hoopt pettycoats* who will surely find out some Scandalous use for his beautiful silk to adorn their butterfly cloaths withal. Give them fine Cloathes, Plenty, and Pleasure and no matter for a good conscience. Take care you be not deluded by one of them now in your old age as Solomon was. I am out of reach of their Gunshot as having neither Plenty nor Pleasure to give them and therefore tis they value me as little as I doe them.

3. Indico Tree thick as a mans little finger and tall as a Mans Loins, tough, strong, and flexible as whalebone, full of small branches and leaves like a Cytisus. In this Country he gives not that deep dye as I have seen but rather a bluish black, whether from his nature or his growing wild and without Cultivation I shall not say. I have sent you seeds enough to try upon, but your being so little in the Country to overlook him will spoyle all.

4. Mechaocan. Tournfort [Tournefort] calls it a sort of Bindweed and ascribes many rare virtues to it among the rest of his apertives; he grows about 2 or 3 yards high, his leaves triangular, thin, and pendulus as a Spanniels ears, the stem thick as a broomstick, hollow within & cuts soft as the pith of a Cabbidge; he bears many branches lolling to all points of the Compass, and on those large red berrys so full of Scarlet Juyce as you cannot touch them without being Smutted. One warme day as I was gathering the berrys and my fingers tinged with the Colour, the Muskito flyes at the same time biting my face vehemently and I with my hand often driveing them away, I so dyed one side of my Chap without my knowledge deep Scarlet, the other side of my beard being grey to my great shame and amazement, as all that saw me laughed me to scorn. I have drawn a tincture out of his berrys and red outside pith, deeper than an Cocheneel can make it. Quaere: how farr he may be useful in painting and dying, he tinges strongly without the help of Allom, boiling, Lye, or any Lixibium to excite the Colour, so as a Canvass bag I carry is so deeply dyed as I think twill never come out, and the paper whence I laid him stains all the sheets near thereunto.

5. Button tree, a large tall plant so-called because his seeds grow like buttons; his wood is firm hard and strong much used in Ships for blocks, pullies &c.

6. Squash, a kinsman of the Pompion or Melon with whom he is comonly Sowen and ripens together, a thin fruit Scalopt and furrowed from a Center to a Circumference & broad as the Crown of a mans hat.

7. Craneberry in a bottle, a drunken Rogue that will neither grow or keep without Swimming in water; he makes the best tarts in the world and therefore highly valued among Gluttons and Epicures for his fine taste.

8. Chestnut tree, the fruit being smal but exceedingly good, the husk so prickly as you dare not touch it.

9. Rhus or Shumach, a small Shrub so abounding in these Countrys as we may furnish enough to serve our Dyers without bringing so many hundred tuns thereof yearly from Portugal and Spain at great prices; it ought to be ground to a powder; I have sent you berrys enough to make trial upon; if any of your acquaintances mynd to encouraging my sending it over, Let them send me over a little Iron Mill like an Oatmeal or Coffee mill to grind it withal, with what Instructions they can pick up among the Dyers, Salters &c. It'l turn to great account.

10. Juniper, one sort bearing a berry the forme of a Pearle, the other flat, the one a white wood, the other white without and red within, both called by the people here a red and white Cedar but abusively, the berrys are very smal but I am told very Spirituous and good, & of a more pungent taste then our sort.

11. Spruce, this tree is highly useful all the Corn drink we have in this Country being brewed therewith yet we have abundance of your stinking hops growing here wild but no body notices them; this healthy Plant would save the lives of many thowsands in Britain if our Ale and Beer were brewed therewithal and by what I can learn preserves the drink also more powerfully than Hopps for many years.

12. Turpentin, this Pine naturally Sweats out the Juyce in hot days but always on that side faceing the South. This Liquor the Natives boyle to a certain consistence so making Rosin.

13. Pitch pine, this tree differs from the other mostly in having farr greater Cones or Apples the leaves broader and tree bigger; in hot weather faceing the south he sweats out Tarr abundantly which the People boyle to a certain hight so making Pitch; the wood of both trees are so fat and Resinous that the Natives slice it into thin fleaks which when lighted at one end serves them as well as any Candles, they carrying them up and down the house out of doors, in the wind & Rain without extinguishing, a most fragrant smell Issueing from them mean while.

14. Amara Dulcis, or bitter sweet, a kind of Creeper and always climbing on other Plants; he gives a pleasant red berry surrounded with yellow leaves in clusters like grapes the Natives hang them up in their houses, set them in pots, Mantlepeeces &c as a great ornament. The taste of the berry is not unpleasant.

15. Oaks, the red a large broad leaf like a Cabbage I am told that a beam of this wood 40 foot long you may blow at one end and a Man shall perceive your breath at the other end proceeding thro' the pores of the tree. Whether the Nutritious vessels, Seed vessels, and Air vessels of this tree be wider than others that causes such sensible Spiration, I leave to you to determine; only this by the way I have seen it so in the long Joynts of some Bambo Canes, and yet by the Collison of a tobacco pipe and that Cane together a languid sort of fire was struck visible enough.

The long leaf they call the white oak from the Colour of the wood I suppose. The small leaf they call the black oak. The Round leaf they call the Dwarf oak. I never saw it so high as my self; at my comeing they told me they had hogs in that Country so tall as that standing they could eat the topp leaves of an Oak; upon enquiry I found this Paradox was nothing else but the lowness of the Plant. He carrys a great bushy head, a firm leaf, sweet and good food for Cattell that hardens and Substantiats the flesh and fat of beasts much sooner firmer and Sweeter then our British feeding. I wish this Plant were propagated plentifully with you for that use in hedge Rows upon heaths, wastes, Commons, &c, tho he grows Sometimes no higher then your pockets yet he rewards you with a Bushie head full of leaves & branches Sweet, hard, firme, and good. I have sent you acorns plenty of all Sorts to try experience upon.

16. Walnuts, Long, The Broad, and Round Sort. These 3 Species are all I have yet seen but there are more of them I'm told. They are very small in respect of ours but I'm Informed much better. They make a great figure in the woods and are by the Natives used in most uses but it vexes me to see whole Trees of them laid on the fire for Lazyness to bring in worser fewel. I hope you'l use them better and even to improve the grain and goodness of them. the Nuts will grow bigger by Cultivation. I have sent you a Specimen of the Sassafras but this is the wrong time of getting his flower or seed and also of all the Species of the Ash; but of these next year.

17. Calamus Aromaticus I can send enough of if any of your ffriends want them.

18. Lime Juyce enough to make a Plantation. Also Lemons and Oranges, Musk & water melons &c. [Note: perhaps some of these items had been obtained in the West Indies en route.]

19. Hazel Nuts exceeding Small but very Sweet. Small for want of Cultivation.

20. Locust tree, and exceeding large, tall, and beautyful plant sometimes 100 foot high, some say 200 or more. he is of great use in building of houses for long Beams, Justing, &c.

21. Tamuns [?] the smallest leaf tree in the world his leaves no bigger than common grass.

22. Alder tree exceeding big and large, with several Apples, Pears, Quinces, Peaches &c of wch I forbear to Speak, any difference from yours being but accidental as proceeding from English seeds at first.

23. Prune tree or Privet very beautiful and fitt for hedging.

24. Fern tree or Citrack very bushy & full of branches, and other sorts not so frondesient. Shoe flower, a tall high plant a large flower and shapen as a mans shoe. Hemelok tree with an Yew-leaf; he seems to be a kinseman of the firr.

25. Poison tree, he grows the bigness of an Elder. I never Saw his leaf, the wood as cold as Ice; when laid on the fire 5 or 6 persons sitting thereabout some will fall a Swooning, fainting or Yawning so continueing for some dayes, others but a few hours and others of the same Company not at all. I handle, cut, and burn him with Impunity and so it is with several.

26. Hickery, a great large fair tree with a leaf the forme and Site of a Walnut but Smaler leaf, bearing a Nut as hard as wood. This Plant is of Singular use as being fitt for Masting Ships, building timber, blocks, pulies, wedges, house timbering, Millwork, Rails, Styles, posts, pails, Canns, Drumms, Hoops &c being as hard, firm, and Solid as Oak, flexible as Ash, tough as Walnut &c. Above all the rest he makes the best fewel in the world, as giveing a most intense heat, Inflammable & easily kindled, smels sweet in burning and will last so well as I have seen a log foot thick serve the back of the fire a whole week and never goe out; but in dressing meat, Warming &c some few chipps or Shaveings being added he makes a better & more dureable fire than Ston coal; he also makes the best Charcoal and is mostly used for fewel tho' fitt for everything. If you and your friends apply your selves, you may fill Britain full of this tree, which will be a great benefit to the nation and as good Service as you can doe to it; hee'l grow any where and will be fitt to plant on our Commons, Wasts, hedge rows &c.

If you encline to have great quantitys of any trees or Seeds send me word in your next, and which of them mostly. The little I send you now will keep you doeing mean while, and if I had not sent them by this first Ship you'd had nothing to Sow next Spring, and Sowe should lost a year. I have got notice of many things and dayly more and more of all which in time & their Season. Our Countys of Northampton, Oxfordshire, Wilts, Dorsetshire, and other places Starved for want of fewel will blesse this undertaking and be mightily relieved thereby. The Scoundrel Elm will be of litle Account when once this Hickory comes to take place. This is one of the healthyest Countrys ere I came in. Always a Serene Air, Shinshine, and no Clouds, Damps or Mists overcasting a little before Ram [i.e., the first sign of the zodiac, or late March] and no more quickly dryed up and mostly fair weather; Summer very hot and about the lenth of ours, but winter violent and pinching cold, but the Country being one entire wood fireing is so plenty as they lay on whole Walnut trees at once, no wood being so much Spared as Oak for the conveniency of building. When they mynd to clear their ground if the wood be good they cut down the trees leaving the roots to rott in the ground, but if otherwayes they set the whole woods on fire, afterward planting their Indian Corn, Roots, Potatoes &c in furrows as the ffrench doe their vines. The soil is plentyful good and Cultivable enough but the People are both Idle, Ignorant, and Poor and proud and which is worse don't care much for being better. They are Courteous, Civil, discreet and hospitable even to a Proverb, exceedingly weaned from all the extravagances of England, Except only in gawdyness of Apparell. They did me the honour to Invite me to a magnificent feast they made to the 7 Indian Princes of the Erocoj [Iroquois], Mohoks &c that came here to mediate a peace between us and the ffrench Indians now at warr with us. The Prince of the Mohoks knew me again perfectly weel I being often in his Company at London in Queen Anns time, he being then one of the 5 Princes that came over to England. He is now a Polite Gentleman, Baptized, a Zealous Christian apparelled as we, Speaks pretty good English, and scarcely distinguishable from an Englishman but by his tawny complexion. When he came to know my designe he Invited me very loveingly up to his Country and Spoke to the rest of the Princes to the same purpose who all very willingly did the same, one of them unfortunately dyed in this town, the other 6 are now with the Frenchefied Indians negotiating the Peace which is not yet concluded. Those 7 Countrys being opened to me will make my Range exceedingly the larger.

2 or 3 dayes agoe I was Invited by the Publick to the Instalment of a new Professor at the University here, where I saw such Learning, Decency, Order, and Decorum in All their proceedings as struck me with Admiration to think a Starr so lately appearing in the hemisphere of Learning, should shine so bright and some of our old ones so dim. Drunkeness, Swearing, Blaspheming, and other Extravagances are little to be seen here, but bridled very Severely by the Magistracy. Plenty of everything and good in their kind, money and Gold sells like Merchandize and Bills Circulate in place of money; any piece of Silver or Gold they pick up as carefully as Diamonds so sending it to England to procure from thence what they stand in need of, the goods sent from hence not being valueable enough to ballance the trade from England hither.

I have sent you Specimens of all Smal plants I could find that were not quite burnt up, the shortness of water and distance from whence I brought them assisted only by my poor legs without a horse and fatigue in travel excuses me from methodizing and laying them curiously, but this I need not speak of; your German Doctor [Dillenius] has Leisure and skill enough so to doe. I Committ you to Gods gratious protection both of you and am

Honoured Sir,
Your faithful and humble
Servt
Tho: More

Direct me at the house of Mr. Slepe Shoemaker in Marleboro Street opposite to Colloll. Dyers doore, Boston.
[On left margin:] It would be too tedious at this time to tell you of all I have already observed among the Indians and seen in their Wigwams or houses.
[Below:] His Matie. pays yearly 20 000 £i for the drawbacks of Pitch and Tarr from hence. I know a ready way to save all this money in his Matys. Pocket and get him 20 000 £i a year more to put in his Pocket. He shall have the same quantity of Pitch and Tar yearly from hence, Hemp enough to serve the Royal Navy, this Country better regulate[d] and peopled then ever and be made more Serviceable both to Britain and itself also. If you can Engage any Eminent men in this work Let me know by your next and I shall send you my proposals which are plain & demonstrative as any proposition in Euclid. If you can procure friends to this great & necessary work I shall send you all things proved in Print which I now have by me, but will not open my Pack till I see I can Sell some of my goods. Send me also some Character or Title from his Maty. to defend me against

Insults to which I may be exposed by some few who care not for such discovery.

I send you some few fruits as Apples, Pears, Quinces &c but am not careful therein all such here being from English seeds differ little or nothing from ours only the Walnuts, Chestnuts &c growing wild in the woods I regard hoping that their Smalness may be cured by Cultivation and bring them in to Garden Management. I hope to send you a berry bearing Shrub next year of more value than a whole County. 6, 8, 10, or 12 of the berrys chewed in the mouth cures faintness, Giddyness, Swoonings, Wearyness, Melancholy, and that taedieum commonly oppressing Nature, Contrarily clearing the heart, reviveing the Spirits & bringing a man to more lively condition then before. The Governour was the first who told me of this Plant being in the Country and promised to get it for me but I have since found it out by the help of my Indian whom I have hired for my Servant. By the help of this & other such unknown Plants they performe such wonderful cures So as being all Galenists, Doctors, & Apothecaries here live like Rats, Glauber & [word undecipherable] with their Chymical disciples not being able to doe so much in 7 yeares as Galen in one day.

The Several sorts of Ash, the red & white cedar, with the Curious Maple commonly called black Walnut for faceing of Cabinets, Scintoirs [?], looking glasses &c I cannot get ready now but I hope I shall by next addition.

What I now send is but a ffleabite to whats a comeing. Send me more brown paper. I have enough of white. The Governour is my great friend & tells me the best hemp in the world may be and is already begun to be raised in this Country, Stronger, longer, & more workable ten times than any we can have elsewhere for the use of our Royal Navy & to encourage the Planters he Intends to allow them a penny each pound for raising. This will be of great use both to Britain and this Country. The Commissioners of the Navy will be glad to know this. Many things more will follow on this so as I would have you & your friends to be first acquainted with this profitable designe. a filament of it as small as a fine threed of it will cut a mans finger to the bone & one as big as a brown thread strong enough to hang a thief. 16, 17, 18 foot high it grows already, and better husbandry will make it higher still. the Country seems to be peculiar to it. This will be a matter of great Concern & draw that trade quite from the Baltic. I made narrow Search for a litle of it to Send you but you may depend on this relation till a Specimen come. Send me word if a parcell of Spruce sent you would not doe well to brew Spruce beer.

[Subscribed on back:]
> To
> Wm Sherrard Esqr. at his lodgings in Barking Alley
> a few Doors from Tower Hill with a Box
>
>> London.
>> Capt. Barlow's Ship
>> by Ratcliffe Cross

[Endorsed by Sherard:]
> Rx Jany 15, 1722/3
> Answ. March 20, 1722/3.

Note 2: *Thomas More's Second Letter to William Sherard, dated Boston, New England, 12 December, 1723* [from *Sherard Letters*, IV, No. 560].

Honoured Sr,

I Reced yours of 20th March last by Mr. Barlow but none since; your Instructions therein I have followed as nicely as I can, but commands and obedience are but sometimes Kinesmen, by reason of accidents, that doe occur [?]. I have provided you abundantly with those seeds you most desire as Oaks of all sorts, and the smaler the accorns the finer and stronger the wood, for building shipp; the bigger being only useful they tell me in house timbering, fencing, Charcoal, &c. but not good for fuel as groeing no light or blaze to purpose. — Turpentin comes of several sorts, some smal that grow no great hight, but runn turpentin plentifully. the greediness and Idleness of the people is such, that when thay have wounded the tree they look not nigh till a week after, by which time he has bled himself to death, & being stopt after two dayes running might have been preserved for many more Incisions. the longest Cones I had of trees an hundred & fforty fifty or sixty foot high, some three or more foot diameter. yet the taler they be, they give the less Turpentin and Rozin in proportion. I suppose because the Juyce is [? torn; used?] to forward the extension of the tree. Such large Plants reputed the best in the world for masting and by several acts of Parliament Invested in the Crown, are here cutt down by thousands, some exported to France, Spain, & Portugal to mast their Shipping, to fight against our selves. I perswaded but had no power to command, the seizing of eleaven of them going to ffrance by way of Lisbon, in one ship, for which I have procured my self many sowre looks from the exporters of them, and our wool also to the ffrench but to be zealous here for the King and Crowns service is accounted a greater cryme then theft and murther, the masting were let goe and wool also upon frivalous pre-

tences, anything being an excuse against the Crown, but no reason strong enough on its behalf, but by those and many such methods, we get great estates. The penalty by act of Parliament is one hundred pound sterling a Mast, which since the Charter given by King William, we have used without controul. Pitch pines you have different sortes. Theyr easily known by the shortness of the Cones. Spruces you have of several sorts, all of them being here accounted a panacea, Chiefly brewed in their beer, drunk in Tea, powdered & given among their meat and now Smoakt among their tobacco. Hemloks you have several sorts, he is accounted a hasty grower and one of the most dureable woods in the world, both wett and dry Insomuch as they use him in all foundation work for houses, wells, stakes in the sea, Keels of ships Ac. they pretend hee'l outlast cedar. I suppose he may [be] the Cedallus or bastard cedar growing here, but the true Cedar of Barmuda He cannot, for that'l last like brass. The spruces and Hemlocks being all together you'l find among them a small seed founed and full of valves like them but little bigger than a large pea, his tree grows to the hight of a Cherry, the branches Joynted like the Equisetum aquaticum, round about the Joynts at equal distances stand a ruft of small leaves like those of the Turpentine pine, but short to the quarter of an Inch. I suppose he is a kinseman of the Pine, his leaves bearing such resemblance, what he is I Cannot tell but is a fair plant in growing. Walnuts you have all sorts as to the other seeds of trees, Buttons, & such you have but less remarkable. Mohock Corn you have one ear of eighteen rows, a thing never heard of before in this Country, and thirty grains each row amounts to 540, each stem carrying three such as frequently it happens among the Mohocks, encreases to 1620 or thereabout out of one grain's sowing. we read that Isaac sowed and reaped 1000 fold which seems to be no Miracle if it were Mohock Corn he sowed, 5 rows all round the topp broke off in rideing which greeves me more than a little; another you have twisted like a rope, I take them both to be new Species in Nature & no accidents because theyr always so in that Country; a third you have whitish 8 rows 45 rows on each 3 of which out of one root or seed amounts to 1080 or thereabout, the parly [perly?] coloured one I take to be an accident for tho they change colour every year yet theyr allways parly Coloured & never the same twice together. the Beans from same Country are very beautyful pleasantly variegate and always so, but one among them you'l find altogether new white at one end and blackish at tother, whole feilds being so, but not very fruitful. They eat very
1. well but grow smal. 1. No. 1 in a litle bag you have a

smal read berry white in the middle but while not fully ripe white and red prettily streaked like a Pomgranate, big as a pea, deep red without, has a thick fat leaf like bo[xwood?] but broader, of a pleasant aromatick tast, Creeps on the ground each leaf emitting small fibres which pin him down like pennyroyal but when he grows among bushes that he cannot creep he stands upright, yet never taler than a writeing pen; he makes the best tea in the world and is counted a great Catholicon among us. Collonel Brown a man of great figure here, told me his body was so big of a dropsie as a sack of malt, but by drinking this tea he soon recovered a very healthy state of body which he has for some years enjoyed, and mynds to drink it to his dying day. I know you are very parsimonius and sparing of your ground, because he gives but litle encrease you'l think him cumbersom, but hee'l well requite your pains, and grow any where. You'l not want Partridges where he stands for hees their beloved food, and that I take to be the reason why we have the best Partridges in the world, he makes a glorious tincture with Rum or Brandy, so disguising the taste Colour and smell thereof as it seems a new thing. I made & presented some of it to persons of figure here, who were delighted with its pleasant taste and startled with the novelty. I made several specimens of him but could not preserve one, his leaves are so deciduous, as generaly most of the Plants here be that they fall off, shift to new papers as often as you will, some of his leaves I have put up with the berrys that you may see and Call them as you please. I have named him Poxdicaria but should be glade to know his true name and Genus.

Among the specimens No. 2 you have the flowers of a 2. tree as hard as Iron, and sinks to the bottom like a stone, tall as an Ash full of pleasant broad flowers, white as snow four leaves on a twig, in forme & size like a wild rose the leaves on the backside of the flower, so delightful in growing that he gives beauty to all the woods round about him. his flowers are now become dilute by drying, has little smell, of no knowen use and very Cumberson to the ground, Countrymen not dareing to meddle with him because he dulls their saws, Chizels, and Utensils to no purpose, fire only being able to deal with him. I saw a strong man with a sharp knife presume to cut a chip out of his bark, at two cuts with all his strength slopeways he made no more incision then the breadth of a straw, and when he cut perpendicular could make no more but like a scratch. No. 3 the white wood as white within as 3. chalk a great large tree fitt for Many uses very beautiful in wainscoting, he is too soft for turning but much used for making chests boards covering houses &c. — No. 4. a 4.

tree of middle size, his wood the Colour of firr, and leaf surprizing figure, the wind russling his leaves make a strange noise, a blow given on the dryed wood resounds like an Echo, I heard of a Chest made of it & got the owner to empty it that so I might try the experiment. upon tryal it gave me the exact resounds of every knock I gave in perfect unison, high low flat sharp and equal time; Quere yt this be not Solomons Almuggins whereof he made viols, Timbiels [timbals?] and musical instruments for the temple, and now at Cremona & other places in the Cremoneze in Italy they make the best fiddles in the world because of the resounding quality of that wood. Quaere also if the hard wood No. 2 be not the Anchorwood of China wherewith the Chinese anchor

5. their Ships. No. 5 of this plant I mean the flowers I made a tincture that tinges cloath as deep as the french Turnsole, and of the glorious blew flowers you'l find among the Specimens I suppose one might be made as beautiful as outremarin itself I have not yet had Time to try it but intend it next summer; I have travel'd thro Six Countrys of New England this year and Doctor Dilenius was all wrong when he represented this as a hospitable Country, for here they bite like sharks and in some things outdoe the very Hollanders themselves. The shells seem to be a Species of the Nautilus and the 2 smal fishes a Species of the Hippocampos or Lamprey, — the long Alga Marina seems new to me for I never saw one like it, — Among your things you have a shineing stone which some thought to be metall and others Carbuncle because of the glorious radiance he gives when the Sun shines on him by day and the Moon by night, he is as great a cheat as the Pope for he has begiuled them all. Metalls we have enough but no body to enquire into them; no King being in Israel every one does whats good in his own eyes, and pretious Stones we have not tho half witted fools think the contrary, he seems to me to be only a congestion of heterogenous particles which agree in a common mass, but afterward all the Similary parts betake themselves to each other, so uniteing into such particular forms as the Lawes of their Natures enchues them unto, like Churchmen and dissenters all agreeing in the general forme or Mass of Civil government yet each forming particular bodys, distinct in matter and forme from each other, some shineing some Lurid and others of several Colours, yet the Vinculum of Government like a hoop keeps them all together. I was curious enough to see these rocks where they grow, but my labour and expense was only rewarded with a fitt of laughter, the wiser sort are well pleased to be so undeceived but the generality are sick of this phrenzie still. — As to the Ratlesnake I have discovered that the Comon preservative we use in

Italy & Germany is good against him also and better then all the Nostrums used in this Country which are many, I have often assaulted other Serpents with Common Garlick, I did him also from which he flyes like fire from flint, the whole process of the story is too long to write, only this in short I bear it always about me in traveling and so am as safe as an unmarryed man from being a Cuckold. I have not yet observed how farr Garlick may be Sanative in cureing his bite, but doe not intend to be the first object of tryal for curiositys sake. — I have seen a pestiferous beast in this Country that is a plague and no plague, for he does much mischief and much good the Indians call him Skunk the bigness of a domestick Cat long tayled streight and tapering, prettily spoted brown and white, prick eard, a Sharp head and Snout like a Fop, whiskered with brown & white hairs alternately, his common pace is up and down a hand-gallop, but not very quick so as a Swift man may outrun him, he lives in holes of Rocks Chinks of stones and inaccessible places, Dogs nor beasts of prey will not willingly meddle with him, if they can help it, for upon the least occasion he squirts out upon them as liquor out of Syringe or Spout, a fluid stuff yellow as the yolk of an egg, thin as water, of such a rotten stinking smell as infects the air round about for some myles, he is smelt comonly from Roxbury to Boston 3 myles semi-diameter & as much tother side being 6 miles diameter answering to 18 miles Circumference, and some adds that this poisoned Creature emits this odious halitus in a Circle, and some say a great deal more, but I speak within compass, Colonel William Dudley a Gentleman of great vertue and veracity told me, one of them got into his barn, and there so pestered it with this Sowre rotten stink, as it was 3 full years ere he could purge it, and yet dayly pains were used to that end but all in vain, windows & doors opened for fresh air twas still worse & worse, this stuff is contained in a Cistus or bladder apart, haveing no Communication with the Urine bladder and being Cast into the fire gives a crack like a musquet without stinking, at ten or 12 yards distance he squirts it out on the objects of his anger, the young Cubs being kept their Masters were soon tyred of them for being naturally a peevish Creature upon the least provocation they squirted out this odious matter, thin as water on Master Mistress children or anybody or thing without respect of persons or degrees of provocation. My Landlords prentice & his father hunting of him in the Country at westwards [?] were both bespattered by him in their faces so as for 9 months, tho' they wroght hard & sweated many times on purpose they could not get out the stink and the Lad says if his Father had not been bestunk as well as he he could not had lodgings in the house, but his ffather gave him lodging because he was so himself. horses it makes to run over fences, rocks, & precipices headlong till they come to the water [two words torn] tumble about for some houres together therein, but to little purpose; Dogs doe the same, but the poor Sheep & Cows fare the worst for no body either come nigh to milk them, nor will the Butchers buy them nor anybody suffer them to Come into the town; they get frequently into Barnes where they suck eggs and kill and eat poultry, bestink ye hay, Corn, & provendar so as Cattle will no more taste it. this poisoned stuff so infuseing itselfe in the pavements, all their houses and barnes being of wood, as the beasts lye All in the open fields & will not come nigh it, they creep into houses by night & there with their sharp teeth, gnaw holes in peoples powdring tubbs, so to come at the flesh as to fill their Carniverous bellys, and the people look on dare not hinder them for fear of being spouted upon by their horrid liquor; the only way yet knowen is to shoot them, but if you miss the mark your in danger. Ye Indians shoot them and throw away the skin, which also smells abominably, but sell ye Carkasses to our people who eat them and say theyr the best of meat, the Cistus & poisoned stuff therein they anoynt their eyes withal agreeing tis the richest Opthalmick on earth, give inwardly & smell to outwardly to cure Epilepsies fitts Meagrims, vertigues &c. wherein it never fails in any Constitution. tis so strong a halitus as one told me he was 8 houres senceless after smelling it, but this may be corrected, afterward it revives the heart, cheares the spirits and works excellent feats in the body, thers no possible means of sending you either himself or his skin because of the direful stinck, but I have agreed with an Indian to get me a vial full as soon as he Can, hee'l hurt nobody unless provokt wherefore I let him alone as he does me, he is so bold as to come within a yard of you, as knowing his stink to be a weapon of offence & defence that man cares not to deal withal. the Cistus is so big as to hold half a pint which sometimes he emptys and is shot with it empty. 100 armed men Cannot make him turn out of ye way, or mend his pace, but they must all goe round about & let him stand still, for hee'l neither goe backward or come foreward, he has also a way of dawbing his Tayle with that execrable matter and like a brush of long hairs flirts it at his agressors, some 10 or 12 yards, they have comonly 4 cubs at a litter in walking the Sire goes foremost, the Dame behind, & the young ones in the middle 2 and 2 in rank and file military order, any man appearing they make ready for a stinking battle, being never yet known to fly but rather dye in the engagement. A Gent. in company with a Quaker that was a stranger being in the field, the Quaker first saw him & assaulted him with a stick among ye bushes, on which he flirted in his face, some whereof happening in his eyes made him blind for a long houre, but afterward recovered a clearer and farr better sight then before, even to read the smalest print without his Spectacles; on which ye Gent merrily told him ye Spirit & Religion of the Skunk was better than his, for he had done him good by restoring his sight, and he like a worser Christian Intended to kill ye poor beast without provocation. I cannot yet learn whether he holds Sympathy with any Creature but all abhorr him & shun his Company. I suppose hee's a Species of the Polecat. — No. 6 6. you have a pod with a seed enclosed which the Natives call Skunkroot because of his stinking smell, ye Indians call him poke or Smoak because they smoak it when they want tobacco, and ere the knowledge of Rum was brought among them by the Christians they used to make a fuddling drink off it at their Gambols and merry makings, that so they may be stupifyed and senseless of the horrour occasioned at their paw wawings by a Daemon takeing away alive allways one of the Company, whose lot 'twil be they cannot tell, but are resolved all to be drunk and so less apprehensible of the danger. I dryed & smoakt som on't but it stunk so wretchedly as to make me spew, but the Indians have a way of dressing it so as to make it less hideous, it has a broad large leaf furrowed & ridged like ye veratum ingrum a litle tapering at the tip of the leaf. No. 7 you have a plant accounted 7. most effectual of all for cureing the bite of the ratlesnake. he grows flat on the ground the leaf full of smal downy hairs, and seems to be a Kinseman of the Plantain. No. 8 the glorious blue flower as he ripens he turns more 8. and more languid. I shall get the seed as soon as I can, & promise my self fine things from his tincture, next Summer. — the yellow peece of wood may be useful in dying — the litle Squash full of limbbs is new to me, — I forbear to send you any soft things whereof I could many, for fear of their perishing by the way. — in the Specimens I have forbore repetition as much as I could, but now & then two of a sort is convenient Lest one should perish by the by. In my travels I lost many because I was not in the way to shift them. The Govermt. of Jerseys, New York, and all the Six Countrys of new England have things to send me some by water some by land many of which are not yet arrived thats the reason I'm so late for many of our seeds are so stubborn they'l not fall untill hard frosts make them tumble, but yet I come soon enough for your sowing time.

[Latter portion of letter, with signature, is lost.]

Index

DATE DUE

GAYLORD   PRINTED IN U.S.A.